DECISION AND ESTIMATION THEORY

DECISION AND ESTIMATION THEORY

James L. Melsa
David L. Cohn

Department of Electrical Engineering
University of Notre Dame

McGraw-Hill Book Company

New York   St. Louis   San Francisco   Auckland   Bogotá
Düsseldorf   Johannesburg   London   Madrid   Mexico
Montreal   New Delhi   Panama   Paris   São Paulo
Singapore   Sydney   Tokyo   Toronto

DECISION AND ESTIMATION THEORY

234567890 FGRFGR 78321098

This book was set in Times Roman by A Graphic Method Inc.
The editors were Frank Cerra and Frances A. Neal;
the cover was designed by Rafael Hernandez;
the production supervisor was Dominick Petrellese.
The drawings were done by J & R Services, Inc.
Fairfield Graphics was printer and binder.

Library of Congress Cataloging in Publication Data

Melsa, James L
    Decision and estimation theory.

    Includes bibliographical references and index.
    1. Statistical decision.   2.   Estimation theory.
I. Cohn, David L., date   joint author. II. Title.
QA279.4.M44   519.5′4   77-22759
ISBN 0-07-041468-8

TO THOSE WHO FIRST TAUGHT US ABOUT DECISIONS

Ann and Louis Melsa
Marjorie and Nathan Cohn

CONTENTS

PREFACE

Decision and estimation theory are basic tools which are used in many areas of communications, control theory, and system theory. This book provides a unified presentation of these important tools. The step-by-step development is designed to provide the reader with a solid background in this complex area.

The book is intended as a textbook for a one-semester course in decision and estimation theory. It is designed for advanced seniors or first-year graduate students. We assume that the reader has had prior exposure to probability and random process theory. This background may have been acquired from a course using one of the many available books such as "Probability, Random Variables, and Stochastic Processes" by A. Papoulis, "An Introduction to Probability and Stochastic Processes" by J. L. Melsa and A. P. Sage, or "Probability and Random Processes" by W. B. Davenport. Alternatively, the student may have been exposed to these concepts elsewhere. The major elements of probability theory and stochastic processes that are required in this text are summarized in Chapter 2. A student who can work the exercises at the end of Chapter 2 probably has sufficient background in this area.

Decision and estimation problems have essentially the same structure. Some sort of *message* is generated at a source which causes an *observation* at a receiver. The message and observation are only stochastically related. The objective is to determine a rule which forms a "best guess" of the message based on the observation.

This book deals with the problem of making decisions about both discrete and continuous messages. Although there are important differences between the discrete and the continuous problems, they are treated in a parallel fashion. Chapters 1 to 7 deal with the discrete decision problems, while Chapters 8 to 11 are concerned with continuous estimation problems.

Chapter 3 begins the treatment of decision problems with the simplest possible problem structure. It considers the case of binary decisions and a single observation. The discussion begins with the fewest assumptions concerning the system model. Subsequent sections add structure and analyze the results of these additions. In Chapter 4, the problem is generalized to include multiple and waveform observations.

The problem is generalized still further in Chapter 5 where multiple decision problems are considered. This chapter ends with the erasure decision problem, which is used as an introduction to the sequential decision problem in Chapter 6. Chapter 6 includes a careful motivation of the Wald test and is one of the major features of the book. The discussion of decision problems is concluded in Chapter 7, which summarizes the composite decision problem and presents some simple nonparametric decision methods.

Chapters 8 to 11 examine the impact of enlarging the message space from a finite number of elements to an uncountably infinite number of elements. Chapter 8 discusses simple estimation structures and parallels the development in Chapter 3. The important case of estimation with gaussian noise is discussed in Chapter 9. In particular, sequential estimation and nonlinear estimation are described. Chapter 10 examines some of the properties of estimators. Finally, the important state estimation problem and the Kalman filter are introduced in Chapter 11.

No work of this nature is prepared in a vacuum. Therefore, we would like to acknowledge those who have established the atmosphere which enabled us to undertake and complete this project. Deans Thomas Martin at Southern Methodist University and Joseph Hogan at University of Notre Dame deserve special mention for the leadership they provided. Our colleagues and students at these two universities, who suffered through the earlier stages with us, also merit recognition. A succession of secretaries typed and retyped the manuscript. And, finally, we acknowledge the readers; they may find, as we did, that the most intensive learning takes place while correcting the mistakes of others.

James L. Melsa
David L. Cohn

DECISION AND ESTIMATION THEORY

INTRODUCTION

1.1 STRUCTURE OF DECISION AND ESTIMATION PROBLEMS

All the decision and estimation problems discussed in this book have the same basic structure. This structure involves four steps: first, something happens; second, this happening is relayed to an observer by some form of signaling mechanism; third, a noisy observation of this signal is made; and finally, the observer must reach a decision concerning the happening. This problem structure is shown schematically in Fig. 1.1-1. We are involved with problems of this sort all the time. Consider, for example, the medical doctor attempting to diagnose a patient's illness. The happening in this case is the illness. The signal is the set of medical tests which the doctor can make, each of which is corrupted by various noise sources including physical abnormalities the patient may have. The doctor then must decide what illness the patient has.

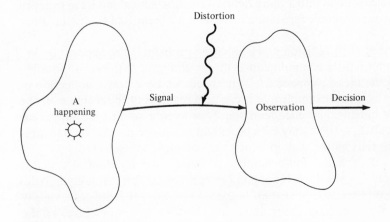

Figure 1.1-1 Structure of decision and estimation problems.

Another example of this type of problem is encountered in modeling a communication system. Suppose that a message is to be sent to a remote location. For the first step, a sender selects a message from a predetermined set of messages. For example, the sender might decide which key on a teletypewriter keyboard to push. The signal corresponding to this message is then transmitted. For example, pushing the key might generate a sequence of pulses that are transmitted over a telephone line. The transmitted signal is distorted by noise in the transmission media so that the signal observed at the receiver does not match the transmitted signal. The receiver must then use the distorted signal to make a best guess of which key was pushed. An appropriate definition of "best guess" here might be to select the key with the highest probability of having been pushed. Alternatively, best guess might mean to select the key which minimizes the probability of error.

A slightly different example arises in a biomedical experiment. An experimentalist may wish to determine if a particular optic nerve in a frog's eyes responds to a light stimulus. In this case, the happening occurs when the experimentalist selects one of the many thousands of nerve fibers. The observations are the electrical measurements made on the nerve when a light stimulus is applied to the frog's eye. In this example, the goal is not to guess which nerve was selected. Rather, there are only three possible decisions: the fiber responds; it does not respond; or more information is needed. If the third decision is reached, the experiment is repeated. The information for the first trial is available in formulating the decision rule for the next trial.

Note the importance of the distortion which occurs to the signal before the observation is made. Without this distortion, the signal would be directly observed and there would be no uncertainty concerning what happened. It is this distortion that makes decision and estimation theory important.

There are many other practical problems that fit this general problem structure, and the methods for formulating and solving these problems are the topic of this book. Although we treat such problems intuitively all the time, it is important that we cast them into a more definitive mathematical model in order to develop a rigorous structure for stating them, solving them, and evaluating their solution.

At the root of each decision and estimation problem is the happening. We shall borrow a term from communication theory and refer to the set of possible happenings as the message space M. This space can be simply a collection of discrete points as in our examples, or it can be a segment of the real line, or the points in an N-dimensional euclidean space, or even a set of time functions. Often, but not always, there may be a probability measure defined on this message space that tells us the way in which the messages are selected.

Generally, if M has a finite number of points, the problem is called a *decision* or *detection problem*. If the number of points are uncountably infinite, the problem is referred to as an *estimation problem*. For the finite case, we say that there are K points in the space and define them as m_k where k takes on the values from 1 to K. For the estimation problem, messages will be generalized as a continuous random vector **m** with dimension K. If the messages are time functions, we shall use the random process $m(t)$.

The concept of a signal space S is used to isolate the portion of the problem where information is generated from the portion where that information is transmitted. In the communication example this distinction was clear. The message was a letter on the key, and the signal was a series of pulses. In the biomedical case, the message was a particular nerve selected and the signal was a reaction of that nerve to the light stimulus. In general, we shall use a lower case s to identify points in the signal space. As with messages, s could be either a discrete or continuous random variable, a random vector, or a stochastic process. The distinction will be made clear as needed for a particular problem. In general, the signal statistical type is not necessarily the same as that of the message. However, on occasion the message and the signal will be identical. We assume that there is a unique and invertible mapping between elements of the message space and elements of the signal space. That is, each message generates a uniquely defined signal, and each signal is generated by only one message.

The third part of our mathematical model is a set of possible observations known as the *observation space* Z. Frequently, we shall be trying to model some physical mechanism that relates the signal and the observation. When this happens, S and Z will be the same statistical type. However, there may be times when there is no physical relationship between S and Z, only a statistical one. In any case, we shall assume that for each point S, there is a conditional probability measure defined on Z. For example, when Z consists of a segment of the real line, the probability density function $p(z|s)$ will be defined for each z in the observation space Z and each s in the signal space S. Often one says that the signals are mapped into the observation space by means of *probabilistic transition mechanism*, or, in the communication sense, this is the *channel model*.

Finally, a decision must be reached. There is as much flexibility in the size of the decision space D as there is in the message space. In many problems, however, D and M actually consist of the same set of points. In this case, the decision is usually a best guess of what the message was. This was the case in our second example but not the third. The relationship between the observation space and the decision space is called the *decision rule*. In a typical decision or estimation problem, the message, signal, observation, and decision spaces are all defined and the relationships between M, S, and Z are specified. The missing piece is the decision or estimation rule, that is, the mapping from the observation to a decision. Therefore, in this book we shall be concerned primarily with designing decision and estimation rules. Typically these rules will be deterministic; in other words, for each observation there will be a unique decision. These four spaces and their interrelations are shown schematically in Fig. 1.1-2.

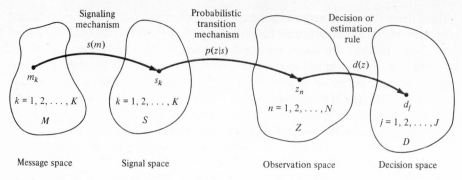

Figure 1.1-2 Decision and estimation problems.

1.2 OUTLINE OF THE BOOK

Following the introductory material of this chapter, Chap. 2 presents a brief review of certain concepts and notations in probability theory that will be used throughout the developments in this book. Following this review in Chap. 2, the remainder of the book can be divided into two broad classes: Chaps. 3 to 7 are directed to solutions of decision problems, while Chaps. 8 to 11 concern estimation problems.

We begin our study of decision theory problems in Chap. 3 with simple binary decision problems having only a single scalar observation. With this class of problems we can introduce most of the concepts within the simplest possible mathematical framework. In the binary decision problem, the message and decision spaces contain only two elements. Several different formulations and solutions of this problem are considered.

In Chap. 4, we will broaden the class of binary decision problems to include those where the observation is more complicated than the single scalar observation. Initially we let the observation be a set of scalar variables, and then we consider time-waveform observations. In particular, we will use the gaussian problem as a focal point for the development of several interesting concepts involving the signal-space approach to decision problems.

Chapter 5 considers another extension of the simple binary decision problem treated in Chap. 3. Here we consider problems for which the decision space has more than two elements. We begin with the general bayesian approach and then develop a more practically meaningful result using the probability-of-error criterion. Finally, we consider erasure decision problems.

In all the decision problems considered in these early chapters, it is assumed that the number of observations is fixed. Sometimes, however, it is possible for the receiver to take additional observations before making a final decision. Such problems are called *sequential decision problems* and are the topic of Chap. 6. We begin with treatment of the bayesian approach to this problem and later consider the Wald sequential-decision-theory approach.

In Chap. 7, we examine a number of methods for handling decision problems when the conditional probability density of the observation is not completely known. We begin with the case where the conditional density is known in its basic form but where there are certain unknown parameters. This type of problem is known as a *composite decision problem*. In the second part of Chap. 7, we consider another class of problems, known as *nonparametric decision problems*, in which the conditional probability density function is assumed to be unknown, except for general properties such as symmetry.

Chapter 8 begins our discussion of estimation problems. Because estimation problems are really an extension of multiple decision problems treated in Chap. 5, it is possible to make use of a great amount of the theory presented in the preceding chapters in the development of estimation methods. Chapter 8 considers the development of several different classes of estimators and shows their general properties and some examples of their use.

In Chap. 9, the general problem of estimating a gaussian vector in the presence of gaussian noise is examined. It is a problem of considerable interest both because it has many applications and because a complete solution is easy to find.

Chapter 10 is directed to the study of the properties of different forms of estimators. One of the major differences between the estimation problem and the decision problem is the difficulty in describing how good a given estimation algorithm is. Chapter 10 attempts to quantify certain desirable properties of estimators and show how they can be developed and used.

The state estimation problem is considered in Chap. 11. In Chaps. 8 to 9, we estimated a constant parameter. Now we wish to estimate the time-varying state of a dynamic system. In particular, our interest is in a class of linear unbiased minimum-error-variance sequential-state estimators referred to as the *Wiener-Kalman filters*.

TWO

REVIEW OF PROBABILITY THEORY

In this chapter, some of the basic notions of probability and random processes will be reviewed. Further details regarding these concepts can be found in any one of several textbooks on probability and stochastic processes, including Melsa and Sage (1973) and Papoulis (1965). The objectives are to refresh the reader's memory and present notation that will be used throughout the book. Whenever possible, the examples will be those that occur most often in decision and estimation. The chapter is divided into three sections: Section 2.1 deals with simple probability theory; Sec. 2.2 introduces random variables; and Sec. 2.3 treats stochastic processes.

In any presentation of probability theory, a choice must be made between exactness and economy of notation. In an introductory presentation of the subject, it is generally best to use the most exact notation possible. The same is also true of advanced presentations which emphasize the mathematical aspects of the topic. In this text, however, probability theory is to be used as a tool to solve a set of interesting problems. Therefore, whenever possible, simple notational forms will be used. One objective of this chapter is to present this simplified notation.

2.1 DISCRETE PROBABILITY THEORY

Probability theory is an attempt to model mathematically a set of real-world situations. A typical situation to be modeled is one where an experiment is performed and the result of the experiment is observed. The probabilistic model, or probability space, consists of three components: a set of possible alternatives, or *sample points*; a set of *events* defined on the sample points; and a *probability measure* defined on the events. The set of sample points, or sample space Ω, can be visualized as the set of all possible outcomes of the experiment.

The events are then the sets of outcomes one wishes to distinguish between, and the probability measure is a reflection of the likelihood of the various events. We shall use the Greek letter ξ to denote the sample points and italic capital letters to indicate the events. Therefore, the event A might be defined as

$$A = \{\xi: \text{some condition on } \xi \text{ is met } \} \qquad (2.1\text{-}1)$$

where the braces indicate "the set of" and the colon means "such that."

The simplest class of probability spaces are those in which the sample space contains a finite number of points K. Within this class the simplest case, and the one we shall be primarily concerned with, is where each of the points in the sample space is an event and thus has a probability assigned to it. When this is true, the probability measure can be any assignment of nonnegative numbers to the sample points as long as these numbers sum to 1. The probability of any particular outcome ξ_k is then just indicated by $P\{\xi = \xi_k\}$ or, if there is no chance for confusion, by $P\{\xi_k\}$.

As an example, suppose that $K = 10$ and that the event A is defined as the set of points ξ_1, ξ_2, and ξ_6. We can simplify the notation of (2.1-1) to write

$$A = \{\xi_1, \xi_2, \xi_6\} \qquad (2.1\text{-}2)$$

If the outcome is ξ_1, ξ_2, or ξ_6, we shall say that the event A has occurred. Since the sample points are mutually exclusive, the probability of event A will be

$$P\{A\} = P\{\xi_1\} + P\{\xi_2\} + P\{\xi_6\} \qquad (2.1\text{-}3)$$

If two events A and B are defined on the same probability space, we can talk of the joint event AB. This event occurs if and only if the outcome is contained in the set of sample points that comprise event A and it is contained in the set of sample points that comprise event B. Also, the union of the two events $A \cup B$ can be defined. This event occurs if and only if A occurs or B occurs or AB occurs. It is well known that the probability of $A \cup B$ is

$$P\{A \cup B\} = P\{A\} + P\{B\} - P\{AB\} \qquad (2.1\text{-}4)$$

If $P\{B\} > 0$, the conditional probability that event A occurs given that B has occurred can be defined as

$$P\{A|B\} = \frac{P\{AB\}}{P\{B\}} \qquad (2.1\text{-}5)$$

Using symmetry, this definition can be used to write *Bayes' rule for events*:

$$P\{A|B\} = \frac{P\{B|A\}P\{A\}}{P\{B\}} \qquad (2.1\text{-}6)$$

The events A and B are said to be *statistically independent* if their joint probability factors

$$P\{AB\} = P\{A\}P\{B\} \qquad (2.1\text{-}7)$$

Note that when this is used in the definition of conditional probability and when $P\{B\} > 0$, the probability of A conditioned on an independent event B is

$$P\{A|B\} = P\{A\} \tag{2.1-8}$$

In other words, when A and B are statistically independent, the probability that A occurs is not affected by knowing that B has occurred.

Example 2.1-1 As an illustration of the use of discrete probability theory, suppose that a friend of yours has five coins in his pocket. Four are fair coins (equally likely to be heads or tails), but one coin has two tails. Otherwise, the coins are indistinguishable. Your friend picks one coin with his eyes closed and begins to flip it. He flips it l times, and each time it comes up tails. What is the probability that he is using the unfair coin?

We shall let A be the event that he selected the unfair coin and B be the event that l tails occurred. Clearly,

$$P\{A\} = \tfrac{1}{5}$$

$$P\{B|A\} = 1$$

The third quantity we need for Bayes' rule is $P\{B\}$, the unconditional probability of l tails. If we let A^c denote the complement of A, we can use the theorem of total probability to write

$$P\{B\} = P\{B|A\}P\{A\} + P\{B|A^c\}P\{A^c\}$$

The probability of l tails given a fair coin is

$$P\{B|A^c\} = 2^{-l}$$

so that

$$P\{B\} = \frac{1 + 2^{-l+2}}{5}$$

Therefore, the probability that your friend is using the unfair coin is

$$P\{A|B\} = \frac{1}{1 + 2^{-l+2}}$$

Note that after two tails, the probability that he is using the unfair coin is $\tfrac{1}{2}$.

2.2 RANDOM VARIABLES

Frequently we shall wish to deal with sample spaces that do not contain a finite number of points. The simplest case is when the number of sample points is countably infinite. This case, however, is not of particular interest, and it can be handled much like the finite case. The situation alters significantly, however, with an uncountably infinite number of points. Here it is not possible to assign probabilities to each sample point, and they will not each be events. Fortunately, our primary interest in this type of sample space is when there is a numerical value associated with each sample point and we define events in terms of this value.

Although we shall generalize the concept later, initially we shall assume that this is a simple variable and not a vector. We shall refer to this variable as $m(\xi)$. If all sets of sample points of the form

$$A_\mu = \{\xi: m(\xi) \leq \mu\}$$

for any finite real number μ are events and have probabilities assoicated with them and if

$$P\{\xi: m(\xi) = -\infty\} = P\{\xi: m(\xi) = \infty\} = 0$$

then we will say that m is a *random variable*. We call the set of probabilities of A_μ the probability *distribution function* of m and write it as

$$F_m(\mu) = P\{A_\mu\} = P\{m \leq \mu\} \tag{2.2-1}$$

where we have adopted a shorthand notation for the set A_μ. Clearly, $F_m(\mu)$ is a nondecreasing function of μ and falls in the range

$$0 = F_m(-\infty) \leq F_m(\mu) \leq F_m(\infty) = 1 \tag{2.2-2}$$

The distribution function is particularly useful. For example, if we wish to compute the probability that m falls in some range, say, μ_1 to μ_2, it will just be

$$P\{\mu_1 < m \leq \mu_2\} = F_m(\mu_2) - F_m(\mu_1)$$

In fact, if M represents any set of intervals on the real line, the probability that m falls in M can be computed from $F_m(\mu)$.

This last fact leads us to the definition of the *probability density function* of m. It is defined as any nonegative function $p_m(\mu)$ such that

$$F_m(\mu) = \int_{-\infty}^{\mu} p_m(\alpha)\, d\alpha \tag{2.2-3}$$

Thus, the density function is essentially the derivative of $F_m(\mu)$, but our definition avoids certain mathematical problems. Since we are interested in engineering applications, not mathematical perfection, when $F_m(\mu)$ contains discontinuities, we shall permit $p_m(\mu)$ to contain impulse functions. Appendix A contains a list of many common probability distributions and their associated density functions. The density function can be used to calculate the probability that the random variable m is contained in an interval M

$$P\{m \in M\} = \int_M p_m(\mu)\, d\mu \tag{2.2-4}$$

When no confusion is possible, we shall refer to the density function as $p(m)$, so that Eq. (2.2-4) would become

$$P\{m \in M\} = \int_M p(m)\, dm$$

Frequently we shall have to deal with probability spaces where there are several numbers assigned to each sample point in the sample space. Thus, an outcome ξ would specify a group of numbers: $m_1(\xi)$, $m_2(\xi)$, ..., $m_I(\xi)$. We shall refer to this group of numbers as the *random vector* $\mathbf{m}(\xi)$ and write it as

$$\mathbf{m}(\xi) = \begin{bmatrix} m_1(\xi) \\ m_2(\xi) \\ \vdots \\ m_I(\xi) \end{bmatrix}$$

Therefore, we have mapped the set of sample points Ω into an *I*-dimensional euclidean space. For the two-dimensional case, each sample point specifies a point on a plane.

In order to define events and assign a probability measure on this type of a sample space, we assume first that each of the m_i is a random variable. Then all sets of the form $\{\xi: m_i(\xi) \leq \mu_i\}$ are events and have probabilities. Since the intersection of events is an event, the sets $\{\xi: m_1(\xi) \leq \mu_1, m_2(\xi) \leq \mu_2, \ldots, m_I(\xi) \leq \mu_I\}$ are also events and have probabilities. We use these probabilities to define the joint probability distribution function:

$$\begin{aligned} F_{\mathbf{m}}(\boldsymbol{\mu}) &= P\{m_1 \leq \mu_1, m_2 \leq \mu_2, \ldots, m_I \leq \mu_I\} \\ &= P\{\mathbf{m} \leq \boldsymbol{\mu}\} \end{aligned} \tag{2.2-5}$$

The joint probability density function for a random vector can be defined by an intergral equation just as the density function for a scalar was. The only difference is that now we have an *I*-fold integral:

$$\begin{aligned} F_{\mathbf{m}}(\boldsymbol{\mu}) &= \int_{-\infty}^{\mu_I} \cdots \int_{-\infty}^{\mu_2} \int_{-\infty}^{\mu_1} p_{\mathbf{m}}(\alpha_1, \alpha_2, \cdots, \alpha_I) \, d\alpha_1 \, d\alpha_2 \cdots d\alpha_I \\ &= \int_{-\infty}^{\boldsymbol{\mu}} p_{\mathbf{m}}(\boldsymbol{\alpha}) \, d\boldsymbol{\alpha} \end{aligned} \tag{2.2-6}$$

If $\mathbf{M}$ represents some set of *I*-fold intervals in an *I*-dimensional euclidean space, the probability that $\mathbf{m}$ is in $\mathbf{M}$ is just

$$P\{\mathbf{m} \in \mathbf{M}\} = \int_{\mathbf{M}} p_{\mathbf{m}}(\boldsymbol{\mu}) \, d\boldsymbol{\mu} \tag{2.2-7}$$

The density function for one of the set of variables, say, m_1, can be found by integrating the joint density over the full range of the other variables:

$$p_{\mathbf{m}_1}(\alpha_1) = \int_{-\infty}^{\infty} \cdots \int_{-\infty}^{\infty} \int_{-\infty}^{\infty} p_{\mathbf{m}}(\boldsymbol{\mu}) \, d\mu_2 \, d\mu_3 \cdots d\mu_I \tag{2.2-8}$$

If the components of $\mathbf{m}$ are *independent*, the joint density function factors

$$p_{\mathbf{m}}(\boldsymbol{\mu}) = p_{m_1}(\mu_1) p_{m_2}(\mu_2) \cdots p_{m_I}(\mu_I) \tag{2.2-9}$$

As before, we shall use the shorthand notation $p(\mathbf{m})$ for the joint density function whenever possible.

Our use of the subscript notation method to distinguish between the various variables is simply a convenience. We could just as easily have given them each different names. For example, we could have a three-variable problem with variables x, y, and z. In this case, the density function of interest would have been $p_{x,y,z}(\alpha, \beta, \gamma)$.

Often we shall encounter a random variable that is defined as a function of other random variables. In this case, we can use Eq. (2.2-7) to find the density function of the function. For example, if a random variable z is defined as

$$z = x + n \qquad (2.2\text{-}10)$$

and if the joint density of x and n is known, then the probability distribution function of z can be found from

$$F_z(\gamma) = P\{z \le \gamma\} = P\{x + n \le \gamma\}$$

But the condition $x + n \le \gamma$ just defines a region of the x, n plane, and so we can use Eq. (2.2-7) to write

$$P\{z \le \gamma\} = \int_{\alpha + \beta \le \gamma} p_{x,n}(\alpha, \beta)\, d\alpha\, d\beta$$

$$= \int_{-\infty}^{\infty} \int_{-\infty}^{\gamma - \alpha} p_{x,n}(\alpha, \beta)\, d\beta\, d\alpha \qquad (2.2\text{-}11)$$

If we do a change of variables to $\beta' = \alpha + \beta$ and change the order of integration, this becomes

$$F_z(\gamma) = P\{z \le \gamma\} = \int_{-\infty}^{\gamma} \int_{-\infty}^{\infty} p_{x,n}(\alpha, \beta' - \alpha)\, d\alpha\, d\beta' \qquad (2.2\text{-}12)$$

So, from the definition of the density function

$$p_z(\gamma) = \int_{-\infty}^{\infty} p_{x,n}(\alpha, \gamma - \alpha)\, d\alpha \qquad (2.2\text{-}13)$$

Note that if x and n are independent, (2.2-13) is just the convolution of $p(x)$ and $p(n)$.

As we did for events, we shall wish to define *conditional probability densities*. In general, the density of $\mathbf{x}$ given $\mathbf{y}$ is defined as

$$p_{\mathbf{x}|\mathbf{y}}(\boldsymbol{\alpha}|\boldsymbol{\beta}) = \frac{p_{\mathbf{x},\mathbf{y}}(\boldsymbol{\alpha}, \boldsymbol{\beta})}{p_{\mathbf{y}}(\boldsymbol{\beta})} \qquad (2.2\text{-}14)$$

Therefore, there is also a *Bayes rule* statement for random variables. Using our shorthand, it is

$$p(\mathbf{x}|\mathbf{y}) = \frac{p(\mathbf{y}|\mathbf{x})p(\mathbf{x})}{p(\mathbf{y})} \qquad (2.2\text{-}15)$$

The problem treated in the following example will be used throughout this text.

Example 2.2-1: If z is the sum of two independent random variables x and n, find the conditional probability density of z given x.

To use the definition in Eq. (2.2-14), we must find the joint density function $p_{x,z}(\alpha, \gamma)$. Note, however, that Eq. (2.2-13) has exactly the form of Eq. (2.2-8), so that

$$p_{x,z}(\alpha, \gamma) = p_{x,n}(\alpha, \gamma - \alpha) \qquad (2.2\text{-}16)$$

Therefore, if x and n are independent, Eq. (2.2-16) factors and

$$p_{z|x}(\gamma|\alpha) = p_n(\gamma - \alpha)$$

Thus, if we know x, the density of z is just the density of n shifted.

Occasionally we shall be interested in probability spaces where random variables are defined on the sample points and where events are also defined on the sample points but not directly in terms of the random variables. For example, consider an experiment to determine whether it is too hot for this time of year. We would determine the temperature, a random variable, and the month, an event. The event and the random variable are related, but the event is not defined in terms of the random variable. In cases like this, we will define a *mixed probability distribution function* of the event A and the random vector $\mathbf{x}$ as the joint probability

$$F_{\mathbf{x}}(\boldsymbol{\alpha}, A) = P\{\mathbf{x} \leq \boldsymbol{\alpha}, A\}$$

Then the *joint density function* of the continuous vector $\mathbf{x}$ and the event A is defined by

$$F_{\mathbf{x}}(\boldsymbol{\alpha}, A) = \int_{-\infty}^{\alpha} p_{\mathbf{x}}(\boldsymbol{\beta}, A) \, d\boldsymbol{\beta} \qquad (2.2\text{-}17)$$

The conditional probability density of $\mathbf{x}$ conditioned on the event A will be of significant interest:

$$p_{\mathbf{x}}(\boldsymbol{\alpha}|A) = \frac{p_{\mathbf{x}}(\boldsymbol{\alpha}, A)}{P\{A\}} \qquad (2.2\text{-}18)$$

Also, we will use the conditional probability of A given that $\mathbf{x} = \boldsymbol{\alpha}$:

$$P\{A|\mathbf{x} = \boldsymbol{\alpha}\} = \frac{p_{\mathbf{x}}(\boldsymbol{\alpha}, A)}{p_{\mathbf{x}}(\boldsymbol{\alpha})} \qquad (2.2\text{-}19)$$

These last two equations can be combined to write the *mixed form of Bayes' rule*:

$$P\{A|\mathbf{x} = \boldsymbol{\alpha}\} = \frac{p_{\mathbf{x}}(\boldsymbol{\alpha}|A)P\{A\}}{p_{\mathbf{x}}(\boldsymbol{\alpha})} \qquad (2.2\text{-}20)$$

Finally, from Eqs. (2.2-16) and (2.2-17), it can be seen that

$$P\{A\} = P\{\mathbf{x} \leq \infty, A\} = \int_{-\infty}^{\infty} p_x(\boldsymbol{\beta}, A) \, d\boldsymbol{\beta} \qquad (2.2\text{-}21)$$

Example 2.2-2 Two friends, Smith and Jones, agree to meet on a given street corner sometime between noon and 1:00 P.M. Each agrees to wait exactly 10 min, but both say that their arrival time will be uniformly distributed over the hour. We wish to determine the probability that the two friends meet.

Letting A denote the event that the two meet, it is clear that if x is the arrival time of Smith in minutes, the conditional probability of A is

$$P\{A|x=\alpha\} = \begin{cases} \dfrac{10+\alpha}{60} & 0 \leq \alpha < 10 \\[2mm] \dfrac{20}{60} & 10 \leq \alpha < 50 \\[2mm] \dfrac{70-\alpha}{60} & 50 \leq \alpha < 60 \end{cases}$$

Therefore, from Eq. (2.2-21),

$$P\{A\} = \int_{-\infty}^{\infty} p_x(\alpha) P(A|x=\alpha) \, d\alpha = \frac{1}{60} \int_{0}^{60} P\{A|x=\alpha\} \, d\alpha$$

$$= \frac{11}{36}$$

The notion of *expected value* will play a significant role in our study. The expected value of a scalar random variable is defined as

$$E\{m\} = \int_{-\infty}^{\infty} mp(m) \, dm \qquad (2.2\text{-}22)$$

When it is convenient, we shall use the simpler notation $\bar{m}$ to denote expected value. The fundamental theorem of expectation states that if x is a function of m, then $\bar{x}$ is given by

$$E\{x\} = \bar{x} = \int_{-\infty}^{\infty} x(m)p(m) \, dm \qquad (2.2\text{-}23)$$

The expected value of certain simple functions of a simple random variable are particularly useful. The mean of a scalar variable $\bar{m}$ gives the average value of the variable, and the *variance*

$$\text{var}\,\{m\} = E\{(m - \bar{m})^2\} \qquad (2.2\text{-}24)$$

is an indication of how much it varies from its mean.

The expected value of a random vector is just a vector whose components are the expected values of the components of the random vector. Thus, the expected value of **m** is just

$$E\{\mathbf{m}\} = \begin{bmatrix} E\{m_1\} \\ E\{m_2\} \\ \vdots \\ E\{m_I\} \end{bmatrix} = \bar{\mathbf{m}} \qquad (2.2\text{-}25)$$

The variance of an I-dimensional random vector is the $I \times I$ matrix

$$\text{var } \{\mathbf{m}\} = E\{(\mathbf{m} - \bar{\mathbf{m}})(\mathbf{m} - \bar{\mathbf{m}})^T\} \qquad (2.2\text{-}26)$$

where $\mathbf{m}^T$ is the transpose of **m**. The component in the ith row and jth column of the matrix is $E\{(m_i - \bar{m}_i)(m_j - \bar{m}_j)\}$. Thus, only the terms on the diagonal are variances in the sense of Eq. (2.2-24). The off-diagonal elements are covariances and are defined formally as

$$\text{cov } \{m_i, m_j\} = E\{(m_i - \bar{m}_i)(m_j - \bar{m}_j)\}$$

The covariance of two I-dimensional random vectors is

$$\text{cov } \{\mathbf{m}, \mathbf{s}\} = E\{(\mathbf{m} - \bar{\mathbf{m}})(\mathbf{s} - \bar{\mathbf{s}})^T\} \qquad (2.2\text{-}27)$$

Two random vectors **m** and **s** are *uncorrelated* if

$$E\{\mathbf{m}\mathbf{s}^T\} = E\{\mathbf{m}\} E\{\mathbf{s}^T\} \qquad (2.2\text{-}28)$$

If **m** and **s** are independent, then they are also uncorrelated. In general, however, two random variables may be uncorrelated without being independent. The reader is reminded that if two random variables are jointly gaussian and uncorrelated, then they are also independent.

2.3 RANDOM PROCESSES

A *random process* or *stochastic process* can be viewed as a probability space with a time function $m(t, \xi)$ assigned to each sample point. However, in order to ensure a valid probability measure, the time functions must be assigned in such a way that for each permissible t, $m(t)$ is a random variable. This fact leads to the formal definition of a random process as a family of random variables $m(t)$ indexed by the parameter t.

Since each $m(t)$ is a random variable, the definition of expected value, variance, and covariance can be applied. The expectation

$$E\{m(t)\} = \int_{-\infty}^{\infty} \mu p_{m(t)}(\mu) \, d\mu = \bar{m}(t) \qquad (2.3\text{-}1)$$

is actually a time function as is the variance

$$\text{var } \{m(t)\} = \int_{-\infty}^{\infty} [\mu - \bar{m}(t)]^2 p_{m(t)}(\mu) \, d\mu \qquad (2.3\text{-}2)$$

The covariance depends on two index parameters t_1 and t_2. We give it the special name

$$C_m(t_1, t_2) = \text{cov } \{m(t_1), m(t_2)\} \qquad (2.3\text{-}3)$$

One additional function that will be of great use is the *autocorrelation function*

$$R_m(t_1, t_2) = E\{m(t_1)m(t_2)\} \qquad (2.3\text{-}4)$$

This is closely related to the covariance and, in fact,

$$C_m(t_1, t_2) = R_m(t_1, t_2) - \bar{m}(t_1)\bar{m}(t_2) \qquad (2.3\text{-}5)$$

In most of what follows, we shall be primarily concerned with *wide-sense stationary* processes whose expected value $\bar{m}(t)$ is a constant and whose autocorrelation function $R_m(t_1, t_2)$ depends only on the difference $\tau = t_1 - t_2$. In this case we introduce the shorthand notation

$$R_m(t_1, t_2) = R_m(t_1 - t_2, 0) = R_m(\tau) \qquad (2.3\text{-}6)$$

where τ is used to emphasize the dependence on a single variable. We shall refer to wide-sense stationary processes as simply *stationary* processes; this should not be confused with *strict-sense stationary*, which is a much stronger condition.

For a wide-sense stationary process the *power spectral density* of the process is the Fourier transform of $R_m(\tau)$:

$$S_m(f) = \int_{-\infty}^{\infty} R_m(\tau)e^{-j2\pi f\tau} \, d\tau \qquad (2.3\text{-}7)$$

Many times, noise processes have power spectral densities that are independent of f for all frequencies of interest. It is frequently desirable to approximate such processes with processes having power spectral densities that are constant for *all f*. We shall refer to these as *white noise processes*, and, as we shall see in Chap. 4, care must be taken in using this approximation.

A vector random process $\mathbf{m}(t)$ is just an l-dimensional generalization of a scalar random process. Instead of assigning a single time function to each sample point, a set of time functions are assigned. Each vector $\mathbf{m}(t)$ is required to be a random vector. Functions and operators equivalent to those in Eqs. (2.3-1) to (2.3-7) can be defined using the vector operations as given in Eqs. (2.2-25) to (2.2-27). The only change is the addition of the index t.

We shall also make use of discrete-time random processes. Here the process is family of random variables indexed by the integer k. All the definitions presented above carry over directly.

We shall also define a *discrete-time white-noise process* as well as the continuous process. The nice thing about the discrete-time version is that its definition is quite simple. The process $m(k)$ is white if

$$\text{cov } \{m(k_1), m(k_2)\} = 0 \qquad \text{for } k_1 \neq k_2$$

This concept is used in the following example.

Example 2.3-1 In general, the state variables of a linear, time-invariant, discrete-time system that is driven by white noise can be written as

$$\mathbf{x}(k + 1) = \mathbf{\Phi}\mathbf{x}(k) + \mathbf{\Gamma}\mathbf{n}(k)$$

where $\mathbf{n}(k)$ is the driving term and $\mathbf{\Phi}$ and $\mathbf{\Gamma}$ are fixed matrices. Letting $\mathbf{V}_n$ be the variance matrix of the noise, we wish to find a recursive expression for the variance matrix of $\mathbf{x}(k)$.

We shall assume that everything is zero-mean. We can use the defining equation to write

$$\mathbf{x}(k + 1)\mathbf{x}^T(k + 1) = [\mathbf{\Phi}\mathbf{x}(k) + \mathbf{\Gamma}\mathbf{n}(k)] \ [\mathbf{\Phi}\mathbf{x}(k) + \mathbf{\Gamma}\mathbf{n}(k)]^T$$

Taking expected values yields

$$\mathbf{V}_x(k + 1) = \mathbf{\Phi}\mathbf{V}_x(k)\mathbf{\Phi}^T + \mathbf{\Gamma}E\{\mathbf{n}(k)\mathbf{x}^T(k)\}\mathbf{\Phi}^T + \mathbf{\Phi}E\{\mathbf{x}(k)\mathbf{n}^T(k)\}\mathbf{\Gamma}^T + \mathbf{\Gamma}\mathbf{V}_n\mathbf{\Gamma}^T$$

But $\mathbf{x}(k)$ depends only on $\mathbf{n}(j)$ for $j < k$ and $\mathbf{n}(k)$ is white. Therefore, the middle two terms are zero and

$$\mathbf{V}_x(k + 1) = \mathbf{\Phi}\mathbf{V}_x(k)\mathbf{\Phi}^T + \mathbf{\Gamma}\mathbf{V}_n\mathbf{\Gamma}^T$$

2.4 SUMMARY

The purpose of this chapter has been to introduce some of the simple concepts and the associated notation of probability and stochastic processes which will be used throughout this book. The problems presented in Sec. 2.5 reinforce or further elaborate these concepts and should be undertaken by those who feel some weakness in this area of their background.

2.5 PROBLEMS

2.5-1 Consider drawing one card from a deck of cards. What is the probability that you draw
   (a) an ace?
   (b) a spade?
   (c) the ace of spades?
   (d) an ace or a spade?

2.5-2 Suppose that you have four boxes labeled A, B, C, and D. The first box contains 12 balls: 2 are labeled B; 4 are labeled C; and 6 are labeled D. Box B contains 4 red balls and 6 white balls; box C, 3 red and 7 white; and box D, 3 red and 6 white. The experiment is to draw a ball from box A and then, depending which ball you draw, draw another ball from box B, C, or D. Assume that all balls in a given box are *equiprobable*.
   (a) What is the probability of drawing a red ball?
   (b) What is the probability that the first ball was labeled B, given that the second ball was red?
   (c) Are the events "drawing a B ball" and "drawing a red ball" statistically independent?
   (d) Are the events "drawing a D ball" and "drawing a red ball" statistically independent?

2.5-3 A real-world experiment is performed in which two fair dice are thrown. If the sum of the two numbers is 4 or less, then event A has occurred. If at least one of the dice shows a 3, then event B has occurred.

(*a*) Construct a probabilistic model of this experiment by describing the sample space, sample points, events, and probability assignment.

(*b*) Describe the events

   (i) AB

   (ii) $A \cup B$

   (iii) AB^C

(*c*) Find the probabilities of these events.

2.5-4 A large family has decided it is time to stop buying so many Christmas presents. Therefore, at Thanksgiving they put all of their names in a hat, and each person draws a name. A drawing will be considered "successful" only if no one draws his or her own name. We wish to compute the probability of a successful drawing as a function of the number of people in the family.

(*a*) Compute the probability of a successful drawing P_N for family sizes of $N = 2$, 3, and 4.

(*b*) Letting $E_i(j)$ be the event that person i picks name j and letting S_N be a successful drawing, prove that

$$P_N = \sum_{j=2}^{N} [P\{S_N, E_j(1)|E_1(j)\} + P\{S_N, E_j^C(1)|E_1(j)\}] P\{E_1(j)\}$$

(*c*) From symmetry, it is clear that the bracketed term does not depend on j, and so it is easiest to evaluate it for $j = 2$. Find a simple arrangement to show that

$$P\{S_N|E_2(1), E_1(2)\} = P\{S_{N-2}\}$$

(*d*) Similarly, argue that

$$P\{S_N, E_2^C(1)|E_1(2)\} = P\{S_{N-1}\}$$

(*e*) Prove that

$$P_N = \sum_{n=2}^{N} \frac{(-1)^n}{n!}$$

satisfies the resulting recursive relationship and matches your answer to part (*a*). Find the value of P_N in the limit of large N.

2.5-5 (Buffon's needle problem) A needle of length x is dropped at random on a large surface on which parallel lines have been drawn. The lines are a distance d apart and $d > x$. We are interested in the event A where

$$A = \{\xi: \text{the needle crosses a line}\}$$

(*a*) Construct a probabilistic model for this experiment by describing a suitable sample space and probability assignment.

(*b*) Find $P(A)$.

This problem was originally proposed by George-Louis Leclerc, Comte de Buffon, an eighteenth-century French naturalist. He was amazed that the solution involved the constant π. Somehow, this no longer seems quite so amazing.

2.5-6 Consider two random variables x and y where

$$F_x(\alpha) = \begin{cases} 0 & \alpha < 0 \\ \alpha & 0 \le \alpha \le 1 \\ 1 & \alpha > 1 \end{cases}$$

and

$$y = 1 - x$$

Find and sketch
   (a) $F_y(\beta)$
   (b) $F_{x,y}(\alpha, \beta)$
Use part (b) to find
   (c) $p_{x,y}(\alpha, \beta)$
   (d) $p_y(\beta)$

2.5-7 Three gamblers A, B, and C each independently draw a number between 0 and 1 according to the density function

$$p_x(\alpha) = \begin{cases} 1 & 0 \le \alpha \le 1 \\ 0 & \text{elsewhere} \end{cases}$$

The gambler with the largest number wins.
   (a) What is the probability that A wins?
   (b) What is the probability that A wins given that he has drawn the number x_0?
   (c) A is now given the option of drawing a second number if he does not like his first number. What strategy should A use to maximize his probability of winning?

2.5-8 Let x be uniformly distributed between 0 and 1. Find the density of y when

$$y = -2 \ln x$$

2.5-9 Let x_1 and x_2 be two statistically independent gaussian random variables with zero mean and variance $\sigma^2 = 1$. Let

$$y = \begin{cases} 1 & \text{when } x_1^2 + x_2^2 > 1 \\ 0 & \text{otherwise} \end{cases}$$

Find the probability density of y.
   Hint: Use the definition of the distribution function of y. Also, you may want to use the change of variables

$$r^2 = x_1^2 + x_2^2$$

$$\theta = \tan^{-1} \frac{x_2}{x_1}$$

2.5-10 Consider two random variables x and y with joint probability density

$$p_{x,y}(\alpha, \beta) = \begin{cases} C & 0 \le \alpha^2 + \beta^2 \le 1 \\ 0 & 0 \text{ otherwise} \end{cases}$$

where C is a constant. If z is defined as

$$z = x^2 + y^2$$

find $p_z(\lambda)$.

2.5-11 Let x and y be independent with densities

$$p_x(\alpha) = \begin{cases} \dfrac{\alpha}{2} & 0 \le \alpha \le 2 \\ 0 & \text{otherwise} \end{cases}$$

$$p_y(\beta) = \begin{cases} 3\beta^2 & 0 \le \beta \le 1 \\ 0 & \text{otherwise} \end{cases}$$

Define

$$z = \frac{e^{xy}}{xy}$$

Find $E[z]$.

2.5-12 Let θ be a random variable and define z by

$$z = \sin \theta$$

(a) Find the density of z when

$$p_\theta(\phi) = \begin{cases} \dfrac{1}{\pi} & -\dfrac{\pi}{2} < \phi \le \dfrac{\pi}{2} \\ 0 & \text{otherwise} \end{cases}$$

(b) Find the density of z where

$$p_\theta(\phi) = \begin{cases} \dfrac{2}{N\pi} & -N\pi + \alpha < \phi \, N\pi + \alpha \\ 0 \end{cases}$$

when α is a constant and N is a constant integer.

2.5-12 Let $x(t)$ be the random process

$$x(t) = \sin(t + \phi)$$

where ϕ is a random variable. Find $p_{x(t)}(\alpha), R_x(t_1,t_2)$, and $S_x(f)$ when it exists for the following cases:

(a) ϕ is uniform over $(0, \pi/2)$
(b) ϕ is uniform over $(0, \pi)$
(c) ϕ is uniform over $(0, 2\pi)$

2.5-13 Let $x(t)$ be a stationary gaussian random process with autocorrelation function

$$R_x(\tau) = \begin{cases} 1 & |\tau| \le 1 \\ 0 & \text{otherwise} \end{cases}$$

and $\qquad\qquad E[x(t)] = \tfrac{1}{2}$

(a) Find var $\{x(t)\}$
(b) If

$$y(t) = x(t) + x(t + \tfrac{1}{2})$$

is $y(t)$ a gaussian random process

(c) Find $R_y(\tau)$.

2.5-14 Let $F(t)$ be a known (nonrandom) function and let $x(t)$ be a gaussian random process with mean function $m(t)$ and correlation function $R(t, s)$.

(a) Find the mean function and the correlation function of

$$y_1(t) = F(t)x(t)$$

(b) Find the mean function and the correlation function of

$$y_2(t) = F(t) + x(t)$$

(c) Prove that $y_1(t)$ and $y_2(t)$ are gaussian random processes.

2.5-15 A discrete-time gaussian process is defined as one where any set of elements

$$\mathbf{x} = [x(1)\, x(2) \cdots x(I)]^T$$

has the density function

$$p_{\mathbf{x}}(\boldsymbol{\alpha}) = (2\pi)^{-1/2}(\det \mathbf{V}_{\mathbf{x}})^{-1/2}\exp\ \{-\tfrac{1}{2}(\boldsymbol{\alpha} - \mathbf{x})^T\mathbf{V}_{\mathbf{x}}^{-1}\ (\boldsymbol{\alpha} - \mathbf{x})\}$$

where the mean of $\mathbf{x}$ is $\bar{\mathbf{x}}$ and the variance of $\mathbf{x}$ is $\mathbf{V}_{\mathbf{x}}$. Two such gaussian processes $\mathbf{x}$ and $\mathbf{y}$ are jointly gaussian if their joint density has the same form.

(a) Let $\mathbf{x}$ and $\mathbf{y}$ be jointly gaussian random processes and define

$$\mathbf{z} = \begin{bmatrix} \mathbf{x} \\ \mathbf{y} \end{bmatrix}$$

Write the density function of $\mathbf{z}$ in terms of $\bar{\mathbf{x}}$, $\bar{\mathbf{y}}$, $\mathbf{V}_{\mathbf{x}}$, $\mathbf{V}_{\mathbf{y}}$ and cov $\{\mathbf{x}, \mathbf{y}\}$.

(b) If $\mathbf{x}$ and $\mathbf{y}$ are zero mean, find $E\{\mathbf{x}|\mathbf{y}\}$ in terms of $\mathbf{y}$, $\mathbf{V}_{\mathbf{x}}$, and $\mathbf{V}_{\mathbf{z}} = \text{var } \{\mathbf{z}\}$.

THREE

BINARY DECISIONS: SINGLE OBSERVATION

In this chapter, we shall consider the simplest class of decision problems: binary decisions with a single observation. Although they represent the simplest class of decision problems, binary decision problems illustrate most of the concepts which underlie all decision theory. By *binary decision*, we mean that there are two messages m_1 and m_2 in the message space M and that the decision space D also has only two elements d_1 and d_2. For convenience, we shall assume a natural pairing of decisions and messages; in other words, if m_1 is sent, then d_1 is the "correct" decision. Our problem is to select the decision rule $d(z)$ which maps the observation space Z into the binary decision space in some optimal manner. Since there are only two decisions, this is equivalent to dividing Z into two *decision regions* Z_1 and Z_2 such that $d(z) = d_1$ if $z \in Z_1$ and $d(z) = d_2$ if $z \in Z_2$. The regions Z_1 and Z_2 must be disjoint $(Z_1 Z_2 = \varnothing)$ in order that each point in Z will yield a unique decision. The regions Z_1 and Z_2 must cover Z $(Z_1 \cup Z_2 = Z)$ in order that each point in Z will have a decision associated with it.

In the following sections of this chapter we shall examine five criteria for designing the decision rule $d(z)$. The approach will be to begin with the criterion which requires the least structure for the decision problem and then to add structural requirements. The reader should not infer that the more structured procedures are necessarily better. In many problems, only limited structural features are known and the simpler procedures are the only applicable ones.

3.1 MAXIMUM-LIKELIHOOD DECISION CRITERION

The nature of the first decision criterion we shall analyze is best illustrated by an example. If Rip Van Winkle awoke from his legendary 20-year nap and found that he felt cold and if he had to decide whether it was summer or winter based only on the temperature, he would probably have decided that it was winter. His decision would have been based on the fact that the probability that it is cold in the winter is higher than the probability that it is cold in the summer. He has made what we shall call a *maximum-likelihood decision.*

The maximum-likelihood decision criterion is the simplest of the techniques we shall examine in this chapter. Unfortunately, its simplicity is also its weakness since it is frequently too simple to adequately represent realistic problems. The method is presented here primarily to introduce the basic elements of decision problems. In addition, the maximum-likelihood decision criterion is introduced since we wish to emphasize the parallel methods in decision and estimation. The maximum-likelihood estimation method, which is introduced in Chap. 8, is a valuable tool.

The basic concept of the maximum-likelihood criterion is to select the decision corresponding to the message which is the most likely cause of the observed phenomenon. Suppose, for example, that we must diagnose whether a patient has disease A or B based on some observed symptoms. Assume that the observed symptoms occur with probability 0.75 if the patient has disease A and with probability 0.10 if the patient has disease B. Based on the maximum-likelihood criterion, we would decide that the patient has disease A since it is the most likely cause of the observed symptoms. If this were the only information available, it would be a good decision. If, however, we knew that disease A is rare and that disease B is common, it might not be. Knowing that A is rare and B is common gives the problem more structure than is compatible with the maximum-likelihood procedure. We shall discuss methods for dealing with more structured problems in Secs. 3.3 and 3.4.

The maximum-likelihood decision techniques require only that we know the conditional probability density functions of the observation given each of the possible messages, that is, $p(z|m_1)$ and $p(z|m_2)$. The criterion can be stated in the following form.

Maximum-likelihood decision criterion Given an observation $z \in Z$, let $d(z) = d_1$ if it is more likely that m_1 generated z than that m_2 generated z.

If the message is m_1, then the probability of receiving an observation in the range $(z, z + dz)$ for sufficiently small dz is $p(z|m_1)\, dz$. On the other hand, if the message is m_2, then the probability of receiving an observation in the range $(z, z + dz)$ is $p(z|m_2)\, dz$. Hence to select the more likely cause of an observation in the range $(z, z + dz)$, we decide d_1 if $p(z|m_1)\, dz > p(z|m_2)\, dz$ and we decide d_2 if $p(z|m_1)\, dz < p(z|m_2)\, dz$. Canceling the common dz on both sides of the inequalities and letting dz approach zero yields the following decision rule:

$$d(z) = \begin{cases} d_1 & \text{if } p(z|m_1) > p(z|m_2) \\ d_2 & \text{if } p(z|m_2) > p(z|m_1) \end{cases} \tag{3.1-1}$$

Now given a particular observation z_0, we may compute $p(z_0|m_1)$ and $p(z_0|m_2)$ and then apply the decision rule given in Eq. (3.1-1). It should be noted that we have not assigned a decision when $p(z|m_1) = p(z|m_2)$. The values of z for which the conditional densities are equal may be arbitrarily assigned to either d_1 or d_2 since m_1 and m_2 are equally likely to have been the cause of the observed z.

Example 3.1-1 To illustrate the maximum-likelihood method, let us determine the decision rule associated with the following example. If the message is m_1, the observation is just the zero-mean unit-variance gaussian random noise n. If the message is m_2, the observation is $1 + n$. A shorthand way of writing this is

$$m_1 : z = n$$

$$m_2 : z = 1 + n$$

This problem is sometimes referred to as a *test of the mean* since the two messages differ only in the mean of the conditional density.
It is easy to determine the conditional probability density of z given m_1 or m_2 as

$$p(z|m_1) = \frac{1}{\sqrt{2\pi}} \exp \frac{-z^2}{2}$$

$$p(z|m_2) = \frac{1}{\sqrt{2\pi}} \exp \frac{-(z-1)^2}{2}$$

Now suppose that we receive an observation $z = 0.6$. Then

$$p(z = 0.6|m_1) = \frac{1}{\sqrt{2\pi}} \exp \frac{-(0.6)^2}{2} = 0.33$$

$$p(z = 0.6|m_2) = \frac{1}{\sqrt{2\pi}} \exp \frac{-(0.6-1)^2}{2} = 0.37$$

Since $p(z = 0.6|m_2) > p(z = 0.6|m_1)$, we would make the decision d_2; that is, $d(0.6) = d_2$.

The preceding example illustrates that the direct application of the decision rule given by Eq. (3.1-1) may be computationally unwieldy. This can sometimes be simplified by performing mathematical operations on the conditional densities. As noted at the beginning of this chapter, an equivalent method for representing the decision rule of Eq. (3.1-1) is to define the decision regions Z_1 and Z_2 as

$$Z_1 = \{z: p(z|m_1) > p(z|m_2)\}$$

$$Z_2 = \{z: p(z|m_1) < p(z|m_2)\} \tag{3.1-2}$$

If we define the *likelihood ratio* $\Lambda(z)$ as

$$\Lambda(z) = \frac{p(z|m_2)}{p(z|m_1)} \tag{3.1-3}$$

then Z_1 and Z_2 may be defined as

$$Z_1 = \{z: \Lambda(z) < 1\} \qquad (3.1\text{-}4)$$

$$Z_2 = \{z: \Lambda(z) > 1\}$$

We shall use the shorthand notation

$$\Lambda(z) \underset{d_1}{\overset{d_2}{\gtrless}} 1 \qquad (3.1\text{-}5)$$

to represent the result described by Eq. (3.1-4). For some cases, the formulation in Eq. (3.1-5) may be easier to evaluate than that in Eq. (3.1-1). Frequently it can be simplified even further. We may operate on the likelihood ratio expression with any operator as long as we uniquely retain the ordering of $\Lambda(z)$ relative to unity. The natural logarithm is often a useful operator especially for gaussian problems. To illustrate the usefulness of Eq. (3.1-5), let us consider again the decision problem of Example 3.1-1.

Example 3.1-2 The likelihood ratio for the decision problem of Example 3.1-1 is given by

$$\Lambda(z) = \frac{p(z|m_2)}{p(z|m_1)} = \frac{(1/\sqrt{2\pi}) \exp\left[-(z-1)^2/2\right]}{(1/\sqrt{2\pi}) \exp\left(-z^2/2\right)}$$

$$= \exp\frac{-[(z-1)^2 - z^2]}{2}$$

$$= \exp\frac{(2z-1)}{2}$$

Hence the decision rule can be written as

$$\exp\frac{(2z-1)}{2} \underset{d_1}{\overset{d_2}{\gtrless}} 1 \qquad (3.1\text{-}6)$$

Now for $z = 0.6$, we have

$$\exp\frac{2(0.6)-1}{2} = 1.105 \underset{d_1}{\overset{d_2}{\gtrless}} 1$$

and $d(0.6) = d_2$ as expected.

The decision rule of Eq. (3.1-6) is in a slightly simpler form than Eq. (3.1-1), but it still requires an exponential operation. Let us take the natural logarithm of both sides of Eq. (3.1-6) to obtain

$$\frac{2z-1}{2} \underset{d_1}{\overset{d_2}{\gtrless}} 0$$

or
$$z \overset{d_2}{\underset{d_1}{\gtrless}} \tfrac{1}{2}$$

Now the decision rule is in a trivially simple form and given any observation we can immediately make a decision. The decision regions for this problem can now be defined in the following way:

$$Z_1 = \{z\colon z < \tfrac{1}{2}\} = (-\infty, \tfrac{1}{2})$$
$$Z_2 = \{z\colon z > \tfrac{1}{2}\} = (\tfrac{1}{2}, \infty)$$

It is instructive to examine graphically the decision rule of Example 3.1-2. Figure 3.1-1 shows a plot of the two conditional densities and the maximum-likelihood decision regions Z_1 and Z_2. We note that Z_1 is the region where $p(z|m_1) > p(z|m_2)$ and Z_2 is the region where $p(z|m_1) < p(z|m_2)$. In this problem the decision rule, which is a single-threshold test on the likelihood ratio as given by Eq. (3.1-5), is also a single-threshold test on the observation, namely,

$$z \overset{d_2}{\underset{d_1}{\gtrless}} \tfrac{1}{2}$$

The maximum-likelihood test does not always correspond to a single-threshold test in terms of the observation. To illustrate this point, let us consider the following example.

Example 3.1-3 Let us determine the maximum-likelihood decision rule associated with the following messages:

$$m_1\colon p(z|m_1) = \frac{1}{\sqrt{2\pi}} \exp \frac{-z^2}{2}$$

$$m_2\colon p(z|m_2) = \frac{1}{2\sqrt{2\pi}} \exp \frac{-z^2}{8}$$

The problem is sometimes referred to as a *test of variance* since the conditional densities differ only in variance. The likelihood ratio for this problem

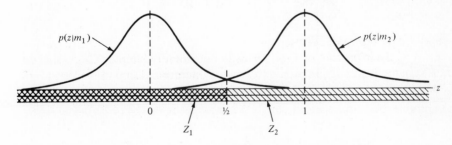

Figure 3.1-1 Graphical representation of the decision rule for Example 3.1-2.

is given by

$$\Lambda(z) = \frac{p(z|m_2)}{p(z|m_1)} = \frac{(1/2\sqrt{2\pi})\exp(-z^2/8)}{(1/\sqrt{2\pi})\exp(-z^2/2)}$$

$$= \tfrac{1}{2}\exp\frac{+3z^2}{8}$$

The decision rule is therefore

$$\frac{1}{2}\exp\frac{3z^2}{8} \overset{d_2}{\underset{d_1}{\gtrless}} 1$$

or

$$\exp\frac{3z^2}{8} \overset{d_2}{\underset{d_1}{\gtrless}} 2$$

Now taking the natural logarithm on both sides yields

$$\frac{3z^2}{8} \overset{d_2}{\underset{d_1}{\gtrless}} \ln 2$$

or

$$z^2 \overset{d_2}{\underset{d_1}{\gtrless}} \tfrac{8}{3}\ln 2$$

An equivalent form for this decision rule is

$$|z| \overset{d_2}{\underset{d_2}{\gtrless}} \sqrt{\tfrac{8}{3}\ln 2} = 1.36$$

Hence, if $|z| > 1.36$, we decide d_2 and if $|z| < 1.36$, we decide d_1. A plot of the conditional densities is shown in Fig. 3.1-2 and reveals the logic of this decision rule. Here the conditional densities for both have zero mean but $p(z|m_2)$ has a larger variance. Hence large values of z are more likely to be the consequence of m_2 than of m_1.

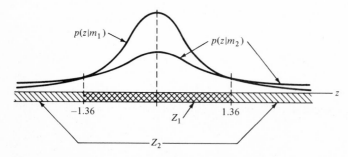

Figure 3.1-2 Graphical representation of the decision rule for Example 3.1-3.

3.2 NEYMAN-PEARSON CRITERION

In this section we consider another method for determining the decision rule $d(z)$ for a simple binary decision problem. Before presenting the Neyman-Pearson decision criterion, it is necessary to introduce some definitions and notation.

There are two types of errors that we can make in a binary decision problem. First, we may decide d_2 when m_1 is true, and second we may decide d_1 when m_2 is true. Each of these errors has a probability associated with it which depends on the decision rule and conditional densities. The following notation will be employed:

$$P\{d_2|m_1\} = \text{Probability of making decision } d_2 \text{ when } m_1 \text{ is true}$$

$$P\{d_1|m_2\} = \text{Probability of making decision } d_1 \text{ when } m_2 \text{ is true}$$

We can express these probabilities in terms of the conditional densities and decision regions as

$$P\{d_2|m_1\} = P\{z \in Z_2|m_1\} = \int_{Z_2} p(z|m_1)\, dz \qquad (3.2\text{-}1)$$

$$P\{d_1|m_2\} = P\{z \in Z_1|m_2\} = \int_{Z_1} p(z|m_2)\, dz \qquad (3.2\text{-}2)$$

The error of deciding d_2 when m_1 is true is sometimes referred to as a *type-one error*, or an *error or the first kind*. Deciding d_1 when m_2 is true is a *type-two error*, or an *error of the second kind*. We shall not make use of this terminology in our study.

In addition to two errors, there are also two correct decisions that we can make in the binary decision problem. We may decide d_1 when m_1 is true and we may decide d_2 when m_2 is true. Again these correct decisions have associated probabilities represented by

$$P\{d_1|m_1\} = \text{Probability of making decision } d_1 \text{ when } m_1 \text{ is true}$$

$$P\{d_2|m_2\} = \text{Probability of making decision } d_2 \text{ when } m_2 \text{ is true}$$

In terms of the conditional densities and decision regions, these probabilities may be expressed as

$$P\{d_1|m_1\} = P\{z \in Z_1|m_1\} = \int_{Z_1} p(z|m_1)\, dz \qquad (3.2\text{-}3)$$

$$P\{d_2|m_2\} = P\{z \in Z_2|m_2\} = \int_{Z_2} p(z|m_2)\, dz \qquad (3.2\text{-}4)$$

Since we must make either decision d_1 or d_2, the probability of error plus the probability of a correct decision must equal 1 for both messages so that

$$P\{d_1|m_1\} + P\{d_2|m_1\} = 1 \qquad (3.2\text{-}5)$$

$$P\{d_1|m_2\} + P\{d_2|m_2\} = 1 \qquad (3.2\text{-}6)$$

We can also obtain this result by substituting Eqs. (3.2-1) and (3.2-3) as

$$P\{d_1|m_1\} + P\{d_2|m_1\} = \int_{Z_1} p(z|m_1)\, dz + \int_{Z_2} p(z|m_1)\, dz$$

$$= \int_Z p(z|m_1)\, dz = 1 \qquad (3.2\text{-}7)$$

The probability $P\{d_2|m_1\}$ is sometimes referred to as the *false-alarm probability*, $P\{d_1|m_2\}$ as the *miss probability*, and $P\{d_2|m_2\}$ as the *detection probability*. These names are the result of the application of decision theory (also called *detection theory*) to a class of problems loosely defined as the *radar problem*. In this class of problems, m_1 is the message that no object is present while m_2 corresponds to the object present situation. Hence the decision d_2 when m_1 is true is a decision that an object is present when, in fact, no object is present, i.e., a false alarm.

In terms of statistical decision theory, $P\{d_2|m_1\}$ is often referred to as the *level of significance* while $P\{d_2|m_2\}$ is the *power of the test*. This terminology arises out of the concept of equating m_1 to the null hypothesis (no change has occurred) and m_2 to the alternative hypothesis (some change has occurred). The power of the test then describes the probability of announcing a change when, in fact, one has occurred. The level of significant represents the probability of incorrectly announcing a change. For a good decision procedure, one would like to make the power $P\{d_2|m_2\}$ as large as possible and the level of significance $P\{d_2|m_1\}$ as small as possible.

It is not possible, however, to simultaneously maximize $P\{d_2|m_2\}$ and minimize $P\{d_2|m_1\}$. As we increase $P\{d_2|m_2\}$, we tend also to increase $P\{d_2|m_1\}$; and conversely as we decrease $P\{d_2|m_1\}$, we also decrease $P\{d_2|m_2\}$. As an exaggerated case, we note that if we let $Z_2 = Z$ and $Z_1 = \varnothing$, then $P\{d_2|m_2\}$ is 1; however, $P\{d_2|m_1\}$ is also 1. The Neyman-Pearson criterion provides a workable solution to this paradox.

Neyman-Pearson decision criterion Fix $P\{d_2|m_1\}$ at a preselected value α_0, then maximize $P\{d_2|m_2\}$.

The Neyman-Pearson decision criterion says that we should maximize the power for a given level of significance. In other words, out of all the decision regions Z_2 for which $P\{d_2|m_1\} = \alpha_0$, we are to select the one for which $P\{d_2|m_2\}$ is maximum. This is a classical problem in optimization theory: maximizing a function subject to a constraint, which can be solved by the use of Lagrange multipliers.

To use this approach we append the constraint $P\{d_2|m_1\} = \alpha_0$ to $P\{d_2|m_2\}$ by the use of an undetermined Lagrange multiplier λ. Therefore we now wish to select the decision region Z_2 in order to maximize:

$$\Gamma = P\{d_2|m_2\} - \lambda[P\{d_2|m_1\} - \alpha_0] \qquad (3.2\text{-}8)$$

The problem is now treated as unconstrained but with λ as a parameter so that the resulting Z_2 will be a function of λ. The Lagrange multiplier is then chosen to satisfy the constraint. Once the constraint is satisfied, the second term on the right side of Eq. (3.2-8) is zero and we have truly maximized $P\{d_2|m_2\}$ subject to the constraint. The minus sign has been chosen in front of λ in Eq. (3.2-8) in order to simplify the final result.

If we substitute Eqs. (3.2-1) and (3.2-4) into Eq. (3.2-8), we obtain the following expression for Γ:

$$
\begin{aligned}
\Gamma &= \int_{Z_2} p(z|m_2)\, dz - \lambda \left[\int_{Z_2} p(z|m_1)\, dz - \alpha_0 \right] \\
&= \int_{Z_2} [p(z|m_2) - \lambda p(z|m_1)]\, dz + \lambda\, \alpha_0
\end{aligned}
\tag{3.2-9}
$$

To maximize Γ by selection of Z_2, we should put into the region Z_2 the values of z for which the integrand is positive. Therefore Z_2 is given by

$$Z_2 = \{z\colon [p(z|m_2) - \lambda p(z|m_1)] > 0\} \tag{3.2-10}$$

and Z_1 is

$$Z_1 = \{z\colon [p(z|m_2) - \lambda p(z|m_1)] < 0\} \tag{3.2-11}$$

It should be remembered that we must select λ such that the constraint

$$P\{d_2|m_1\} = \alpha_0 = \int_{Z_2} p(z|m_1)\, dz \tag{3.2-12}$$

is satisfied. The basic approach is to compute $P\{d_2|m_1\}$ as a function of λ and then find the value(s) of λ which make $P\{d_2|m_1\}$ equal to α_0.

If we make use of the likelihood ratio

$$\Lambda(z) = \frac{p(z|m_2)}{p(z|m_1)}$$

we can write Z_1 and Z_2 as

$$Z_1 = \{z\colon \Lambda(z) < \lambda\}$$
$$Z_2 = \{z\colon \Lambda(z) > \lambda\} \tag{3.2-13}$$

We can also represent the decision rule in our shorthand notation as

$$\Lambda(z) \overset{d_2}{\underset{d_1}{\gtrless}} \lambda \tag{3.2-14}$$

A comparison of Eqs. (3.1-5) and (3.2-14) indicates that the maximum-likelihood and Neyman-Pearson decision rules are identical in form, namely, a test of likelihood ratio against a threshold. In the maximum-likelihood decision rule, the threshold is always unity, while in the Neyman-Pearson decision rule we must select the threshold λ in order to satisfy the constraint of Eq. (3.2-12). Let us consider a simple example to illustrate the use of the Neyman-Pearson decision criterion and the selection of λ.

Example 3.2-1 We treat again the binary decision problem of Example 3.1-1 with the following conditional density:

$$p(z|m_1) = \frac{1}{\sqrt{2\pi}} \exp \frac{-z^2}{2}$$

$$p(z|m_2) = \frac{1}{\sqrt{2\pi}} \exp \frac{-(z-1)^2}{2}$$

We require that $P\{d_2|m_1\} = 0.25$. The likelihood ratio is given by

$$\Lambda(z) = \exp \frac{(2z-1)}{2}$$

and the decision rule is

$$\exp \frac{2z-1}{2} \underset{d_1}{\overset{d_2}{\gtrless}} \lambda$$

Let us take the natural logarithm of both sides of this expression to obtain

$$\frac{2z-1}{2} \underset{d_1}{\overset{d_2}{\gtrless}} \ln \lambda$$

or

$$z \underset{d_1}{\overset{d_2}{\gtrless}} \ln \lambda + \tfrac{1}{2}$$

The decision region Z_2 is therefore

$$Z_2 = \{z\colon z > \ln \lambda + \tfrac{1}{2}\}$$

Now we must select λ such that $P\{d_2|m_1\} = 0.25$. We know that

$$P\{d_2|m_1\} = \int_{Z_2} p(z|m_1)\, dz = \int_{\ln \lambda + 1/2}^{\infty} \frac{1}{\sqrt{2\pi}} e^{-z^2/2}\, dz$$

Using Table B.1 in App. B, we find that

$$Q(0.674) = \int_{0.674}^{\infty} \frac{1}{\sqrt{2\pi}} e^{-z^2/2}\, dz = 0.25$$

so that we have

$$\ln \lambda + \tfrac{1}{2} = 0.674$$

Solving for λ yields

$$\lambda = 1.19$$

We note, however, that it is really not necessary to obtain λ since the decision rule is expressed in terms of $\ln \lambda + \tfrac{1}{2}$ and is therefore

$$z \underset{d_1}{\overset{d_2}{\gtrless}} 0.674$$

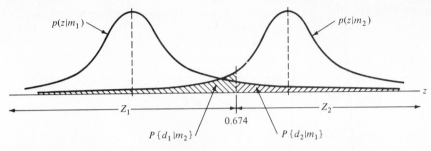

Figure 3.2-1 Decision rule for Example 3.2-1.

This decision rule is illustrated in Fig. 3.2-1 where the error probabilities are shown graphically.

Example 3.2-2 For this example, the conditional probabilities are given by

$$p(z|m_1) = \begin{cases} \frac{3}{2}(1-z)^2 & 0 \le z < 2 \\ 0 & \text{otherwise} \end{cases}$$

$$p(z|m_2) = \begin{cases} \frac{3}{4}z(2-z) & 0 \le z < 2 \\ 0 & \text{otherwise} \end{cases}$$

The likelihood ratio is

$$\Lambda(z) = \frac{\frac{3}{4}z(2-z)}{\frac{3}{2}(1-z)^2} = \frac{z(2-z)}{2(1-z)^2}$$

Since $z(2-z) = 1 - (1-z)^2$, we can write $\Lambda(z)$ as

$$\Lambda(z) = \frac{1}{2}\left[\frac{1}{(1-z)^2} - 1 \right]$$

A plot of $\Lambda(z)$ versus z is shown in Fig. 3.2-2 with Z_1 and Z_2 represented in terms of λ. If ζ is defined by $\Lambda(\zeta) = \lambda$, then the decision regions are given by

$$Z_1 = \{z: 0 \le z \le \zeta \text{ or } 2 - \zeta \le z \le 2\}$$
$$Z_2 = \{z: \zeta \le z \le 2 - \zeta\}$$

Now we must select λ and hence ζ such that $P\{d_2|m_1\} = \alpha_0$. Let us choose $\alpha_0 = 0.2$ in order to be able to calculate a specific value for λ. The error probability $P\{d_2|m_1\}$ is given by

$$P\{d_2|m_1\} = \int_{\zeta}^{2-\zeta} \frac{3}{2}(1-z)^2 \, dz$$

$$= (1 - \zeta)^3$$

Hence we must select λ such that

$$(1 - \zeta)^3 = 0.2$$

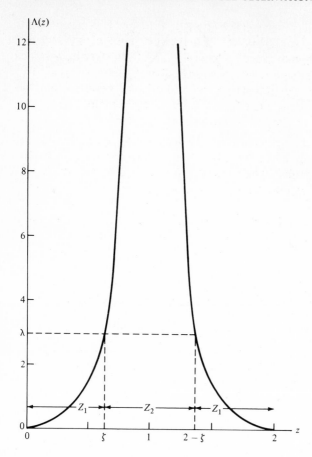

Figure 3.2-2 Example 3.2-2.

The solution of this cubic equation yields

$$\zeta = 0.415$$

so that

$$Z_1 = \{z: |z - 1| > 0.585\}$$
$$Z_2 = \{z: |z - 1| < 0.585\}$$

Notice that, once again, it is not necessary to calculate λ in order to determine the decision rule.

As noted previously in this section, one would ideally like to simultaneously maximize $P\{d_2|m_2\}$ and minimize $P\{d_2|m_1\}$. However, the simultaneous optimization is not possible, and the Neyman-Pearson criterion was offered as an approach to the design of decision rules. By the use of the Neyman-Pearson criterion, the decision rule is completely specified by the selection of α_0; however, no logical procedure has been provided for selecting α_0.

The use of a *receiver operating characteristic* (ROC) can provide some guidance in the selection of α_0. The receiver operating characteristic is a plot of the probability of detection (power) $P\{d_2|m_2\}$ for the Neyman-Pearson decision rule versus the probability of false alarm (level of significance) $P\{d_2|m_1\}$ as a function of one or more parameters. The ROC may be obtained by determining $P\{d_2|m_2\}$ as a function of $\alpha_0 = P\{d_2|m_1\}$ and varying α_0 from zero to one. Alternatively, one may determine both $P\{d_2|m_2\}$ and $P\{d_2|m_1\}$ as functions of the threshold λ and then vary λ from zero to infinity.

Example 3.2-3 In order to illustrate this procedure, let us determine the ROC for the problem of Example 3.2-1. Here, however, we will assume that the expected value of z when m_2 is true is $\mu > 0$ rather than unity. Hence the conditional densities of z are given by

$$p(z|m_1) = \frac{1}{\sqrt{2\pi}} \exp \frac{-z^2}{2}$$

$$p(z|m_2) = \frac{1}{\sqrt{2\pi}} \exp \frac{-(z-\mu)^2}{2}$$

It is easy to show that the Neyman-Pearson decision rule is

$$z \underset{d_2}{\overset{d_1}{\gtrless}} \frac{\ln \lambda}{\mu} + \frac{\mu}{2}$$

The false-alarm probability is therefore

$$P\{d_2|m_1\} = \int_{\frac{\ln \lambda}{\mu} + \frac{\mu}{2}}^{\infty} \frac{1}{\sqrt{2\pi}} \exp \frac{-z^2}{2} \, dz = Q\left(\frac{\ln \lambda}{\mu} + \frac{\mu}{2}\right)$$

while the probability of detection is

$$P\{d_2|m_2\} = \int_{\frac{\ln \lambda}{\mu} + \frac{\mu}{2}}^{\infty} \frac{1}{\sqrt{2\pi}} \exp \frac{-(z-\mu)^2}{2} \, dz$$

Using the transformation $v = z - \mu$, we obtain

$$P\{d_2|m_2\} = \int_{\frac{\ln \lambda}{\mu} - \frac{\mu}{2}}^{\infty} \frac{1}{\sqrt{2\pi}} \exp \frac{-v^2}{2} \, dv = Q\left(\frac{\ln \lambda}{\mu} - \frac{\mu}{2}\right)$$

Now for any given value of μ, we may vary λ from zero to infinity and obtain $P\{d_2|m_1\}$ and $P\{d_2|m_2\}$ by the use of the table in App. B. The resulting ROC is shown in Fig. 3.2-3 for $\mu = 0$, 1, and 2.

Although the ROC shown in Fig. 3.2-3 has been developed for a specific example, it is representative of ROCs. In particular, it is possible to show (Van Trees, 1968) that all ROCs associated with tests where $P\{d_2|m_2\}$ is a continuous function of $P\{d_2|m_1\}$ have the following properties:

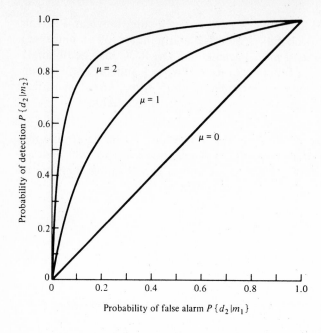

Figure 3.2-3 Receiver operating characteristic for Example 3.2-3.

1. All likelihood-ratio tests have ROCs which are concave downward.
2. All likelihood-ratio tests have ROCs which are on or above the $P\{d_2|m_2\} = P\{d_2|m_1\}$ line.
3. The slope of the ROC at any point is equal to the value of the threshold λ required to achieve the $P\{d_2|m_2\}$ and $P\{d_2|m_1\}$ which define that point.

The first property is illustrated by the following argument: Suppose the nonconcave curve of Fig. 3.2-4 was an ROC. If decision rule $d(z)$ is used to achieve point 1 and $d'(z)$ is used to achieve point 2, then a rule that used $d(z)$ half of the time and $d'(z)$ half of the time would operate at point 3. Clearly point 3 would have a higher $P\{d_2|m_2\}$ than the corresponding point on the ROC. Since this contradicts the definition of the ROC, the curve must be concave downward.

The second property is just a special case of the first since all ROC curves must end on or above the $P\{d_2|m_1\} = P\{d_2|m_2\}$ line. The third property can be established by first writing the probabilities $P\{d_2|m_2\}$ and $P\{d_2|m_1\}$ in terms of the likelihood ratio as

$$P\{d_2|m_2\} = P\{\Lambda > \lambda|m_2\} = \int_\lambda^\infty p(\Lambda|m_2)\, d\Lambda \tag{3.2-15}$$

and
$$P\{d_2|m_1\} = P\{\Lambda > \lambda|m_1\} = \int_\lambda^\infty p(\Lambda|m_1)\, d\Lambda \tag{3.2-16}$$

Here $p(\Lambda|m_1)$ and $p(\Lambda|m_2)$ are the probability density functions of Λ given m_1 and m_2. The likelihood ratio has been treated as simply a complicated transformation of the random observation z.

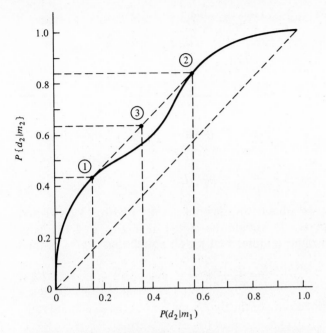

Figure 3.2-4 Nonconvex ROC curve.

Taking the derivative of $P\{d_2|m_2\}$ and $P\{d_2|m_1\}$ with respect to λ yields

$$\frac{dP\{d_2|m_2\}}{d\lambda} = -p(\lambda|m_2)$$

$$\frac{dP\{d_2|m_1\}}{d\lambda} = -p(\lambda|m_1)$$

The slope of the ROC is the ratio of these two derivatives:

$$\frac{dP\{d_2|m_2\}}{dP\{d_2|m_1\}} = \frac{p(\lambda|m_2)}{p(\lambda|m_1)} \qquad (3.2\text{-}17)$$

Now to establish the desired result, we need to show that

$$\frac{p(\lambda|m_2)}{p(\lambda|m_1)} = \lambda \qquad (3.2\text{-}18)$$

Let the set Z_λ be defined as the set of z such that $\Lambda(z)$ is between λ and $\lambda + d\lambda$ or

$$Z_\lambda = \{z: \lambda \le \Lambda(z) \le \lambda + d\lambda\} \qquad (3.2\text{-}19)$$

Then for $d\lambda$ sufficiently small, the conditional probabilities that $\Lambda(z)$ is between λ and $\lambda + d\lambda$ are

$$P\{\lambda \le \Lambda(z) \le \lambda + d\lambda|m_2\} = p(\lambda|m_2)\,d\lambda = \int_{Z_\lambda} p(z|m_2)\,dz \qquad (3.2\text{-}20)$$

and $\qquad P\{\lambda \le \Lambda(z) \le \lambda + d\lambda|m_1\} = p(\lambda|m_1)\,d\lambda = \int_{Z_\lambda} p(z|m_1)\,dz \qquad (3.2\text{-}21)$

But for each $z \in Z_\lambda$, we know that $\Lambda(z)$ is between λ and $\lambda + d\lambda$, so that

$$\lambda p(z|m_1) \leq p(z|m_2) \leq (\lambda + d\lambda)p(z|m_1)$$

Using this to bound the right side of Eq. (3.2-20) gives

$$\lambda \int_{Z_\lambda} p(z|m_1) \, dz < p(\lambda|m_2) \, d\lambda < (\lambda + d\lambda) \int_{Z_\lambda} p(z|m_1) \, dz \quad (3.2\text{-}22)$$

Then, by using Eq. (3.2-21) to replace the integrals in Eq. (3.2-22), the ratio $p(\lambda|m_2)/p(\lambda|m_1)$ is bounded in the following manner:

$$\lambda \leq \frac{p(\lambda|m_2)}{p(\lambda|m_1)} \leq \lambda + d\lambda$$

As $d\lambda$ approaches zero, we obtain the desired results of Eq. (3.2-18) and establish the third property. It should be noted that Eq. (3.2-18) is a valuable result in its own right; it states that for all z such that $\Lambda(z) = \lambda$, then

$$\frac{p(\lambda|m_2)}{p(\lambda|m_1)} = \frac{p(z|m_2)}{p(z|m_1)} = \lambda \quad (3.2\text{-}23)$$

In other words, the likelihood ratio of the likelihood ratio is the likelihood ratio.

Example 3.2-4 Let us determine the ROC for the decision problem with the condtional probability densities

$$p(z|m_1) = \begin{cases} e^{-z} & z \geq 0 \\ 0 & \text{otherwise} \end{cases}$$

$$p(z|m_2) = \begin{cases} \tau e^{-\tau z} & z \geq 0 \\ 0 & \text{otherwise} \end{cases}$$

where $\tau > 1$.

The likelihood ratio for this problem is given by

$$\Lambda(z) = \tau e^{-(\tau - 1)z}$$

and the Neyman-Pearson decision rule is

$$\tau e^{-(\tau - 1)z} \underset{d_1}{\overset{d_2}{\gtrless}} \lambda$$

After a few simple manipulations, we can write this decision rule as

$$z \underset{d_2}{\overset{d_1}{\gtrless}} \frac{1}{1 - \tau} \ln \frac{\lambda}{\tau} = \lambda'$$

Hence the false-alarm probability is given by

$$P\{d_2|m_1\} = \int_0^{\lambda'} e^{-z} \, dz = 1 - e^{-\lambda'}$$

while the probability of detection is

$$P\{d_2|m_2\} = \int_0^{\lambda} \tau e^{-\tau z} \, dz = 1 - e^{-\tau\lambda'}$$

Now varying λ' from zero to infinity for various values of τ yields the ROC shown in Fig. 3.2-5. Note that the slope of the ROC is

$$\frac{dP\{d_2|m_2\}}{dP\{d_2|m_1\}} = \frac{dP\{d_2|m_2\}/d\lambda'}{dP\{d_2|m_1\}/d\lambda'} = \frac{\tau e^{-\tau\lambda'}}{e^{-\lambda'}} = \tau e^{-(\tau - 1)\lambda'}$$

But from the definition of λ' we have

$$\lambda = \tau e^{-(\tau - 1)\lambda'}$$

and so the slope is exactly λ.

Let us return to the use of the ROC for determining the α_0 parameter of the Neyman-Pearson decision rule. By examining the ROC associated with a given decision problem, we can obtain some feeling of the trade-off of decreasing $P\{d_2|m_1\}$ versus increasing $P\{d_2|m_2\}$. In general, we sould like to select a value for $P\{d_2|m_1\}$ which generates a test at the "knee" of the ROC. If $P\{d_2|m_1\}$ is increased above that value, this will result in a smaller increase in $P\{d_2|m_2\}$ and hence a poor trade-off. Correspondingly, if $P\{d_2|m_1\}$ is decreased, $P\{d_2|m_2\}$ will decrease even more.

For example, consider the ROC of Fig. 3.2-5. If $\tau = 16$, then a reasonable value for $P\{d_2|m_1\}$ would be 0.1 to 0.2. Making $P\{d_2|m_1\}$ larger than 0.2 will

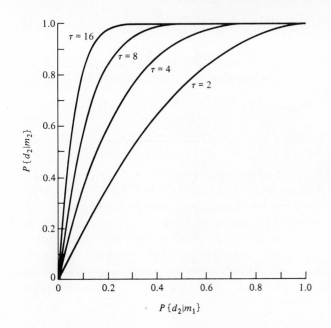

Figure 3.2-5 Receiver operating characteristics for Example 3.2-4.

cause only a small increase in $P\{d_2|m_2\}$, while a $P\{d_2|m_1\}$ smaller than 0.1 will cause a large decrease in $P\{d_2|m_2\}$.

There are problems in which it may be necessary to make $P\{d_2|m_1\}$ smaller than the value at the knee. In this case, one must simply pay the penalty in a reduced value of $P\{d_2|m_2\}$ or try to modify the problem in some way, for example, increasing τ in Example 3.2-4. Note that the ROC also gives us some information concerning the effect of changing various parameters. In Example 3.2-4, increasing τ above 16 would be desirable only if a very small value of $P\{d_2|m_1\}$ is required.

3.3 PROBABILITY-OF-ERROR CRITERION

In the preceding section, we introduced the error probabilities $P\{d_2|m_1\}$ and $P\{d_1|m_2\}$. In this section we examine another decision-rule criterion based on the total probability of error P_e defined as

$$
\begin{aligned}
P_e &= P\{\text{make an incorrect decision}\} \\
&= P\{\text{decide } d_2 \text{ when } m_1 \text{ is true or decide } d_1 \text{ when } m_2 \text{ is true}\} \\
&= P\{(d_2 \text{ and } m_1) \text{ or } (d_1 \text{ and } m_2)\}
\end{aligned} \tag{3.3-1}
$$

The *probability-of-error criterion* says to select the decision regions so as to minimize this total probability of error.

Since the messages m_1 and m_2 are mutual exclusive, we can write P_e as

$$P_e = P\{d_2, m_1\} + P\{d_1, m_2\} \tag{3.3-2}$$

and by the use of conditional probabilities this becomes

$$P_e = P\{d_2|m_1\}P\{m_1\} + P\{d_1|m_2\}P\{m_2\} \tag{3.3-3}$$

Here $P\{m_1\}$ and $P\{m_2\}$ are referred to as the *a priori probabilities*; they represent the probability that the message m_k will be the message selected. Since m_1 and m_2 are mutually exclusive and exhaustive, i.e., either but not both m_1 or m_2 must be true, we know that

$$P\{m_1\} + P\{m_2\} = 1 \tag{3.3-4}$$

Quite often $P\{m_1\} = P\{m_2\} = 0.5$; this will be referred to as the *equally likely message* case.

For some problems, especially communication problems, the a priori probabilities are dependent on the source-coding procedure used. We will not consider such cases here but will assume that the a priori probabilities are given in the basic decision problem statement. For actual problems it may be necessary to conduct extensive experiments to determine these probabilities. The probability-of-error criterion is sometimes referred to as the *ideal observer criterion*.

In order to show how to select the decision regions to minimize P_e, we first write it in terms of Z_2. Since specification of Z_2 automatically describes Z_1, we will minimize P_e by selecting those z which should be in Z_2. By the use of Eq. (3.2-2), we can write $P\{d_1|m_2\}$ as

$$P\{d_1|m_2\} = \int_{Z_1} p(z|m_2)\, dz$$

$$= \int_{Z_1} p(z|m_2)\, dz + \int_{Z_2} p(z|m_2)\, dz - \int_{Z_2} p(z|m_2)\, dz \quad (3.3\text{-}5)$$

where in the second form we have added and substracted the same quantity. Now the first two terms in the second form sum to 1, and so we obtain

$$P\{d_1|m_2\} = 1 - \int_{Z_2} p(z|m_2)\, dz \quad (3.3\text{-}6)$$

We can also obtain Eq. (3.3-6) by noting that

$$P\{d_1|m_2\} = 1 - P\{d_2|m_2\}$$

$$= 1 - \int_{Z_2} p(z|m_2)\, dz$$

In either case we have been able to write $P\{d_1|m_2\}$ in terms of Z_2.

To write $P\{d_2|m_1\}$ as a function of Z_2, we use Eq. (3.2-1) to show that

$$P\{d_2|m_1\} = \int_{Z_2} p(z|m_1)\, dz \quad (3.3\text{-}7)$$

so that P_e given by Eq. (3.3-3) can be written as

$$P_e = P\{m_1\} \int_{Z_2} p(z|m_1)\, dz + P\{m_2\}\left[1 - \int_{Z_2} p(z|m_2)\, dz\right]$$

$$= P\{m_2\} + \int_{Z_2} [P\{m_1\}p(z|m_1) - P\{m_2\}p(z|m_2)]\, dz \quad (3.3\text{-}8)$$

To minimize P_e by the selection of Z_2, we should put into the decision region Z_2 the values of z for which the integrand in Eq. (3.3-8) is negative. Therefore Z_2 is given by

$$Z_2 = \{z\colon [P\{m_1\}p(z|m_1) - P\{m_2\}p(z|m_2)] < 0\} \quad (3.3\text{-}9)$$

and Z_1 is the set z's not in Z_2, or

$$Z_1 = \{z\colon [P\{m_1\}p(z|m_1) - P\{m_2\}p(z|m_2)] > 0\} \quad (3.3\text{-}10)$$

In terms of the likelihood ratio

$$\Lambda(z) = \frac{p(z|m_2)}{p(z|m_1)}$$

the decision regions can be written as

$$Z_2 = \left\{z\colon \Lambda(z) > \frac{P\{m_1\}}{P\{m_2\}}\right\}$$

$$Z_1 = \left\{z\colon \Lambda(z) < \frac{P\{m_1\}}{P\{m_2\}}\right\} \quad (3.3\text{-}11)$$

and the decision rule is

$$\Lambda(z) \underset{d_1}{\overset{d_2}{\gtrless}} \frac{P\{m_1\}}{P\{m_2\}} \tag{3.3-12}$$

Once again, we note that the decision rule consists of comparing the likelihood ratio to a threshold; here, however, the threshold is determined by the ratio of a priori probabilities. To illustrate the use of this criterion, let us consider again the simple problem of Example 3.1-1.

Example 3.3-1 The conditional densities are given by

$$p(z|m_1) = \frac{1}{\sqrt{2\pi}} \exp \frac{-z^2}{2}$$

$$p(z|m_2) = \frac{1}{\sqrt{2\pi}} \exp \frac{-(z-1)^2}{2}$$

We assume that $P\{m_1\} = 0.25$ and therefore $P\{m_2\} = 0.75$. The likelihood ratio is

$$\Lambda(z) = \exp \frac{2z-1}{2}$$

and the decision rule is therefore

$$\exp \frac{2z-1}{2} \underset{d_1}{\overset{d_2}{\gtrless}} \frac{1}{3}$$

If we take the natural logarithm on both sides of this expression, we obtain

$$\frac{2z-1}{2} \underset{d_1}{\overset{d_2}{\gtrless}} -1.1$$

or

$$z \underset{d_1}{\overset{d_2}{\gtrless}} -0.6$$

The decision region Z_2 is therefore

$$Z_2 = \{z: z > -0.6\}$$

and

$$Z_1 = \{z: z < -0.6\}$$

The two error probabilities are given by

$$P\{d_1|m_2\} = \int_{Z_1} p(z|m_2)\, dz = \int_{-\infty}^{-0.6} \frac{1}{\sqrt{2\pi}} e^{-(z-1)^2/2}\, dz = 0.0048$$

and

$$P\{d_2|m_1\} = \int_{Z_2} p(z|m_1)\, dz = \int_{-0.6}^{\infty} \frac{1}{\sqrt{2\pi}} e^{-z^2/2}\, dz = 0.7258$$

Therefore the total probability of error is given by

$$P_e = P\{m_1\}P\{d_2|m_1\} + P\{m_2\}P\{d_1|m_2\}$$
$$= 0.25(0.7258) + 0.75(0.0048)$$
$$= 0.1851$$

It may be instructive to compute the total probability of error for the maximum-likelihood and Neyman-Pearson decision rules determined in Examples 3.1-2 and 3.2-1, respectively. For the maximum-likelihood decision rule, the error probabilities are given by

$$P\{d_1|m_2\} = \int_{-\infty}^{0.5} \frac{1}{\sqrt{2\pi}} e^{-(z-1)^2/2} \, dz = 0.3085$$

$$P\{d_2|m_1\} = \int_{0.5}^{\infty} \frac{1}{\sqrt{2\pi}} e^{-z^2/2} \, dz = 0.3085$$

so that P_e is

$$P_e = 0.25(0.3085) + 0.75(0.3085) = 0.3085$$

For the Neyman-Pearson decision rule, the error probability $P\{d_2|m_1\}$ was constrained to be 0.25 and

$$P\{d_1|m_2\} = \int_{-\infty}^{0.674} \frac{1}{\sqrt{2\pi}} e^{-(z-1)^2/2} \, dz = 0.3722$$

Therefore the probability of error is given by

$$P_e = 0.25(0.25) + 0.75(0.3722) = 0.3417$$

We observe that both the maximum-likelihood and Neyman-Pearson decision rules lead to a higher value for P_e. Of course, this is not surprising since neither of these decision rules was based on minimizing P_e. If, however, we had selected a Neyman-Pearson decision rule with $\alpha_0 = 0.7258$, then the Neyman-Pearson and the probability-of-error decision rules would be equivalent. In general, we do not know the value of α_0 which will establish this equivalence until the probability-of-error decision rule is determined. Such a value always exists.

If the two messages are equally likely, that is, $P\{m_1\} = P\{m_2\} = 0.5$, then the probability-of-error decision rule is equivalent to the maximum-likelihood decision rule. This fact is easily observed if we let $P\{m_1\} = P\{m_2\} = 0.5$ in Eq. (3.3-12) to obtain

$$\Lambda(z) \underset{d_1}{\overset{d_2}{\gtrless}} \frac{0.5}{0.5} = 1$$

This decision rule is identical to the maximum-likelihood decision rule of Eq. (3.1-5). Stated in another way, the maximum-likelihood decision rule will yield a minimum probability-of-error decision only if the two messages are equally likely.

The probability-of-error decision rule has another interesting interpretation. Consider the general probability-of-error decision rule given by Eq. (3.3-12):

$$\frac{p(z|m_2)}{p(z|m_1)} \overset{d_2}{\underset{d_1}{\gtrless}} \frac{P\{m_1\}}{P\{m_2\}}$$

Let us multiply both sides of this expression by $P\{m_2\}/P\{m_1\}$ to obtain the following result:

$$\frac{p(z|m_2)P\{m_2\}}{p(z|m_1)P\{m_1\}} \overset{d_2}{\underset{d_1}{\gtrless}} 1 \qquad (3.3\text{-}13)$$

By using the mixed Bayes rule [Eq. (2.2-20)], we can rewrite Eq. (3.3-13) as

$$\frac{P(m_2|z)p(z)}{P(m_1|z)p(z)} = \frac{P(m_2|z)}{P(m_1|z)} \overset{d_2}{\underset{d_1}{\gtrless}} 1 \qquad (3.3\text{-}14)$$

This result says that we should decide d_1 if $P(m_1|z) > P(m_2|z)$ and decide d_2 if $P(m_2|z) > P(m_1|z)$. In other words, we should select the decision corresponding to the message with the larger a posteriori probability, i.e., the probability of m_k given z. Hence we see that the probability-of-error criterion is identical to the maximum a posteriori (MAP) decision criterion:

Maximum a posteriori (MAP) decision criterion Given an observation z, select d_1 if m_1 is more likely than m_2.

The reader is urged to compare the statement of the MAP decision criterion and the maximum-likelihood criterion in Sec. 3.1.

Example 3.3-2 As a final example of the probability-of-error criterion, let us consider a generalization of the problem presented in Example 3.3-1. The conditional densities are given by

$$p(z|m_1) = \frac{1}{\sqrt{2\pi}\sigma} \exp \frac{-(z-\mu_1)^2}{2\sigma^2}$$

$$p(z|m_2) = \frac{1}{\sqrt{2\pi}\sigma} \exp \frac{-(z-\mu_2)^2}{2\sigma^2}$$

with $(\mu_2 - \mu_1) > 0$. The likelihood ratio is given by

$$\Lambda(z) = \frac{\exp\left[-(z-\mu_2)^2/2\sigma^2\right]}{\exp\left[-(z-\mu_1)^2/2\sigma^2\right]}$$

$$= \exp \frac{(2z(\mu_2 - \mu_1) - (\mu_2^2 - \mu_1^2))}{2\sigma^2}$$

The probability-of-error decision rule is therefore

$$\exp \frac{(2z(\mu_2 - \mu_1) - (\mu_2^2 - \mu_1^2))}{2\sigma^2} \mathop{\gtrless}\limits_{d_1}^{d_2} \frac{P\{m_1\}}{P\{m_2\}}$$

Let us take the logarithm on both sides and define

$$\Lambda_0 = \frac{P\{m_1\}}{P\{m_2\}}$$

so that the decision rule becomes

$$\frac{2z(\mu_2 - \mu_1) - (\mu_2^2 - \mu_1^2)}{2\sigma^2} \mathop{\gtrless}\limits_{d_1}^{d_2} \ln \Lambda_0$$

After some algebraic manipulation we obtain the following form for the decision rule:

$$z \mathop{\gtrless}\limits_{d_1}^{d_2} \sigma \left[\frac{\sigma}{(\mu_2 - \mu_1)} \ln \Lambda_0 + \frac{\mu_2 + \mu_1}{2\sigma} \right] = \eta$$

Next let us determine the error probabilities. The false-alarm probability is given by

$$P\{d_2|m_1\} = \int_\eta^\infty \frac{1}{\sqrt{2\pi}\sigma} \exp \frac{-(z - \mu_1)^2}{2\sigma^2} \, dz$$

By making the substitution $\xi = (z - \mu_1)/\sigma$, this becomes

$$P\{d_2|m_1\} = \int_{\frac{\eta - \mu_1}{\sigma}}^\infty \frac{1}{\sqrt{2\pi}} \exp \frac{-\xi^2}{2} \, d\xi = Q\left(\frac{\sigma}{\mu_2 - \mu_1} \ln \Lambda_0 + \frac{\mu_2 - \mu_1}{2\sigma} \right)$$

Now let $\delta = (\mu_2 - \mu_1)/\sigma$ so that we have

$$P\{d_2|m_1\} = Q\left(\frac{\delta}{2} + \frac{\ln \Lambda_0}{\delta} \right)$$

In a completely similar manner, we express the miss probability as

$$P\{d_1|m_2\} = Q\left(\frac{\delta}{2} - \frac{\ln \Lambda_0}{\delta} \right)$$

so that the total probability of error is given by

$$P_e = P\{m_1\} \, Q\left(\frac{\delta}{2} + \frac{\ln \Lambda_0}{\delta} \right) + P\{m_2\} \, Q\left(\frac{\delta}{2} - \frac{\ln \Lambda_0}{\delta} \right)$$

Now we note that by the definition of Λ_0

$$P\{m_2\} = \frac{1}{1 + \Lambda_0}$$

and
$$P\{m_1\} = \frac{\Lambda_0}{1 + \Lambda_0}$$

so that P_e becomes

$$P_e = \frac{1}{1 + \Lambda_0}\left[\Lambda_0 Q\left(\frac{\ln \Lambda_0}{\delta} + \frac{\delta}{2}\right) + Q\left(\frac{\delta}{2} - \frac{\ln \Lambda_0}{\delta}\right)\right]$$

Hence we see that the minimum probability of error depends only on Λ_0 and δ. The parameter $\delta = (\mu_2 - \mu_1)/\sigma$ is often referred to as the *signal-to-noise ratio*. It is possible to show that for any given Λ_0 that P_e decreases as δ increases.

3.4 BAYES RISK CRITERION

In the preceding sections we examined three ad hoc methods for decision-rule design. In this section, we consider the Bayes decision criterion which employs a systematic procedure of assigning a cost to each correct and incorrect decision and then minimizing the total average cost. If we let C_{jk} be the cost of making decision d_j when m_k is true, then for the binary decision problem there are four possible costs:

$$C_{11} = \text{Cost of deciding } d_1 \text{ when } m_1 \text{ is true}$$
$$C_{12} = \text{Cost of deciding } d_1 \text{ when } m_2 \text{ is true}$$
$$C_{21} = \text{Cost of deciding } d_2 \text{ when } m_1 \text{ is true}$$
$$C_{22} = \text{Cost of deciding } d_2 \text{ when } m_2 \text{ is true}$$

If we assume a natural pairing of d_j and m_k, then we note that C_{11} and C_{22} are costs associated with correct decisions while C_{12} and C_{21} are associated with incorrect decisions.

It may seem strange to talk of a cost associated with a correct decision. Although we can and often will set $C_{11} = C_{22} = 0$, there is nothing inconsistent in assigning a cost to a correct decision. For example, the cost of making a correct medical diagnosis might be the risks involved in the treatment. In addition, there are many problems in which there is no natural pairing of messages and decisions except as associated with relative costs of various decision/message combinations. In Chap. 5, for example, we shall assume that the number of messages and the number of decisions is not equal and hence a natural pairing does not exist.

The expected or average cost is given by

$$B = E\{C_{jk}\} = C_{11}P\{d_1, m_1\} + C_{12}P\{d_1, m_2\}$$
$$+ C_{21}P\{d_2, m_1\} + C_{22}P\{d_2, m_2\} \qquad (3.4\text{-}1)$$

Since $P\{d_j, m_k\} = P\{d_j|m_k\}P\{m_k\}$, Eq. (3.4-1) becomes

$$B = (C_{11}P\{d_1|m_1\} + C_{21}P\{d_2|m_1\})P\{m_1\}$$
$$+ (C_{12}P\{d_1|m_2\} + C_{22}P\{d_2|m_2\})P\{m_2\} \qquad (3.4\text{-}2)$$

The average cost can also be written as

$$B = E\{C_{jk}\} = E\{C_{jk}|m_1\}P\{m_1\} + E\{C_{jk}|m_2\}P\{m_2\}$$

$$= B_1 P\{m_1\} + B_2 P\{m_2\} \tag{3.4-3}$$

A comparison of Eqs. (3.4-2) and (3.4-3) reveals that

$$B_1 = E\{C_{jk}|m_1\} = C_{11}P\{d_1|m_1\} + C_{21}P\{d_2|m_1\} \tag{3.4-4}$$

$$B_2 = E\{C_{jk}|m_2\} = C_{12}P\{d_1|m_2\} + C_{22}P\{d_2|m_2\} \tag{3.4-5}$$

Here B_1 and B_2 are referred to as *conditional costs*; B_k is the average cost assuming that m_k is true. (We shall make extensive use of the concept of conditional costs in Sec. 3.5.)

Because we know that

$$P\{d_1|m_1\} = 1 - P\{d_2|m_1\}$$

$$P\{d_1|m_2\} = 1 - P\{d_2|m_2\}$$

then the conditional costs can be written as

$$B_1 = C_{11} + (C_{21} - C_{11})P\{d_2|m_1\} \tag{3.4-6}$$

$$B_2 = C_{12} - (C_{12} - C_{22})P\{d_2|m_2\} \tag{3.4-7}$$

Therefore the average cost is given by

$$B = C_{11}P\{m_1\} + (C_{21} - C_{11})P\{d_2|m_1\}P\{m_1\} + C_{12}P\{m_2\}$$

$$- (C_{12} - C_{22})P\{d_2|m_2\}P\{m_2\}$$

$$= C_{11}P\{m_1\} + C_{12}P\{m_2\} + (C_{21} - C_{11})P\{m_1\} \int_{Z_2} p(z|m_1) \, dz$$

$$- (C_{12} - C_{22})P\{m_2\} \int_{Z_2} p(z|m_2) \, dz$$

Combining the two integrals yields

$$B = C_{11}P\{m_1\} + C_{12}P\{m_2\} + \int_{Z_2} [(C_{21} - C_{11})P\{m_1\}p(z|m_1)$$

$$- (C_{12} - C_{22})P\{m_2\}p(z|m_2)] \, dz \tag{3.4-8}$$

The Bayes decision criterion can be stated as follows:

Bayes decision criterion Select the decision region Z_2 in order to minimize the average cost B as given by Eq. (3.4-8).

The first two terms in Eq. (3.4-8) are not a function of Z_2 and hence are not involved in the minimization. We can minimize the integral if we assign to Z_2 all the values of z for which

$$(C_{21} - C_{11})P\{m_1\}p(z|m_1) - (C_{12} - C_{22})P\{m_2\}p(z|m_2) < 0 \tag{3.4-9}$$

Therefore the decision rule can be written as

$$(C_{12} - C_{22})P\{m_2\}p(z|m_2) \overset{d_2}{\underset{d_1}{\gtrless}} (C_{21} - C_{11})P\{m_1\}p(z|m_1) \qquad (3.4\text{-}10)$$

Now if we assume[†] that $(C_{12} - C_{22}) > 0$, and then if we divide both sides of Eq. (3.4-10) by $(C_{12} - C_{22})P\{m_2\}$, the Bayes decision rule takes the familiar form of a likelihood-ratio test:

$$\Lambda(z) \overset{d_2}{\underset{d_1}{\gtrless}} \frac{(C_{21} - C_{11})P\{m_1\}}{(C_{12} - C_{22})P\{m_2\}} \qquad (3.4\text{-}11)$$

For most problems both $(C_{12} - C_{22})$ and $(C_{21} - C_{11})$ will be positive since the cost of an incorrect decision is generally greater than the cost of a correct decision.

Example 3.4-1 Let us determine the Bayes decision rule associated with the following conditional probabilities:

$$p(z|m_1) = \tfrac{1}{2}e^{-|z|}$$

$$p(z|m_2) = e^{-2|z|}$$

The costs are given by

$$C_{11} = C_{22} = 0$$

$$C_{12} = 1$$

$$C_{21} = 2$$

and $P\{m_2\} = 0.75$. The likelihood ratio is

$$\Lambda(z) = \frac{e^{-2|z|}}{\tfrac{1}{2}e^{-|z|}} = 2e^{-|z|}$$

The Bayes decision rule is therefore

$$2e^{-|z|} \overset{d_2}{\underset{d_1}{\gtrless}} \frac{(2-0)0.25}{(1-0)0.75} = \frac{2}{3}$$

or
$$|z| \overset{d_2}{\underset{d_1}{\lessgtr}} -\ln \tfrac{1}{3} = 1.10$$

In order to determine the Bayes risk, we need to find the false-alarm

---

[†] If $(C_{12} - C_{22})$ is not positive, then we may either renumber the decisions to make it positive or change the direction of the inequalities in Eq. (3.4-11).

and detection probabilities. The false-alarm probability is given by

$$P\{d_2|m_1\} = \int_{-1.1}^{1.1} \tfrac{1}{2}e^{-|z|} \, dz = \int_0^{1.1} e^{-z} \, dz = 0.67$$

while the detection probability is

$$P\{d_2|m_2\} = \int_{-1.1}^{1.1} e^{-2|z|} \, dz = 2\int_0^{1.1} e^{-2z} \, dz = 0.89$$

Now using Eqs. (3.4-3), (3.4-6), and (3.4-7) we find that

$$B_1 = 0 + (2-0)\,0.67 = 1.34$$
$$B_2 = 1 - (1-0)\,0.89 = 0.11$$
$$B = (1.34)(0.25) + (0.11)(0.75) = 0.42$$

The Bayes cost formulation can be viewed as a generalization of the probability-of-error method. Note that if we assign the costs as

$$C_{11} = C_{22} = 0$$
$$C_{12} = C_{21} = 1$$

then B is identical to P_e.

3.5 MIN-MAX CRITERION

The Bayes criterion discussed in Sec. 3.4 provides a very flexible method for designing decision rules. However, there are many practical problems in which the a priori probabilities of the messages m_1 and m_2 may not be known. In this case, the min-max criterion may often be successfully employed. Basically the min-max criterion says that one should use the Bayes decision rule which corresponds to the least favorable $P\{m_1\}$.

For the purpose of this section, it is convenient to recognize that the average risk is a function of two quantities: the a priori probability $P\{m_1\}$ and the decision region Z_2. Hence, we shall write the average risk as $B(P\{m_1\}, Z_2)$, which is given by Eq. (3.4-3), repeated here for reference:

$$B(P\{m_1\}, Z_2) = B_1(Z_2)P\{m_1\} + B_2(Z_2)[1 - P\{m_1\}] \qquad (3.5\text{-}1)$$

where

$$B_1(Z_2) = C_{11} + (C_{21} - C_{11}) \int_{Z_2} p(z|m_1) \, dz \qquad (3.5\text{-}2)$$

$$B_2(Z_2) = C_{12} - (C_{12} - C_{22}) \int_{Z_2} p(z|m_2) \, dz \qquad (3.5\text{-}3)$$

The min-max decision criterion can be expressed in the following form:

Min-max decision criterion The min-max decision region Z_2^* is defined by

$$\max_{P\{m_1\}} B(P\{m_1\}, Z_2^*) = \min_{Z_2} \max_{P\{m_1\}} B(P\{m_1\}, Z_2)$$

$$< \max_{P\{m_1\}} B(P\{m_1\}, Z_2) \qquad (3.5\text{-}4)$$

for all $Z_2 \neq Z_2^*$. In other words, Z_2^* is the decision region which yields the minimum cost for the least favorable $P\{m_1\}$.

Under very mild restrictions, it is possible to show that the minimization and maximization operations are interchangeable so that

$$\min_{Z_2} \max_{P\{m_1\}} B(P\{m_1\}, Z_2) = \max_{P\{m_1\}} \min_{Z_2} B(P\{m_1\}, Z_2) \qquad (3.5\text{-}5)$$

The minimization of $B(P\{m_1\}, Z_2)$ with respect to Z_2 is simply the Bayes criterion, so that

$$\min_{Z_2} B(P\{m_1\}, Z_2) = B^o(P\{m_1\}) \qquad (3.5\text{-}6)$$

where $B^o(P\{m_1\})$ is the minimum (Bayes) cost associated with the a priori probability $P\{m_1\}$. Therefore Eq. (3.5-5) says that we may find the min-max decision rule by finding the Bayes decision rule for the least favorable $P\{m_1\}$, that is, the $P\{m_1\}$ which maximizes $B^o(P\{m_1\})$. The procedure is therefore to find $B^o(P\{m_1\})$ either numerically or analytically and then to determine the $P\{m_1\}$ for which $B^o(P\{m_1\})$ is maximum. The Bayes decision rule for the $P\{m_1\}$ which maximizes $B^o(P\{m_1\})$ is the min-max decision rule.

Example 3.5-1 To illustrate the use of the min-max design procedure, let us consider a decision problem with the following conditional probabilities:

$$p(z|m_1) = e^{-z} \qquad \text{for } z > 0$$

$$p(z|m_2) = 2e^{-2z} \qquad \text{for } z > 0$$

We shall use the following costs:

$$C_{11} = C_{22} = 0$$

$$C_{12} = 2$$

$$C_{21} = 1$$

In terms of $P\{m_1\}$, the Bayes decision rule takes the following form:

$$\Lambda(z) = \frac{2e^{-2z}}{e^{-z}} \underset{d_1}{\overset{d_2}{\gtrless}} \frac{1}{2} \frac{P\{m_1\}}{(1 - P\{m_1\})}$$

or
$$e^{-z} \underset{d_1}{\overset{d_2}{\gtrless}} \frac{P\{m_1\}}{4(1 - P\{m_1\})}$$

Taking logarithms on both sides and dividing by -1 yields

$$z \underset{d_1}{\overset{d_2}{\lessgtr}} T$$

where
$$T = \ln \frac{4(1 - P\{m_1\})}{P\{m_1\}}$$

This decision rule is only valid if $P\{m_1\} \leq 0.8$. For $P\{m_1\} > 0.8$, T becomes negative and $Z_1 = Z$; that is, we always decide d_1.

Now for $P\{m_1\} \leq 0.8$, we may express the minimum Bayes cost as a function of $P\{m_1\}$ as

$$B^o(P\{m_1\}) = P\{m_1\} \int_0^T e^{-z} \, dz + 2(1 - P\{m_1\}) \int_T^\infty 2e^{-2z} \, dz$$

$$= P\{m_1\}(1 - e^{-T}) + 2(1 - P\{m_1\})e^{-2T}$$

Substituting for T yields

$$B^o(P\{m_1\}) = \frac{9\mathbf{P}^2\{m_1\} - 8P\{m_1\}}{8(P\{m_1\} - 1)} \tag{1}$$

for $P\{m_1\} \leq 0.8$. For $P\{m_1\} > 0.8$, $B^o(P\{m_1\})$ is given by

$$B^o(P\{m_1\}) = 2(1 - P\{m_1\}) \tag{2}$$

Figure 3.5-1 shows a plot of $B^o(P\{m_1\})$ as a function of $P\{m_1\}$. We note that the value of $P\{m_1\}$ which maximizes $B^o(P\{m_1\})$ is less than 0.8, so that Eq. (1) is the correct expression for $B^o(P\{m_1\})$.

We can obtain the value of $P\{m_1\}$ which maximizes $B^o(P\{m_1\})$ by setting $dB^o(P\{m_1\})/dP\{m_1\}$ equal to zero and solving for $P\{m_1\}$. The resulting value of $P\{m_1\}$ is $\frac{2}{3}$. Now we substitute this value into the expression for T to obtain the following min-max decision rule:

$$z \underset{d_1}{\overset{d_2}{\lessgtr}} \ln 2 = 0.69$$

As the preceding example illustrates, the procedure for finding the min-max decision rule can be somewhat difficult. The following theorem offers an alternative procedure for finding the min-max decision rule.

Theorem 3.5-1 If there exists a decision region Z_2^* such that the conditional risks $B_1(Z_2^*)$ and $B_2(Z_2^*)$ are equal and Z_2^* is a Bayes decision region for some $P\{m_1\}$, then Z_2^* is a min-max decision region.

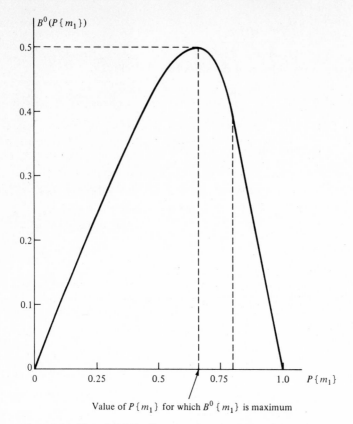

Figure 3.5-1 Plot of $B^o(P\{m_1\})$ versus $P\{m_1\})$ for Example 3.5-1.

To prove this theorem, let us assume that there exists a Z_2^* satisfying the conditions of the theorem which is not a min-max decision region. Then there exists a $Z_2' \neq Z_2^*$ such that

$$\max_{P\{m_1\}} \; B(P\{m_1\}, Z_2') < \max_{P\{m_1\},} \; B(P\{m_1\}, Z_2^*) \qquad (3.5\text{-}7)$$

by definition of a min-max decision region. Now, using Eq. (3.5-1), we can write $B(P\{m_1\}, Z_2^*)$ as

$$B(P\{m_1\}, Z_2^*) = B_1(Z_2^*)P\{m_1\} + B_2(Z_2^*)(1 - P\{m_1\})$$

But $B_1(Z_2^*) = B_2(Z_2^*)$, so that

$$B(P\{m_1\}, Z_2^*) = B_1(Z_2^*) = B_2(Z_2^*)$$

which is independent of $P\{m_1\}$. Therefore

$$\max_{P\{m_1\}} \; B\{P\{m_1\}, Z_2^*\} = B_1(Z_2^*) = B_2(Z_2^*)$$

so that Eq. (3.5-7) implies that

$$\max_{P\{m_1\}} B(P\{m_1\}, Z_2') < B_1(Z_2^*)$$

$$\max_{P\{m_1\}} B(P\{m_1\}, Z_2') < B_2(Z_2^*)$$

Therefore we can conclude that

$$B(P\{m_1\}, Z_2') < B(P\{m_1\}, Z_2^*)$$

for all $P\{m_1\}$. But Z_2^* is a Bayes decision region for some $P\{m_1\}$, say, α^*. Therefore

$$B(\alpha^*, Z_2^*) < B(\alpha^*, Z_2')$$

This yields a contradiction, which means Z_2^* must be a min-max decision region.

Example 3.5-2 Let us consider again the decision problem of Example 3.5-1. We know that all Bayes decision rules must be of the form

$$\Lambda(z) = 2e^{-z} \underset{d_1}{\overset{d_2}{\gtrless}} T$$

where $T \geq 0$. We can simplify the decision rule to the form

$$z \underset{d_1}{\overset{d_2}{\lessgtr}} T' = \ln \frac{2}{T}$$

Therefore $Z_2 = (0, T')$, and the conditional costs are given by

$$B_1(Z_2) = \int_0^{T'} e^{-z} \, dz = 1 - e^{-T'}$$

and

$$B_2(Z_2) = 2 \int_{T'}^{\infty} 2e^{-2z} \, dz = 2e^{-2T'}$$

Equating the conditional costs yields the following expression for T':

$$1 - e^{-T'} = 2e^{-2T'}$$

By letting $T' = \ln(1/x)$, we obtain a simple quadratic equation for x:

$$1 - x = 2x^2$$

This equation is easily solved to yield $x = \frac{1}{2}$ and -1. The -1 value is meaningless since it would lead to an undefined value for T'. Using $x = \frac{1}{2}$, we find that $T' = \ln 2$ as obtained previously. The likelihood-ratio threshold $T = 2e^{-T'} = 1$, and we have a valid Bayes decision rule.

As Example 3.5-2 illustrates, Theorem 3.5-1 is generally an easier method for determining the min-max decision rule than the basic definition. Although rare, there are problems for which Theorem 3.5-1 cannot be used. In other words, there are problems for which there is no Bayes decision rule with equal conditional risk. This condition will occur whenever $B^o(P\{m_1\})$ has its maximum at a point where the derivative of $B^o(P\{m_1\})$ with respect to $P\{m_1\}$ is either nonzero or undefined. The usual situations which have this property are when the maximum occurs for $P\{m_1\}$ equal to 0 or 1 or when the maximum occurs at an interior point for which the derivative is discontinuous.

To graphically illustrate Theorem 3.5-1, recall that the min-max decision region Z_2^* must be the minimum Bayes cost region for some value of $P\{m_1\}$. If we plot the cost for several such regions as functions of $P\{m_1\}$, Eq. (3.5-1) tells us that we will obtain a series of straight lines, as shown in Fig. 3.5-2. We have used Z_2^i to denote the optimum decision region when $P\{m_1\} = P_i$. $B^o(P\{m_1\})$ is the convex $\cap$ curve that is tangent to all such lines (see Prob. 3.7-24). If there is a line whose slope is zero, its maximum cost will be lower than the maximum cost for all of the other lines.

Setting the derivative of Eq. (3.5-1) equal to zero yields

$$B_1\{Z_2^*\} = B_2\{Z_2^*\} \tag{3.5-8}$$

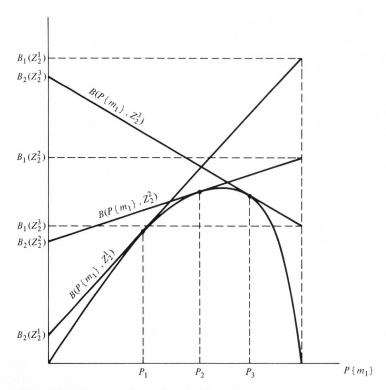

Figure 3.5-2 Bayes cost for various decision rules.

as required by Theorem 3.5-1. If such a region exists, it is tangent to $B^*(P\{m_1\})$ for $P\{m_1\} = P^*$ where P^* is defined by

$$\left.\frac{dB^o(P\{m_1\})}{dP\{m_1\}}\right|_{P\{m_1\}=P^*} = 0 \qquad (3.5\text{-}9)$$

In other words, minimizing the maximum cost (i.e., finding the horizontal line) is identical to maximizing the minimum cost (i.e., finding the peak of the $B^o(P\{m_1\})$ curve. Clearly this method will not work if there is no P^* which satisfies Eq. (3.5-9).

3.6 SUMMARY

In this chapter, we have examined five different criteria for designing the decision rule for a simple binary decision problem. Each of these criteria has resulted in a likelihood-ratio test of the form

$$\frac{p(z|m_2)}{p(z|m_1)} = \Lambda(z) \underset{d_1}{\overset{d_2}{\gtrless}} T$$

The only difference between the various criteria is in the way that the threshold T is selected.

The different criteria also make use of differing amounts of information and problem specification. The maximum-likelihood criterion uses only the conditional probabilities of the observation. The Neyman-Pearson criterion requires the additional specification of the false-alarm probability, while the probability-of-error criterion uses the a priori probabilities. The Bayes risk criterion requires the additional specification of costs for all decisions. The min-max criterion uses the Bayes costs but assumes that the a priori probabilities are unknown.

3.7 PROBLEMS

3.7-1 Determine the decision rule for the messages

$$m_1: p(z|m_1) = \begin{cases} e^{-z} & \text{for } z \geq 0 \\ 0 & \text{otherwise} \end{cases}$$

$$m_2: p(z|m_2) = \begin{cases} e^{z-1} & \text{for } z \leq 1 \\ 0 & \text{otherwise} \end{cases}$$

with $P\{m_1\} = 0.5$ using (a) probability-of-error-criterion; (b) Neyman-Pearson criterion with $P\{d_2|m_1\} = 0.1$; and (c) min-max criterion (probability-of-error costs). In each case, find the total (average) probability of error.

3.7-2 Find the decision rule using Neyman-Pearson criterion for the messages

$$m_1: p(z|m_1) = \begin{cases} 1 & 0 \leq z \leq 1 \\ 0 & \text{otherwise} \end{cases}$$

$$m_2: p(z|m_2) = \begin{cases} e^{-z} & z \geq 0 \\ 0 & \text{otherwise} \end{cases}$$

with $P\{d_2|m_1\} = 0.2$. Determine (*a*) a value for $P\{m_1\}$ such that the probability-of error decision rule will be the same as the Neyman-Pearson decision rule found previously; and (*b*) assuming that the messages are equally likely, a set of costs such that the Bayes decision rule is also equal to the Neyman-Pearson rule.

3.7-3 Consider the binary decision problem with

$$m_1: p(z|m_1) = \begin{cases} \frac{2}{9}(z + 2) & -2 \leq z \leq 1 \\ 0 & \text{otherwise} \end{cases}$$

$$m_2: p(z|m_2) = \begin{cases} \frac{2}{9}(2 - z) & -1 \leq z \leq 2 \\ 0 & \text{otherwise} \end{cases}$$

(*a*) Determine the minimum probability-of-error decision rule if $P\{m_1\} = \frac{1}{3}$.
(*b*) Determine the Neyman-Pearson decision rule for $P\{d_2|m_1\} = 0.1$.
(*c*) Determine the min-max decision rule for $C_{11} = C_{22} = 0$ and $C_{12} = 2C_{21}$.
(*d*) Determine the total probability of error for the decision rules of parts (*a*), (*b*), and (*c*).
(Assume that $P\{m_1\} = \frac{1}{3}$).
(*e*) For the costs of part (*c*), plot the minimum Bayes risk as a function of $P\{m_1\}$ for $0 \leq P\{m_1\} \leq 1$.

3.7-4 Consider the binary decision problem with

$$m_1: p(z|m_1) = \begin{cases} \dfrac{2}{\pi} \cos^2 z & 0 \leq z \leq \pi \\ 0 & \text{otherwise} \end{cases}$$

$$m_2: p(z|m_2) = \begin{cases} \dfrac{2}{\pi} \sin^2 z & 0 \leq z \leq \pi \\ 0 & \text{otherwise} \end{cases}$$

Find the Neyman-Pearson decision rule for $P\{d_2|m_1\} = 0.1$

3.7-5 Find the min-max decision rule for the messages

$$m_1: p(z|m_1) = \begin{cases} 0.1 & 0 \leq z \leq 10 \\ 0 & \text{otherwise} \end{cases}$$

$$m_2: p(z|m_2) = \begin{cases} 0.2 & 5 \leq z \leq 10 \\ 0 & \text{otherwise} \end{cases}$$

Let $C_{11} = C_{22} = 0$ and $C_{12} = C_{21} = 1$. Compute the min-max risk. If the min-max decision rule is used and $P\{m_1\} = 0$, find the actual probability of error.

3.7-6 For the binary decision problem where

$$p(z|m_1) = \frac{1}{\sqrt{2\pi}} e^{-z^2/2}$$

$$p(z|m_2) = \tfrac{1}{2} e^{-|z|}$$

it is known that many decision design criteria lead to a test of the form

$$\frac{p(z|m_2)}{p(z|m_1)} \underset{d_1}{\overset{d_2}{\gtrless}} T$$

for some T. Describe the decision region Z_1 as a function of T for $0 \le T \le \infty$.

3.7-7 Consider the binary decision problem with

$$m_1: p(z|m_1) = \begin{cases} e^{-z} & z > 0 \\ 0 & \text{otherwise} \end{cases}$$

$$m_2: p(z|m_2) = \begin{cases} \tfrac{1}{2}z & 0 < z < 2 \\ 0 & \text{otherwise} \end{cases}$$

and $P\{m_1\} = \tfrac{1}{3}$. Determine (*a*) the minimum probability-of-error test, (*b*) the Neyman-Pearson test with $P\{d_2|m_1\} = 0.1$, and (*c*) the min-max test with probability-of-error costs.

3.7-8 Find the ideal-observer decision rule if

$$m_1: p(z|m_1) = \frac{1}{\sqrt{2\pi}} e^{-z^2/2}$$

$$m_2: p(z|m_2) = \frac{1}{2\sqrt{2\pi}} e^{-z^2/8}$$

Assuming $P\{m_1\} = \tfrac{1}{2}$. Find the resulting P_e in terms of

$$Q(\alpha) = \int_\alpha^\infty \frac{1}{\sqrt{2\pi}} e^{-z^2/2} \, dz$$

3.7-9 Find the min-max decision rule for the message structure of Prob. 3.7-8. Assume ideal-observer costs.

3.7-10 Suppose you are observing the neural discharge in the optic nerve of a frog. You know that ambient light in the room causes the nerve to fire as a Poisson process an average of s_1 times per second. In other words,

$$P\{n \text{ firings in 1 s}|\text{no stimulus}\} = \frac{s_1{}^n}{n!} e^{-s_1} \qquad n = 0, 1, 2, \ldots$$

You also know that if you have correctly positioned your light stimulus, the rate increases to s_2:

$$P\{n \text{ firings in 1 s}|\text{stimulus}\} = \frac{s_2{}^n}{n!} e^{-s_2}$$

(*a*) If you observe z firings in 1 s, what is the maximum-likelihood decision rule to determine if the stimulus is on?

(*b*) What is the probability that you say that it is on when, in fact, it is off?

(*c*) How does this probability change if you observe for 2 s instead of 1 s?

3.7-11 Suppose the conditional densities of an observation are

$$p(z|m_1) = \begin{cases} 2e^{-2z} & z \geq 0 \\ 0 & z < 0 \end{cases}$$

$$p(z|m_2) = \begin{cases} e^{-z} & z \geq 0 \\ 0 & z < 0 \end{cases}$$

(a) Find the maximum-likelihood decision rule.

(b) What decision rule minimizes $P\{d_2|m_1\}$ and satisfies $P\{d_2|m_2\} \leq 1 - e^{-1}$?

(c) What decision rule selects the most probable message if $P\{m_1\} = \frac{1}{3}$ and $P\{m_2\} = \frac{2}{3}$?

(d) What decision rule minimizes probability of error if $P\{m_1\} = \frac{2}{3}$ and $P\{m_2\} = \frac{1}{3}$; and what is the probability of error?

(e) If the costs $C_{11} = 0$, $C_{22} = 1$, $C_{12} = 2$, $C_{21} = 3$ are assigned, and if $P\{m_1\} = P\{m_2\} = \frac{1}{2}$, what is the minimum cost and how can it be achieved?

3.7-12 Suppose that z is the product of the signal s and a zero-mean gaussian random-variable n. If $s_1 = 1$ and $s_2 = 2$, find the likelihood-ratio test and describe the decision regions Z_1 and Z_2.

3.7-13 For a binary decision problem it is found that the conditional probability densities of the observation are those shown in Fig. 3.7-1.

(a) Find the minimum probability-of-error decision rule as a function of the probability of message 1, $P\{m_1\}$.

(b) Find and sketch the minimum probability of error as a function of $P\{m_1\}$.

(c) On the same set of axes, plot the probability of error that results if it is wrongly assumed that

    (i) $P\{m_1\} = 0.1$
    (ii) $P\{m_1\} = 0.3$
    (iii) $P\{m_1\} = 0.5$
    (iv) $P\{m_1\} = 0.7$

(d) Find the min-max decision rule and plot its probability of error on the same set of axes.

3.7-14 Consider the binary decision problem where

$$p(z|m_1) = 2(1 - z) \qquad 0 \leq z \leq 1$$

$$p(z|m_2) = 2z \qquad 0 \leq z \leq 1$$

and $C_{11} = C_{22} = 0$, $C_{21} = 1$, $C_{12} = 2$.

(a) Plot the expected Bayes risk B as a function of $P\{m_1\}$ if the decision rule is the one which gives minimum B when $P\{m_1\} = \frac{1}{4}$.

(b) Repeat (a) for $P\{m_1\} = \frac{1}{2}$; plot on the same axis.

(c) Repeat (a) for $P\{m_1\} = \frac{3}{4}$; plot on the same axis.

(d) Sketch the curve of minimum B for each $P\{m_1\}$.

(e) Find the min-max test and plot its performance.

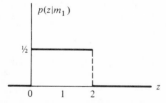
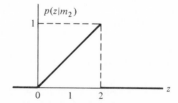

Figure 3.7-1 Problem 3.7-13.

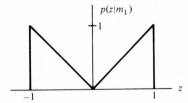

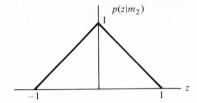

Figure 3.7-2 Problem 3.7-15.

3.7-15 For a binary decision problem with observation z and probability densities as shown in Fig. 3.7-2,

    (*a*) find the maximum-likelihood decision rule.

    (*b*) find the minimum probability-of-error decision rule when $P\{m_1\} = \frac{1}{2}$.

    (*c*) find the minimum Bayes cost rule when

$$P\{m_1\} = \tfrac{1}{3} \qquad C_{11} = 0 \qquad C_{12} = 3 \qquad C_{21} = 2 \qquad C_{22} = 2.$$

3.7-16 For the binary decision problem with

$$p(z|m_1) = \tfrac{1}{2}e^{-|z|}$$

$$p(z|m_2) = e^{-2|z|}$$

    (*a*) Find the Neyman-Pearson decision rule for $P\{d_2|m_1\} = 1 - e^{-0.5}$.

    (*b*) Find the P_e decision rule if $P\{m_1\} = \frac{2}{3}$. What is the minimum P_e?

    (*c*) Use P_e costs and find the min-max decision rule. What is the associated min-max Bayes cost?

3.7-17 A binary decision problem has the following conditional densities

$$p(z|m_1) = \begin{cases} 2z & 0 \le z \le 1 \\ 0 & \text{otherwise} \end{cases}$$

$$p(z|m_2) = \begin{cases} 2 - 2z & 0 \le z \le 1 \\ 0 & \text{otherwise} \end{cases}$$

Assume P_e costs and

    (*a*) Find the Bayes decision rule if $P\{m_1\} = \frac{1}{4}$ and the associated optimum cost.

    (*b*) Repeat part (*a*) with $P\{m_1\} = \frac{3}{4}$.

Now suppose that $P\{m_1\} = \frac{1}{2}$ and we use a randomized decision rule in which we use the decision rule of part (*a*) with probability 0.5 and the decision rule of part (*b*) with probability 0.5. Find the cost for this decision rule and show that it is greater than the cost associated with the Bayes decision rule for $P\{m_1\} = 0.5$.

3.7-18 It seems reasonable that for P_e costs the min-max decision rule will correspond to $P\{m_1\} = 0.5$ or the maximum-likelihood decision rule. Show that this statement is false in general; use a counter example if you wish. Under what conditions on $p(z|m_1)$ and $p(z|m_2)$ will this statement be true?

3.7-19 Consider the binary decision problem with

$$m_1: \; p(z|m_1) = \begin{cases} \frac{1}{5} & 0 \le z \le 5 \\ 0 & \text{otherwise} \end{cases}$$

$$m_2: p(z|m_2) = \frac{1}{\sqrt{2\pi}} e^{-z^2/2}$$

$$P\{m_1\} = 0.4$$

(a) Find the Neyman-Pearson decision rule with $P\{d_2|m_1\} = 0.2$.

(b) Find the minimum probability-of-error decision rule.

(c) Find the min-max decision rule; use probability-of-error costs.

3.7-20 Consider the decision problem with

$$p(z|m_1) = \begin{cases} e^{-z} & z > 0 \\ 0 & \text{otherwise} \end{cases}$$

$$p(z|m_2) = \begin{cases} e^{z-1} & z < 1 \\ 0 & \text{otherwise} \end{cases}$$

(a) Find the maximum-likelihood decision rule.

(b) Find the probability-of-error decision rule if $P\{m_1\} = \frac{1}{3}$.

(c) Find the total P_e for both (a) and (b) if $P\{m_1\} = \frac{1}{3}$.

3.7-21 Consider the observation

$$z = s_k n$$

where n is a zero-mean gaussian random variable with unit variance. Let $s_1 = s$ and $s_2 = 1$. Find the Neyman-Pearson test with $P\{d_2|m_1\} = 0.20$. What is the power of the test?

3.7-22 Consider the following decision problem ($\mu > 0$):

$$p(z|m_1) = \frac{1}{\sigma\sqrt{2\pi}} e^{-z^2/\sigma^2}$$

$$p(z|m_2) = \frac{1}{\sigma\sqrt{2\pi}} e^{-(z-\mu)^2/2\sigma^2}$$

Find the relationship between μ and σ such that $P\{d_2|m_1\} = 0.1$ and the minimum possible value of $P\{d_1|m_2\} = 0.1$

3.7-23 Consider the following decision problem:

$$p(z|m_1) = \begin{cases} \frac{1}{2}|z - 1| & |z| < 1 \\ 0 & \text{otherwise} \end{cases}$$

$$p(z|m_2) = \begin{cases} \frac{1}{8}|z - 2| & |z| < 2 \\ 0 & \text{otherwise} \end{cases}$$

If $C_{11} = 1$, $C_{22} = 2$, $C_{21} = 3$, $C_{12} = 4$ and $P\{m_1\} = 0.25$, find the Bayes decision rule. Using the same Bayes costs, find the min-max decision rule. Find the optimum Bayes cost in both cases.

3.7-24 A function $f(x)$ is defined as convex $\cap$ over a range X if for any $x_1 \in X$, $x_2 \in X$ and $0 \le \theta \le 1$ it is true that

$$f(\theta x_1 + (1 - \theta)x_2) \ge \theta f(x_1) + (1 - \theta) f(x_2)$$

Using an argument similar to that used for the ROC curve, prove that $B^\circ(P\{m_1\})$ is a convex $\cap$ function of $P\{m_1\}$ for $0 \le P\{m_1\} \le 1$.

3.7-25 Consider the binary decision problem with

$$m_1: p(z|m_1) = \begin{cases} \frac{1}{2}e^{-z} & z \geq 0 \\ e^{+2z} & z \leq 0 \end{cases}$$

$$m_2: p(z|m_2) = \begin{cases} e^{-2z} & z \geq 0 \\ \frac{1}{2}e^{z} & z \leq 0 \end{cases}$$

Let $P\{m_1\} = 0.5$.

(a) Find the P_e decision rule.

(b) Find the Neyman-Pearson decision rule with $\alpha_0 = 0.2$.

(c) Find the min-max decision rule using P_e costs.

(e) In all cases find the associated probability of error; assume that $P\{m_1\} = 0.5$.

3.7-26 Consider the binary decision problem with

$$m_1: p(z|m_1) = \begin{cases} 1 & 0 \geq z \geq 1 \\ 0 & \text{otherwise} \end{cases}$$

$$m_2: p(z|m_2) = \begin{cases} e^{-z} & z \geq 0 \\ 0 & \text{otherwise} \end{cases}$$

Find the ROC for this problem.

3.7-27 Consider the binary decision rule for the problem

$$m_1: p(z|m_1) = \frac{1}{\sqrt{2\pi}} e^{-z^2/2}$$

$$m_2: p(z|m_2) = \frac{1}{2\sqrt{2\pi}} e^{-(z-1)^2/8}$$

Find the P_e decision rule if $P\{m_1\} = 0.5$.

CHAPTER
FOUR

BINARY DECISIONS: MULTIPLE OBSERVATIONS

In this chapter we shall broaden the class of binary decision problems to include those where the observation is more complicated than a single scalar variable. Initially, we shall let it be a set of scalar variables (i.e., a vector), and then we shall consider time-waveform observations. Frequently, a multiple-variable observation is a good model for practical situations. For example, a doctor who is trying to determine whether or not a patient is ill has many observation variables at his disposal: temperature, blood presure, respiration rate, and a host of other quantities. This set of variables cannot be represented as a single point on the real line. Indeed, if I different variables are observed, the set defines a point in an I-dimensional euclidean space. As another example, in many communication situations the observation is actually a time waveform. Although the waveform may be finite in time, usually it cannot be represented by any finite number of variables. Thus this case would seem to be even more complex than the multiple-variable case. We shall see, however, that the two cases are quite similar and can be solved by generalizing the results for the single-variable case.

4.1 VECTOR OBSERVATIONS

In order to illustrate the concept of multiple observations, let us consider a simple example. As before, the two points in the message space will be denoted m_1 and m_2. The signal space will also have two points, but the signals associated with the points will be two-dimensional vectors s_1 and s_2. For this model, the mapping from signal to observation space will be by the addition of a two-dimensional noise vector to the signal vector. Thus, the observation z is a two-dimensional vector, and the observation space can be represented by a two-dimensional plane.

We shall use the maximum-likelihood decision criterion to map from the observation space to the decision space. Recall from Chap. 3 that the maximum-likelihood decision criterion says to select d_1 if it is more likely that m_1 generated the observation than that m_2 did. For the scalar observation z, this led to forming the ratio of the probability density of z given m_2 to the probability density of z given m_1 and to selecting d_2 if this ratio was bigger than 1.

In Chap. 3, z was a scalar, but the same reasoning applies to vectors. When the message is m_2, the joint probability that the first component of the observation is between z_1 and $z_1 + dz_1$ and that the second component is between z_2 and $z_2 + dz_2$ for small enough dz_1 and dz_2 is $p(z_1, z_2|m_1)\, dz_1\, dz_2$. Similarly, the probability of the same event when the message is m_2 is $p(z_1, z_2|m_2)\, dz_1\, dz_2$. Clearly, then, using the vector notation $\mathbf{z}$ for the two elements z_1 and z_2, the maximum-likelihood decision rule becomes

$$\Lambda(\mathbf{z}) = \frac{p(\mathbf{z}|m_2)}{p(\mathbf{z}|m_1)} \overset{d_2}{\underset{d_1}{\gtrless}} 1 \qquad (4.1\text{-}1)$$

As in Chap. 3, $\Lambda(\mathbf{z})$ is the *likelihood ratio* of the observation $\mathbf{z}$.

For example we shall let the observation $\mathbf{z}$ be the sum of the signal vector and a random-noise vector:

$$\mathbf{z} = \mathbf{s} + \mathbf{n} \qquad (4.1\text{-}2)$$

That is z_1, the first component of the observation, is the sum of the first component of the signal and the first component of the noise; z_2 is a similar sum. Thus, when the message is m_k,

$$z_1 = s_{k,1} + n_1 \qquad (4.1\text{-}3a)$$

$$z_2 = s_{k,2} + n_2 \qquad (4.1\text{-}3b)$$

For a given message m_k, $\mathbf{z}$ is the sum of a constant $\mathbf{s}_k$ and a random vector $\mathbf{n}$. Therefore the conditional density function of $\mathbf{z}$ is

$$p_z(\boldsymbol{\gamma}|m_k) = p_n(\boldsymbol{\gamma} - \mathbf{s}_k) \qquad (4.1\text{-}4)$$

For our example let

$$\mathbf{s}_1 = \begin{bmatrix} 0 \\ 0 \end{bmatrix} \qquad (4.1\text{-}5a)$$

$$\mathbf{s}_2 = \begin{bmatrix} 1 \\ 1 \end{bmatrix} \qquad (4.1\text{-}5b)$$

and let n_1 and n_2 be independent, zero-mean, unit-variance gaussian random variables. Then, the density function of $\mathbf{n}$ (see App. A) is

$$p_n(\boldsymbol{\eta}) = \frac{1}{2\pi} \exp \frac{-(\eta_1^2 + \eta_2^2)}{2} \qquad (4.1\text{-}6)$$

If Eq. (4.1-6) is substituted into Eq. (4.1-4) and the result used in Eq. (4.1-1), the decision rule becomes

$$\exp\left\{-\tfrac{1}{2}[(z_1-1)^2+(z_2-1)^2-z_1^2-z_2^2]\right\} \underset{d_1}{\overset{d_2}{\gtrless}} 1 \qquad (4.1\text{-}7)$$

This rule can be simplified by taking natural logarithms and combining terms to yield

$$z_1 + z_2 \underset{d_1}{\overset{d_2}{\gtrless}} 1 \qquad (4.1\text{-}8)$$

Note that the decision rule depends only on the sum of z_1 and z_2, not on the actual value of each of them. At first it might seem a little surprising that our two-dimensional observation z can be reduced to a one-dimensional variable $(z_1 + z_2)$ without altering the decision-rule performance. However, recall that the general form of the decision rule given in Eq. (4.1-1) was to compare the ratio $\Lambda(z)$ with the appropriate threshold. Since the ratio is just a one-dimensional variable, it would seem that any two-variable problem can be reduced to a one-variable problem. Thus, the only surprising part of Eq. (4.1-8) should be that the one variable is so simple.

The decision rule in Eq. (4.1-8) has an interesting graphical interpretation. In Fig. 4.1-1 the **Z** space is shown with the two signal points marked. The conditional densities of z are indicated by the concentric circles which denote equiprobable contours. Note that for each z, the decision rule is to pick the decision corresponding to the closest signal point.

The major result of Chap. 3 was that for a single random-variable observation, any of a large number of decision-rule design criteria could be realized by means of a likelihood-ratio test. The preceding discussion illustrates that for a two-dimensional vector observation and for a maximum-likelihood decision criterion, the decision rule again is a likelihood-ratio test. The only difference is that $\Lambda(z)$ is a function of a vector rather than a scalar. In fact, all the decision-rule criteria of Chap. 3 can stated for vector observations, and, using the vector probability results of Chap. 2, all can be reduced to likelihood-ratio tests of the form

$$\Lambda(\mathbf{z}) = \frac{p(\mathbf{z}|m_2)}{p(\mathbf{z}|m_1)} \underset{d_1}{\overset{d_2}{\gtrless}} \lambda \qquad (4.1\text{-}9)$$

where the value of the threshold λ is determined by the particular decision design criterion.

For the case of the maximum-likelihood criterion, the preceding argument can easily be generalized to the l-dimensional case. The only change is that the differential element $dz_1\, dz_2$ must be replaced by $dz_1\, dz_2 \ldots dz_l$.

For the Neyman-Pearson criterion, one can still fix $P\{d_2|m_1\}$ at a preselected value α_0 and then maximize $P\{d_2|m_2\}$. For a vector observation, the integrals which define these quantities are l-dimensional integrals. Other

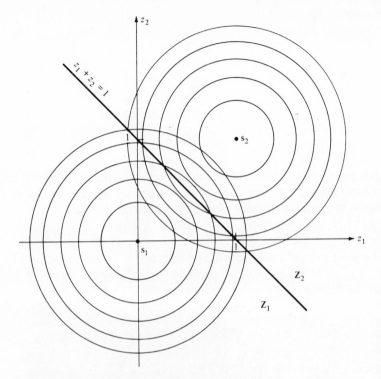

Figure 4.1-1 Signal-space picture of two-dimensional gaussian observation.

than that, all the arguments of Chap. 3 apply, and the criterion reduces to a likelihood-ratio test.

Finally, the Bayes cost criterion and, by implication, the minimum probability-of-error criterion also are just likelihood-ratio tests. Again all that needs to change is that the integrals over the decision regions are now I-fold integrals rather than simple one-dimensional integrals.

We have argued that regardless of the dimensionality of the vector **z**, the decision rule can be formulated as a threshold test on the likelihood ratio $\Lambda(\mathbf{z})$. Since the decision rule is just a description of a mapping from the observation space **Z** to the decision space **D**, any operation on **z** that produces the same mapping can be used as a decision rule. For example, any monotonic function of $\Lambda(\mathbf{z})$ can be compared with an appropriate threshold and yield the same mapping as the likelihood-ratio test. This technique was used in the example at the beginning of the chapter to simplify the decision rule in Eq. (4.1-7). There it was found that a threshold test on the sum of the two observation variables produced the same decision rule as the more complicated likelihood-ratio test. We could say, then, that the sum was a *sufficient statistic* for that problem. In other words, it provided enough information about the observation to enable us to make a proper decision. We shall define a sufficient statistic as follows:

Sufficient statistic A function $l(\mathbf{z})$ is a sufficient statistic if any likelihood-ratio decision rule $d(\mathbf{z})$ can be written as a function of $l(\mathbf{z})$.

It should be noted that since the threshold in the likelihood-ratio test can take on any value, and since a sufficient statistic must be able to mirror this test, it must be possible to determine the value of the likelihood-ratio from the sufficient statistic. The sufficient statistic can be quite useful, however, in simplifying decision-rule implementation and analyzing system performance, as the following example illustrates.

Example 4.1-1 Suppose that as in the previous text example, the observation is formed by adding an independent zero-mean, unit-variance gaussian random variable to each component of the signal vector. That is,

$$\mathbf{z} = \mathbf{s} + \mathbf{n} \tag{4.1-10}$$

where $\mathbf{n}$ and $\mathbf{s}$ are I-dimensional vectors and where

$$\mathbf{s}_1 = \begin{bmatrix} 0 \\ 0 \\ \vdots \\ 0 \end{bmatrix} \tag{4.1-11a}$$

$$\mathbf{s}_2 = \begin{bmatrix} s_1 \\ s_2 \\ \vdots \\ s_I \end{bmatrix} \tag{4.1-11b}$$

Since the noise components are independent, the density of $\mathbf{n}$ is the product of I gaussian densities. Therefore, the likelihood ratio is

$$\Lambda(\mathbf{z}) = \frac{\displaystyle\prod_{i=1}^{I} [1/\sqrt{2\pi}] \, \exp -\tfrac{1}{2}(z_i - s_i)^2}{\displaystyle\prod_{i=1}^{I} [1/\sqrt{2\pi}] \, \exp -\tfrac{1}{2}z_i^2} \tag{4.1-12}$$

which can be simplified by taking the natural logarithm and combining terms:

$$\ln \Lambda(\mathbf{z}) = \sum_{i=1}^{I} s_i z_i - \tfrac{1}{2} \sum_{i=1}^{I} s_i^2 \tag{4.1-13}$$

Finally, if the second sum is combined with the logarithm of the original threshold, the decision rule can be stated as a threshold test on the weighted sum of the z_i:

$$l(\mathbf{z}) = \sum_{i=1}^{I} s_i z_i \underset{d_1}{\overset{d_2}{\gtrless}} \ln \lambda + \tfrac{1}{2} \sum_{i=1}^{I} s_i^2 = \lambda' \tag{4.1-14}$$

The statistic which has been identified as $l(\mathbf{z})$ is obviously a sufficient statistic for this problem, and it will serve to illustrate the useful properties of sufficient statistics. First, it can be used as the basis for designing the decision device shown in Fig. 4.1-2. The components of **z** enter the device from the left, starting with z_1 at time 1. They enter the delay line and are shifted to the right, one stage each time unit. After I time units, z_1 is in the rightmost stage and z_I is in the leftmost. The circles are used to represent multipliers, and the output of each multiplier is the product of the labeled value and the contents of the corresponding delay-line stage. Thus, at time I, the output of the summer is $l(\mathbf{z})$. This number is sampled and fed into the threshold device to be compared with λ', and the decision is made. It is interesting to note that if the input to this device is a single pulse of unit height, the output of the summer will be the sequence

$$\{s_I, s_{I-1}, \ldots, s_2, s_1, 0, 0, \ldots\}$$

In order to compute the performance of this system, we would have to compute the conditional probabilities that **z** will be in $\mathbf{Z}_1$ or $\mathbf{Z}_2$. In their most general interpretation, $\mathbf{Z}_1$ and $\mathbf{Z}_2$ are subsets of an I-dimensional space. Thus it would seem that the integrals which define these probabilities will be difficult to write down, let alone calculate. However, since $l(\mathbf{z})$ is a sufficient statistic, it will tell in which decision region **z** lies. In fact, $\mathbf{Z}_1$ and $\mathbf{Z}_2$ can be defined by

$$\mathbf{Z}_1 = \{\mathbf{z}: l(\mathbf{z}) < \lambda'\} \qquad (4.1\text{-}15a)$$

$$\mathbf{Z}_2 = \{\mathbf{z}: l(\mathbf{z}) > \lambda'\} \qquad (4.1\text{-}15b)$$

Therefore, the conditional probability that $\mathbf{z} \in \mathbf{Z}_1$ (or $\mathbf{Z}_2$) is just the conditional probability that $l(\mathbf{z})$ is less than (greater than) λ'. The error probabilities are therefore

$$P\{d_2|m_1\} = \int_{\lambda'}^{\infty} p(l|m_1)\, dl$$

$$P\{d_1|m_2\} = \int_{-\infty}^{\lambda'} p(l|m_2)\, dl$$

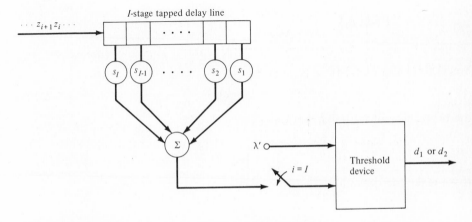

Figure 4.1-2 Optimum decision device for additive gaussian noise.

Since $l(\mathbf{z})$ is a weighted sum of gaussian variables, it is a simple gaussian variable whose variance is constant and whose mean depends on the message. Hence to find the densities $p(l|m_1)$ and $p(l|m_2)$, we need only find the means and the variance of $l(\mathbf{z})$. The conditional means are just

$$E\{l(\mathbf{z})|m_1\} = E\left\{\sum_{i=1}^{l} s_i n_i\right\} = 0$$

$$E\{l(\mathbf{z})|m_2\} = E\left\{\sum_{i=1}^{l} s_i(n_i + s_i)\right\}$$

$$(4.1\text{-}16a)$$

$$= \sum_{i=1}^{l} s_i^2 = \|\mathbf{s}_2\|^2 = \mathbf{s}_2^T \mathbf{s}_2 \qquad (4.1\text{-}16b)$$

The last equality uses the fact that the sum of the squares of the components of a vector is just the square of the length of the vector. The variance of $l(\mathbf{z})$ for either message is

$$\text{var } \{l(\mathbf{z})|m_k\} = \sum_{i=1}^{l} s_i^2 = \|\mathbf{s}_2\|^2 \qquad (4.1\text{-}17)$$

The probability density $p(l|m_1)$ is therefore

$$p(l|m_1) = \frac{1}{\sqrt{2\pi} \, \|\mathbf{s}_2\|} \exp\left\{\frac{-l^2}{2\|\mathbf{s}_2\|^2}\right\}$$

so that $P\{d_2|m_1\}$ becomes

$$P\{d_2|m_1\} = \int_{\lambda'}^{\infty} \frac{1}{\sqrt{2\pi} \, \|\mathbf{s}_2\|} \exp\left\{\frac{-l^2}{2\|\mathbf{s}_2\|^2}\right\} dl \qquad (4.1\text{-}18)$$

If we make the substitution

$$\xi = \frac{l}{\|\mathbf{s}_2\|}$$

then we have

$$P\{d_2|m_1\} = \int_{\frac{\lambda'}{\|\mathbf{s}_2\|}}^{\infty} \frac{1}{\sqrt{2\pi}} e^{-\xi^2/2} \, d\xi = Q\left(\frac{\lambda'}{\|\mathbf{s}_2\|}\right)$$

Since, from Eq. (4.1-14), λ' is given by

$$\lambda' = \ln \lambda + \tfrac{1}{2}\|\mathbf{s}_2\|^2$$

the probability of false alarm becomes

$$P\{d_2|m_1\} = Q\left(\frac{\ln \lambda}{\|\mathbf{s}_2\|} + \frac{\|\mathbf{s}_2\|}{2}\right)$$

If we make the definition

$$\delta = \|\mathbf{s}_2\|$$

then we have the familiar form

$$P\{d_2|m_1\} = Q\left(\frac{\delta}{2} + \frac{\ln \lambda}{\delta}\right) \qquad (4.1\text{-}19a)$$

In a similar fashion we can show that

$$P\{d_1|m_2\} = Q\left(\frac{\delta}{2} - \frac{\ln \lambda}{\delta}\right) \qquad (4.1\text{-}19b)$$

These error probabilities are identical to what we would obtain if we used the results of Example 3.3-2 and treated $l(\mathbf{z})$ as a scalar observation. In this case

$$\mu_1 = 0$$
$$\mu_2 = \|\mathbf{s}_2\|^2$$

and $$\sigma = \|\mathbf{s}_2\|$$

so that δ is given by

$$\delta = \frac{\mu_2 - \mu_1}{\sigma} = \frac{\|\mathbf{s}_2\|^2}{\|\mathbf{s}_2\|} = \|\mathbf{s}_2\|$$

as before.

In order to more fully understand the behavior of the optimal decision device derived previously, let us examine its function for the $I = 2$ case. Figure 4.1-3 shows the $\mathbf{Z}$ space with the points $\mathbf{s}_1$ and $\mathbf{s}_2$ indicated. Since the noise is additive, $\mathbf{z}$ is just the result of adding the noise vector $\mathbf{n}$ to the

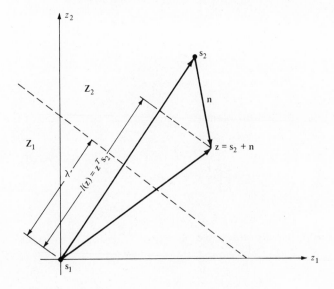

Figure 4.1-3 Signal-space picture for $I = 2$.

appropriate signal vector **s**. The figure shows this procedure for signal s_2 and for some particular noise **n**. Now, the sufficient statistic is computed from

$$l(\mathbf{z}) = \sum_{i=1}^{2} s_i z_i = \mathbf{s}_2^T \mathbf{z} \tag{4.1-20}$$

Thus, since the dot product of two vectors is the projection of one on the other, $l(\mathbf{z})$ is just the projection of **z** on s_2. This is also indicated in Fig. 4.1-3.

The threshold test described by Eq. (4.1-15) partitions the **Z** space into the two regions $\mathbf{Z}_1$ and $\mathbf{Z}_2$. Since $l(\mathbf{z})$ is measured parallel to s_2, the boundary between $\mathbf{Z}_1$ and $\mathbf{Z}_2$ is perpendicular to s_2. Therefore, of the two-dimensional noise vector, only the component parallel to s_2 will effect the decision. It is this component which determines the error probabilities given in Eq. (4.1-19).

Although l-dimensional pictures are a bit more difficult to draw, the same structure holds for the general case. That is, for l-dimensional signal and noise vectors, $l(\mathbf{z})$ is still just the projection of **z** on s_2. Note from Eqs. (4.1-18) and (4.1-19) that the conditional probabilities are completely determined by the length of s_2. Thus, if it was possible to make the vector longer, it would not matter which dimensions were increased. In fact, a one-dimensional vector would yield the same performance if it had the same length. The technique of considering l-dimensional pictures of signal points is called *signal-space analysis*, and it will continue to be of use.

Example 4.1-2 Consider the decision problem with

$$p(\mathbf{z}|m_1) = p(z_1, z_2, \ldots, z_l|m_1) = \prod_{i=1}^{l} \tfrac{1}{2} e^{-|z_i|}$$

and

$$p(\mathbf{z}|m_2) = p(z_1, z_2, \ldots, z_l|m_2) = \prod_{i=1}^{l} e^{-2|z_i|}$$

The likelihood-ratio test for this problem is

$$\Lambda(\mathbf{z}) = \frac{\displaystyle\prod_{i=1}^{l} e^{-2|z_i|}}{\displaystyle\prod_{i=1}^{l} \tfrac{1}{2} e^{-|z_i|}} = \prod_{i=1}^{l} \frac{1}{2} e^{-|z_i|} \underset{d_1}{\overset{d_2}{\gtrless}} \lambda$$

If we take the logarithm on both sides, we have

$$\sum_{i=1}^{l} [\ln \tfrac{1}{2} - |z_i|] \underset{d_1}{\overset{d_2}{\gtrless}} \ln \lambda$$

or
$$l(\mathbf{z}) = \sum_{i=1}^{I} |z_i| \underset{d_1}{\overset{d_2}{\gtrless}} - \ln \lambda - I \ln 2$$

Here it is not easy to find the probability densities of l. One possible approach is to use the central limit theorem to approximate the densities by gaussian densities. Another approach is to use numerical methods to find the densities and associated error probabilities.

4.2 THE GENERAL GAUSSIAN PROBLEM

Example 4.1-1 is one step toward the general gaussian problem. Further steps would include letting the signal vector $\mathbf{s}_1$ be nonzero, letting the variance of the noise components n_i depend on i, letting the n_i be dependent variables, and, finally, letting the statistics of $\mathbf{n}$ be dependent on the message. Instead of working each of these cases separately, we shall simply solve the general case and then examine the effect of various simplifications. The only constraint will be that the conditional probability density function of $\mathbf{z}$ be an Ith-order gaussian density. This general problem will be used extensively in later work.

The general form of the density function of an Ith-order gaussian vector $\mathbf{z}$ with mean $\mathbf{s}$ and variance matrix $\mathbf{V}$ is

$$p(\mathbf{z}) = \frac{1}{(2\pi)^{I/2}(\det \mathbf{V})^{1/2}} \exp \left[-\frac{1}{2}(\mathbf{z} - \mathbf{s})^T \mathbf{V}^{-1} (\mathbf{z} - \mathbf{s}) \right] \qquad (4.2\text{-}1)$$

where it is assumed that $\mathbf{V}$ is positive definite and symmetric. The components of $\mathbf{s}$ are the expected values of the components of $\mathbf{z}$:

$$E\{z_i\} = s_i \qquad \text{for } i = 1, 2, \ldots, I \qquad (4.2\text{-}2)$$

and the elements of $\mathbf{V}$ are the (co)variances of z_i and z_j:

$$v_{ij} = \text{cov } \{z_i, z_j\} \qquad \text{for } i, j = 1, \ldots, I \qquad (4.2\text{-}3)$$

For the general gaussian problem the conditional densities $p(\mathbf{z}|m_1)$ and $p(\mathbf{z}|m_2)$ are given by

$$p(\mathbf{z}|m_1) = \frac{1}{(2\pi)^{I/2}(\det \mathbf{V}_1)^{1/2}} \exp \left[-\frac{1}{2}(\mathbf{z} - \mathbf{s}_1)^T \mathbf{V}_1^{-1}(\mathbf{z} - \mathbf{s}_1) \right]$$

and
$$p(\mathbf{z}|m_2) = \frac{1}{(2\pi)^{I/2}(\det \mathbf{V}_2)^{1/2}} \exp \left[-\frac{1}{2}(\mathbf{z} - \mathbf{s}_2)^T \mathbf{V}_2^{-1}(\mathbf{z} - \mathbf{s}_2) \right]$$

The likelihood ratio is therefore

$$\Lambda(\mathbf{z}) = \frac{(\det \mathbf{V}_1)^{1/2} \exp \left[-\frac{1}{2}(\mathbf{z} - \mathbf{s}_2)^T \mathbf{V}_2^{-1}(\mathbf{z} - \mathbf{s}_2) \right]}{(\det \mathbf{V}_2)^{1/2} \exp \left[-\frac{1}{2}(\mathbf{z} - \mathbf{s}_1)^T \mathbf{V}_1^{-1}(\mathbf{z} - \mathbf{s}_1) \right]} \qquad (4.2\text{-}4)$$

Taking logarithms, the likelihood-ratio test for the general gaussian problem can be stated as

$$(\mathbf{z} - \mathbf{s}_1)^T \mathbf{V}_1^{-1}(\mathbf{z} - \mathbf{s}_1) - (\mathbf{z} - \mathbf{s}_2)^T \mathbf{V}_2^{-1}(\mathbf{z} - \mathbf{s}_2) \underset{d_1}{\overset{d_2}{\gtrless}} 2 \ln \lambda + \ln \frac{\det \mathbf{V}_2}{\det \mathbf{V}_1} \quad (4.2\text{-}5)$$

where λ is the threshold for the particular decision-rule design criterion selected.

The expression in Eq. (4.2-5) is not particularly easy to interpret in its most general form. For example, the left-hand side is a quadratic expression in $\mathbf{z}$ and hence does not represent a gaussian variable. However, various simplifications of the general problem do lead to interesting decision rules. We shall now consider some of these simplifications.

If the two covariance matrices are the same, the decision rule reduces to

$$(\mathbf{z} - \mathbf{s}_1)^T \mathbf{V}^{-1}(\mathbf{z} - \mathbf{s}_1) - (\mathbf{z} - \mathbf{s}_2)^T \mathbf{V}^{-1}(\mathbf{z} - \mathbf{s}_2) \underset{d_1}{\overset{d_2}{\gtrless}} 2 \ln \lambda \quad (4.2\text{-}6)$$

The assumption of equal covariances is true whenever the noise does not depend on which signal is sent. Multiplying out the matrices and combining terms yields

$$l(\mathbf{z}) = (\mathbf{s}_2 - \mathbf{s}_1)^T \mathbf{V}^{-1}\mathbf{z} \underset{d_1}{\overset{d_2}{\gtrless}} \ln \lambda + \tfrac{1}{2}(\mathbf{s}_2^T \mathbf{V}^{-1}\mathbf{s}_2 - \mathbf{s}_1^T \mathbf{V}^{-1}\mathbf{s}_1) = \lambda' \quad (4.2\text{-}7)$$

Since $l(\mathbf{z})$ is a weighted sum of jointly gaussian variables, it is gaussian. The variance of $\mathbf{z}$ is independent of the message so the variance of $l(\mathbf{z})$ is

$$\text{var } \{l(\mathbf{z})|m_k\} = (\mathbf{s}_2 - \mathbf{s}_1)^T \mathbf{V}^{-1}(\mathbf{s}_2 - \mathbf{s}_1) \qquad \text{for } k = 1, 2 \quad (4.2\text{-}8)$$

The expected value of l if m_1 is true is

$$E\{l|m_1\} = E\{(\mathbf{s}_2 - \mathbf{s}_1)^T \mathbf{V}^{-1}(\mathbf{s}_1 + \mathbf{n})\} = (\mathbf{s}_2 - \mathbf{s}_1)^T \mathbf{V}^{-1}\mathbf{s}_1 \quad (4.2\text{-}9a)$$

while $\qquad E\{l|m_2\} = E\{(\mathbf{s}_2 - \mathbf{s}_1)^T \mathbf{V}^{-1}(\mathbf{s}_2 + \mathbf{n})\} = (\mathbf{s}_2 - \mathbf{s}_1)^T \mathbf{V}^{-1}\mathbf{s}_2 \quad (4.2\text{-}9b)$

If we define $\Delta\mathbf{s}$ as

$$\Delta\mathbf{s} = \mathbf{s}_2 - \mathbf{s}_1$$

then $\qquad\qquad\qquad \text{var } \{l|m_k\} = \Delta\mathbf{s}^T \mathbf{V}^{-1}\Delta\mathbf{s}$

$$E\{l|m_1\} = \Delta\mathbf{s}^T \mathbf{V}^{-1}\mathbf{s}_1$$

and $\qquad\qquad\qquad E\{l|m_2\} = \Delta\mathbf{s}^T \mathbf{V}^{-1}\mathbf{s}_2$

The probability of false alarm is given by

$$P\{d_2|m_1\} = \int_{\lambda'}^{\infty} p(l|m_1)\, dl \quad (4.2\text{-}10)$$

From the preceding result we know that $p(l|m_1)$ is

$$p(l|m_1) = K \exp \{-\tfrac{1}{2}(l - \Delta\mathbf{s}^T \mathbf{V}^{-1}\mathbf{s}_1)(\Delta\mathbf{s}^T \mathbf{V}^{-1}\, \Delta\mathbf{s})^{-1}(l - \Delta\mathbf{s}^T \mathbf{V}^{-1}\mathbf{s}_1)\} \quad (4.2\text{-}11)$$

where K is the normalizing constant. Let us substitute Eq. (4.2-11) into Eq. (4.2-10) and make the transformation

$$\xi = \frac{l - \mathbf{\Delta s}^T \mathbf{V}^{-1} \mathbf{s}_1}{\sqrt{\mathbf{\Delta s}^T \mathbf{V}^{-1} \mathbf{\Delta s}}}$$

so that $P\{d_2|m_1\}$ becomes

$$P\{d_2|m_1\} = \int_{\frac{\lambda' - \mathbf{\Delta s}^T \mathbf{V}^{-1} \mathbf{s}_1}{\sqrt{\mathbf{\Delta s}^T \mathbf{V}^{-1} \mathbf{\Delta s}}}}^{\infty} \frac{1}{\sqrt{2\pi}} e^{-\xi^2/2} \, d\xi$$

$$= Q\left(\frac{\lambda' - \mathbf{\Delta s}^T \mathbf{V}^{-1} \mathbf{\Delta s}}{\sqrt{\mathbf{\Delta s}^T \mathbf{V}^{-1} \mathbf{\Delta s}}}\right) \qquad (4.2\text{-}12)$$

From Eq. (4.2-7) we know that λ' is

$$\lambda' = \ln \lambda + \tfrac{1}{2}(\mathbf{s}_2^T \mathbf{V}^{-1} \mathbf{s}_2 - \mathbf{s}_1^T \mathbf{V}^{-1} \mathbf{s}_1)$$

so that

$$\lambda' - \mathbf{\Delta s}^T \mathbf{V}^{-1} \mathbf{s}_1 = \ln \lambda + \tfrac{1}{2}(\mathbf{s}_2{}^T \mathbf{V}^{-1} \mathbf{s}_2 - \mathbf{s}_1{}^T \mathbf{V}^{-1} \mathbf{s}_1) - (\mathbf{s}_2 - \mathbf{s}_1)^T \mathbf{V}^{-1} \mathbf{s}_1$$

$$= \ln \lambda + \tfrac{1}{2}\mathbf{\Delta s}^T \mathbf{V}^{-1} \mathbf{\Delta s}$$

Now let us define

$$\delta^2 = \mathbf{\Delta s}^T \mathbf{V}^{-1} \mathbf{\Delta s} \qquad (4.2\text{-}13)$$

so that $P\{d_2|m_1\}$ can be written, as before, as

$$P\{d_2|m_1\} = Q\left(\frac{\delta}{2} + \frac{\ln \lambda}{\delta}\right) \qquad (4.2\text{-}14)$$

In a completely similar fashion, we can show that

$$P\{d_1|m_2\} = Q\left(\frac{\delta}{2} - \frac{\ln \lambda}{\delta}\right) \qquad (4.2\text{-}15)$$

These error-probability results are identical to those obtained previously. The distance measure defined by Eq. (4.2-13) is consistent with the other definitions of δ made in Examples 3.3-2 and 4.1-1.

Example 4.2-1 If the noise is white with unit variance, then the covariance matrix $\mathbf{V}$ is the identity matrix. For this case, the decision rule of Eq. (4.2-7) becomes

$$l(\mathbf{z}) = (\mathbf{s}_2 - \mathbf{s}_1)^T \mathbf{z} \underset{d_1}{\overset{d_2}{\gtrless}} \ln \lambda + \tfrac{1}{2}(\mathbf{s}_2^T \mathbf{s}_2 - \mathbf{s}_1^T \mathbf{s}_1) \qquad (4.2\text{-}16)$$

If $\mathbf{s}$ is the all-zero vector, this is exactly the decision rule that was encountered in Example 4.1-1. Note, however, that even when $\mathbf{s}_1$ is not zero, the sufficient statistic is still just the projection of the observation $\mathbf{z}$ onto the line that joins the two signal vectors in the signal space $(\mathbf{s}_2 - \mathbf{s}_1)$. The resultant variable is still a gaussian random variable. Therefore, the signal-space picture is useful here, too, and it can be shown that performance depends only on the distance between the two signals $\|s_2 - s_1\|$.

If V is the product of a scalar v and I, then the problem models the addition of an independent gaussian noise of variance v to each component of s. The sufficient statistic then becomes

$$l(\mathbf{z}) = \frac{1}{v}\, \Delta \mathbf{s}^T \mathbf{z}$$

and the squared distance is

$$\delta^2 = \frac{\|\Delta \mathbf{s}\|^2}{v}$$

The appearance of v in the denominator of δ^2 indicates that the performance of a system would decrease as v increases. (That should not be surprising.) Also note that system performance is determined by the ratio of $\|\Delta \mathbf{s}\|^2$ to v. If $\|\Delta \mathbf{s}\|^2$ is taken as a measure of signal energy, then δ^2 becomes a signal-to-noise ratio. In fact, it can be interpreted as such even in the most general case.

Suppose that the various noise components were independent but had different variances. In particular, assume that

$$V = \begin{bmatrix} v_1 & & & & & \\ & v_2 & & & 0 & \\ & & v_3 & & & \\ & & & \ddots & \\ 0 & & & & v_I \end{bmatrix} \tag{4.2-17}$$

Then $l(\mathbf{z})$ is

$$l(\mathbf{z}) = \sum_{i=1}^{I} \frac{\Delta s_i z_i}{v_i} \tag{4.2-18}$$

and the terms $\Delta s_i z_i$ are weighted according to their reliability. For a fixed Δs_i, the larger the noise variance v_i, the less the term effects the decision variable.

An interesting interpretation of this result is the following: Suppose that after receiving the vector $\mathbf{z}$, it was altered by multiplying each component by $1/\sqrt{v_i}$. In other words, suppose the observation $\mathbf{z}'$ was formed:

$$\mathbf{z}' = \begin{bmatrix} z_1/\sqrt{v_1} \\ z_2/\sqrt{v_2} \\ \vdots \\ z_I/\sqrt{v_I} \end{bmatrix} \tag{4.2-19}$$

Now, would a decision based on $\mathbf{z}'$ be better than, worse than, or the same as one based on $\mathbf{z}$? Clearly it cannot be better since $\mathbf{z}'$ was obtained from $\mathbf{z}$. It cannot be worse since one way of using $\mathbf{z}'$ is to reconstruct $\mathbf{z}$. Thus, it must be the same. In fact, we can prove the following theorem.

Theorem 4.2-1 Invariance of decision rule If $\mathbf{f}(\mathbf{z})$ is an invertible function of $\mathbf{z}$, then an optimal decision rule based on $\mathbf{z}' = \mathbf{f}(\mathbf{z})$ will yield the same performance as one based on $\mathbf{z}$.

PROOF Let $\mathbf{f}^{-1}(\mathbf{z}')$ be the inverse of $\mathbf{f}(\mathbf{z})$; that is,

$$\mathbf{f}^{-1}(\mathbf{f}(\mathbf{z})) = \mathbf{z}$$

Then if $d(\mathbf{z})$ is the optimal decision rule for $\mathbf{z}$, the same performance can be obtained for $\mathbf{z}'$ by using the rule $d(\mathbf{f}^{-1}(\mathbf{z}'))$. Similarly, if the optimum rule for $\mathbf{z}'$ is $d'(\mathbf{z}')$, $\mathbf{z}$ will yield the same performance with the rule $d'(\mathbf{f}(\mathbf{z}))$.

It turns out that we have already designed a decision rule for the $\mathbf{z}'$ given by Eq. (4.2-19). Note that the conditional mean of $\mathbf{z}'$ is

$$E\{\mathbf{z}'|m_k\} = \begin{bmatrix} s_{k,1}/\sqrt{v_1} \\ s_{k,2}/\sqrt{v_2} \\ \vdots \\ s_{k,I}/\sqrt{v_I} \end{bmatrix} = \mathbf{s}'_k \qquad (4.2\text{-}20)$$

and its variance matrix is just the identity matrix. Thus, we have transformed this problem into the simple one of Example 4.2-1. Using the sufficient statistic result obtained in Eq. (4.2-16) yields

$$l(\mathbf{z}') = \Delta \mathbf{s}'^T \mathbf{z}'$$

$$= \sum_{i=1}^{I} \frac{(s_{2,i} - s_{1,i})}{\sqrt{v_i}} \frac{z_i}{\sqrt{v_i}} \qquad (4.2\text{-}21)$$

which matches (4.2-18) and δ^2 is

$$\delta^2 = \|\Delta \mathbf{s}'\|^2$$

$$= \sum_{i=1}^{I} \frac{(s_{2,i} - s_{1,i})^2}{v_i} \qquad (4.2\text{-}22)$$

Therefore, the optimum decision rule can be viewed as a two-step process: First the signal is normalized so that each component of $\mathbf{z}$ contains a noise of unit variance, and then the decision rule for this simpler type of noise is used. In fact, the decision rule for any fixed $\mathbf{V}$ can also be considered to be a two-step process. The first step transforms the problem to an equivalent one with independent noise components, and the second step employs the best decision rule for this new problem.

In order to establish this result, we must first show that any gaussian vector can be reversibly transformed to a gaussian vector with independent components. To do so, a rotated set of coordinate axes must be used. Figure 4.2-1

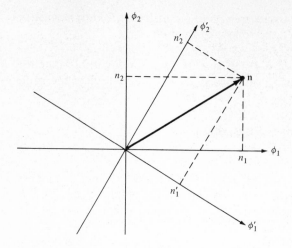

Figure 4.2-1 Rotation of coordinates.

illustrates such a rotation for the $I = 2$ case and can serve as the model for the more general case. We shall use $\mathbf{n}$ to denote the original gaussian vector and $\mathbf{n}'$ to denote the "new" vector. The word *new* is in quotes since $\mathbf{n}'$ and $\mathbf{n}$ actually describe the same point in I-space but use different coordinate systems. The components of $\mathbf{n}'$ will be the projections of $\mathbf{n}$ onto a new set of axes vectors $\boldsymbol{\phi}_i'$:

$$n_i' = \boldsymbol{\phi}_i'^T \mathbf{n} \qquad i = 1, 2, \ldots, I \tag{4.2-23}$$

We shall assume for the moment that we can find a set of $\boldsymbol{\phi}_i'$ such that the n_i' are independent. We shall use β_i for the variance of each n_i'. Then, since the components of $\mathbf{n}'$ are to be independent, the second moments of $\mathbf{n}'$ are

$$E\{n_i' n_j'\} = \beta_i \delta_{ij} = \begin{cases} \beta_i & i = j \\ 0 & i \neq j \end{cases} \tag{4.2-24}$$

Using Eq. (4.2-23) to represent n_i' and n_j', this becomes

$$E[\boldsymbol{\phi}_i'^T \mathbf{n} \mathbf{n}^T \boldsymbol{\phi}_j'] = \boldsymbol{\phi}_i'^T \mathbf{V} \boldsymbol{\phi}_j' = \beta_i \delta_{ij} \tag{4.2-25}$$

It can be shown [see, for example, Van Trees (1968)] that the only $\boldsymbol{\phi}_i'$ that can satisfy Eq. (4.2-25) are those that satisfy

$$\beta_i \boldsymbol{\phi}_i' = \mathbf{V} \boldsymbol{\phi}_i' \tag{4.2-26}$$

These $\boldsymbol{\phi}_i'$ are the *eigenvectors* of $\mathbf{V}$. Since Eq. (4.2-26) only determines $\boldsymbol{\phi}_i'$ to within a constant, we can normalize it so that $\boldsymbol{\phi}_i'^T \boldsymbol{\phi}_i' = 1$; the associated β_i are the *eigenvalues*. It can also be shown that it is always possible to select the $\boldsymbol{\phi}_i'$ so that they form an orthonormal set. Before applying these to the decision problem, we shall illustrate the procedure with the following example.

Example 4.2-2 For the zero-mean gaussian random vector $\mathbf{n}$, with variance matrix

$$\mathbf{V} = \begin{bmatrix} 2 & 2 \\ 2 & 5 \end{bmatrix}$$

find a linear transformation to a vector $\mathbf{n}'$ such that $\mathbf{n}'$ has independent components.

From Eq. (4.2-26), the β's must satisfy

$$\det\,[\mathbf{V} - \beta\mathbf{I}] = 0$$

The determinant becomes

$$(2 - \beta)\,(5 - \beta) - 4 = 0$$

and so the eigenvalues are

$$\beta_1 = 6$$

$$\beta_2 = 1$$

Now, Eq. (4.2-26) can be used to solve for the ϕ_i'. For ϕ_1', it becomes

$$6\phi_1' = \begin{bmatrix} 6\phi_{11}' \\ 6\phi_{12}' \end{bmatrix} = \begin{bmatrix} 2\phi_{11}' + 2\phi_{12}' \\ 2\phi_{11}' + 5\phi_{12}' \end{bmatrix}$$

so that

$$\phi_{11}' = \tfrac{1}{2}\phi_{12}'$$

Since the ϕ' are to be normalized, ϕ_1' is

$$\phi_1' = \begin{bmatrix} \dfrac{1}{\sqrt{5}} \\ \dfrac{2}{\sqrt{5}} \end{bmatrix}$$

Similarly,

$$\phi_2' = \begin{bmatrix} \dfrac{-2}{\sqrt{5}} \\ \dfrac{1}{\sqrt{5}} \end{bmatrix}$$

Figure 4.2-2 shows a plot of the original axes and the new axes.

For the general gaussian problem with equal variance matrices, suppose that the first step in the decision device is to transform the received signal so that it has independent components. Since this is a reversible operation, it will not alter performance. Now the decision is to be based on $\mathbf{z}'$ where

$$z_i' = \mathbf{z}^T\phi_i' = \phi_i'^T\mathbf{z} \tag{4.2-27}$$

and where the ϕ_i' are the normalized eigenvectors of $\mathbf{V}$. The conditional mean of $\mathbf{z}'$ is clearly

$$E\{\mathbf{z}'|m_k\} = \sum_{i=1}^{I} (\mathbf{s}_k{}^T\phi_i')\phi_i' = \mathbf{s}_k' \tag{4.2-28}$$

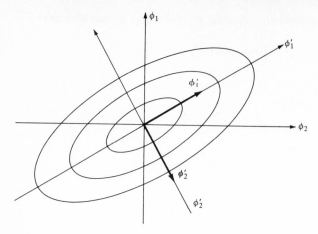

Figure 4.2-2 Rotation of axes for Example 4.2-2.

and its variance matrix is

$$
\mathbf{V}' =
\begin{bmatrix}
\beta_1 & & & 0 \\
& \beta_2 & & \\
0 & & \ddots & \\
& & & \beta_I
\end{bmatrix}
\tag{4.2-29}
$$

The sufficient statistic for this type of problem is given in Eq. (4.2-18). It is just

$$
l(\mathbf{z}') = \sum_{i=1}^{I} \frac{\Delta s'_i \, z'_i}{\beta_i}
\tag{4.2-30}
$$

which, if one has computed the β_i, is a much simpler expression than the one in Eq. (4.2-7). However, the theorem of reversibility assures us that the two expressions are identical. To prove this, note that since the $\boldsymbol{\phi}'_i$ are the eigenvectors of $\mathbf{V}$ as given in Eq. (4.2-26), they can be written as

$$
\boldsymbol{\phi}'_i = \beta_i \mathbf{V}^{-1} \boldsymbol{\phi}'_i
\tag{4.2-31}
$$

which can be used to write the $\Delta s'_i$.

$$
\Delta s'_i = \Delta \mathbf{s}^T \boldsymbol{\phi}'_i
$$
$$
= \beta_i \Delta \mathbf{s}^T \mathbf{V}^{-1} \boldsymbol{\phi}'_i
\tag{4.2-32}
$$

If Eq. (4.2-32) is used in Eq. (4.2-30), the sufficient statistic becomes

$$
l(\mathbf{z}') = \sum_{i=1}^{I} \Delta \mathbf{s}^T \mathbf{V}^{-1} \boldsymbol{\phi}'_i z'_i
$$

$$
= \Delta \mathbf{s}^T \mathbf{V}^{-1} \left(\sum_{i=1}^{I} \boldsymbol{\phi}'_i \boldsymbol{\phi}'^{T}_i \right) \mathbf{z} = \Delta \mathbf{s}^T \mathbf{V}^{-1} \mathbf{z}
\tag{4.2-33}
$$

The second line was obtained by using Eq. (4.2-27) and recognizing that

$$\sum_{i=1}^{l} \boldsymbol{\phi}_i' \boldsymbol{\phi}_i'^T = \mathbf{I}$$

This, however, is exactly the same as the general expression for the sufficient statistic in Eq. (4.2-7). Therefore the processes of transforming the observation with correlated noise to one with uncorrelated noise does not alter system performance. It is called a *whitening process*, and the name has more significance when the same ideas are applied to waveform problems.

Another interesting subset of the general gaussian problem is the class of constant mean problems. Here the mean vectors $\mathbf{s}_1$ and $\mathbf{s}_2$ are identical, and the sufficient statistic is

$$l(\mathbf{z}) = \tfrac{1}{2}(\mathbf{z} - \mathbf{s})^T(\mathbf{V}_1^{-1} - \mathbf{V}_2^{-1})(\mathbf{z} - \mathbf{s}) \qquad (4.2\text{-}34)$$

where the constant mean is denoted $\mathbf{s}$. Since the mean is always subtracted from $\mathbf{z}$, and since it does not appear elsewhere in the problem, it can be ignored. This class of problems is developed in the problems.

4.3 WAVEFORM OBSERVATIONS AND ADDITIVE GAUSSIAN NOISE

In many decision problems, the observation is a continuous waveform rather than a set of numbers. In this section, a method of reducing a waveform problem to a vector problem will be presented and applied to gaussian noise processes. Although the derivations are lengthy, the final result has a pleasing intuitive interpretation.

One simple way of representing a waveform as the limiting form of a vector would be to define the vector as samples of the waveform and let the samples become dense. Thus, if $z(t)$ is a waveform over the interval $[0, T]$, then a vector $\mathbf{z}_\epsilon$ can be formed of samples $z(t)$ spaced by ϵ seconds.

$$\mathbf{z}_\epsilon = \begin{bmatrix} z(0) \\ z(\epsilon) \\ z(2\epsilon) \\ \cdots \\ z(l\epsilon) \end{bmatrix} \qquad (4.3\text{-}1)$$

The number of elements in the vector is selected so that

$$l\epsilon \leq T < (l + 1)\epsilon \qquad (4.3\text{-}2)$$

It would seem that if the samples are dense enough, $z(t)$ can be reconstructed from $\mathbf{z}_\epsilon$ and sampling is a reversible process. A waveform $z_\epsilon(t)$ that approximates $z(t)$ can be formed from the elements of $\mathbf{z}_\epsilon$ by using the function $\delta_\epsilon(t)$ which is shown in Fig. 4.3-1. The approximating function is

$$z_\epsilon(t) = \sum_{i=0}^{l} \sqrt{\epsilon} z(i\epsilon) \delta_\epsilon(t - i\epsilon) \qquad (4.3\text{-}3)$$

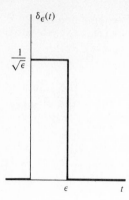

Figure 4.3-1 The pulse function $\delta_\epsilon(t)$.

Figure 4.3-2 shows the relation between $z(t)$ and $z_\epsilon(t)$. If $z(t)$ is well behaved, the limit of $z_\epsilon(t)$ as ϵ goes to zero is well defined and is, in fact, $z(t)$. However, if $z(t)$ is not well behaved, for example, if it has an uncountably infinite number of discontinuities, the limit is not defined and the approach does not work.

Usually when one is interested in engineering applications, it is possible to ignore sticky mathematical questions concerning whether or not functions are well behaved. Unfortunately this is not the case here; problems arise when the function to be sampled contains a *white-noise* component. White noise is usually defined as a random process whose power spectral density is a constant. Thus, its autocorrelation function is a delta function:

$$R_n(\tau) = V\delta(\tau) \tag{4.3-4}$$

If one attempts to "sample" such a process by measuring it at a given instant of time, the resulting random variable would have an infinite variance; clearly, this is not a valid model for a physical system.

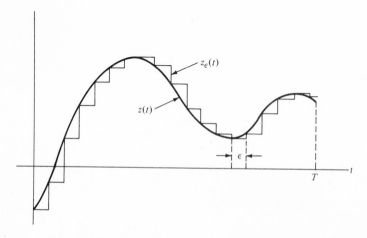

Figure 4.3-2 Sampled waveform.

The source of the problem lies in the definition of white noise. It is usually introduced as a model for a noise process whose power spectral density is flat for all *frequencies of interest*. An ideal instantaneous sampler is influenced by energy from all frequencies. Thus, for a sampler all frequencies are of interest, and there is a conflict with the white-noise model.

In order to resolve the conflict, let us look more closely at how a sampler might actually function. The waveform to be sampled is converted to a voltage, and at the *sampling instant* this voltage is used to charge a capacitor. This process actually takes a finite amount of time, say, ϵ seconds. After the capacitor is fully charged, it is discharged through a measuring device. Thus, the sample at the ith sampling instant is actually

$$z_i = \frac{1}{\epsilon} \int_{i\epsilon}^{(i+1)\epsilon} z(t)\, dt \qquad (4.3\text{-}5)$$

where the $1/\epsilon$ coefficient is selected to scale z_i correctly. Therefore, a sampler can be represented by a linear system with impulse response $\delta_\epsilon(t)$ whose output is sampled in the classic sense.

It should be clear that for a well-behaved $z(t)$ and a small ϵ, this representation of sampling will yield essentially the same sample value as the classic representation. In addition, it has the distinct advantage of being well defined for a broader class of functions. For example, if $n(t)$ is a zero-mean white gaussian noise process with spectral density V, then its *sampled value* at the time $t = i\epsilon$ is

$$n_i = \frac{1}{\epsilon} \int_{i\epsilon}^{(i+1)\epsilon} n(t)\, dt \qquad (4.3\text{-}6)$$

For a nonzero ϵ, n_i is a zero-mean gaussian variable with variance

$$
\begin{aligned}
\text{var}\,\{n_i\} &= E\left\{ \frac{1}{\epsilon} \int_{i\epsilon}^{(i+1)\epsilon} n(t)\, dt\, \frac{1}{\epsilon} \int_{i\epsilon}^{(i+1)\epsilon} n(\tau)\, d\tau \right\} \\
&= \frac{1}{\epsilon^2} \int_{i\epsilon}^{(i+1)\epsilon} \int_{i\epsilon}^{(i+1)\epsilon} R_n(t,\tau)\, dt\, d\tau \\
&= \frac{V}{\epsilon} \qquad (4.3\text{-}7)
\end{aligned}
$$

In order to treat a waveform as a sequence of samples, it must be shown that in the limit of dense sampling, the sequence actually represents the waveform. For a continuous deterministic waveform, this is trivial. However, for a white-noise process $n(t)$, as defined previously, it is quite difficult.

Rather than show that a white-noise process can be approached by a time function based on n_i, we shall turn the problem around and show that it is possible to use n_i to construct a random process with all the statistical attributes of $n(t)$. To begin with, define the random process $n_\epsilon(t)$ as

$$n_\epsilon(t) = \sum_{i=0}^{I} n_i \sqrt{\epsilon}\, \delta_\epsilon(t - i\epsilon + \gamma) \qquad (4.3\text{-}8)$$

The additional parameter γ is a random variable uniformly distributed between 0 and ϵ; it is included to make $n_\epsilon(t)$ a stationary process.

The autocorrelation function of $n_\epsilon(t)$ is

$$R_\epsilon(\tau) = E\{n_\epsilon(t)n_\epsilon(t - \tau)\}$$

$$= \begin{cases} \dfrac{V}{\epsilon} \dfrac{\epsilon - |\tau|}{\epsilon} & |\tau| \leq \epsilon \\[3em] 0 & |\tau| > \epsilon \end{cases} \qquad (4.3\text{-}9)$$

Now, it is clear that $n_\epsilon(t)$ is a zero-mean gaussian process, and the limit of $R_\epsilon(t)$ is

$$\lim_{\epsilon \to 0} R_\epsilon(\tau) = V\delta(t) \qquad (4.3\text{-}10)$$

Thus, as ϵ goes to zero, $n_\epsilon(t)$ has all the properties of $n(t)$.

The expression in Eq. (4.3-8) is one example of expressing a random process as an expansion over a complete set of orthonormal functions. In this case, the functions were just delayed replicas of the simple pulse function shown in Fig. 4.3-1, but any complete set of orthonormal function can be used, as we shall see later.

To illustrate the usefulness of the sequence of the samples representation of processes, consider the following case. The signal is one of the two waveforms $s_1(t)$ or $s_2(t)$ which are nonzero only over the interval $[0, T]$. The observation is the sum of the signal waveform and a sample function from a white gaussian noise process $n(t)$:

$$z(t) = s(t) + n(t) \qquad 0 \leq t \leq T \qquad (4.3\text{-}11)$$

We wish to find the optimum receiver for a likelihood-ratio test. In the sequence-of-samples representation, we have the vector observation

$$\mathbf{z} = \mathbf{s} + \mathbf{n} \qquad (4.3\text{-}12)$$

where the n_i are independent zero-mean gaussian variables with variance V/ϵ, as given by Eq. (4.3-6). The components of $\mathbf{z}$ are given by Eq. (4.3-5), while the $s_{k,i}$ are defined by

$$s_{k,i} = \frac{1}{\epsilon} \int_{i\epsilon}^{(i+1)\epsilon} s_k(t)\, dt \qquad k = 1,2$$

From Sec. 4.2, the sufficient statistic is

$$l(\mathbf{z}) = \Delta \mathbf{s}^T \mathbf{V}^{-1} \mathbf{z}$$

$$= \frac{\epsilon}{V} \sum_{i=0}^{I} (s_{2,i} - s_{1,i}) z_i$$

Now we will show that the limit of $l(\mathbf{z})$ is

$$\lim_{\epsilon \to 0} l(\mathbf{z}) = l(z(t)) = \frac{1}{V} \int_0^T [s_2(t) - s_1(t)] z(t) \, dt$$

$$= \frac{1}{V} \int_0^T \Delta s(t) z(t) \, dt \qquad (4.3\text{-}13)$$

To establish this result, we need to prove

$$\int_0^T \Delta s(t) z(t) \, dt = \lim_{\epsilon \to 0} \epsilon \sum_{i=0}^{I} \Delta s_i z_i$$

We know that

$$z(t) = \lim_{\epsilon \to 0} z_\epsilon(t) = \lim_{\epsilon \to 0} \sum_{i=0}^{I} \sqrt{\epsilon} \, z_i \delta_\epsilon(t - i\epsilon)$$

and

$$\Delta s(t) = \lim_{\epsilon \to 0} \Delta s_\epsilon(t) = \lim_{\epsilon \to 0} \sum_{j=0}^{I} \sqrt{\epsilon} \, \Delta s_j \delta_\epsilon(t - j\epsilon)$$

Therefore

$$\int_0^T \Delta s(t) z(t) \, dt = \lim_{\epsilon \to 0} \int_0^T \epsilon \sum_{j=0}^{I} \Delta s_j \delta_\epsilon(t - j\epsilon) \sum_{i=0}^{I} z_i \delta_\epsilon(t - i\epsilon) \, dt \qquad (4.3\text{-}14)$$

But the product $\delta_\epsilon(t - j\epsilon)\delta_\epsilon(t - i\epsilon)$ is nonzero only if $i == j$ so that Eq. (4.3-14) becomes

$$\int_0^T \Delta s(t) z(t) \, dt = \lim_{\epsilon \to 0} \epsilon \sum_{i=0}^{I} \Delta s_i z_i \int_0^T \delta_\epsilon^2(t - i\epsilon) \, dt$$

Because $\delta_\epsilon(t)$ is orthonormal, the integral is just 1 and we have established Eq. (4.3-13) as desired.

The threshold for this test was given by

$$\lambda' = \ln \lambda + \tfrac{1}{2}(\mathbf{s}_2^T \mathbf{V}^{-1} \mathbf{s}_2^T - \mathbf{s}_1^T \mathbf{V}^{-1} \mathbf{s}_1)$$

$$= \ln \lambda + \frac{\epsilon}{2V} \sum_{i=0}^{I} (s_{2,i}^2 - s_{1,i}^2)$$

which for small ϵ is

$$\lim_{\epsilon \to 0} \lambda' = \ln \lambda + \frac{1}{2V} \int_0^T [s_2^2(t) - s_1^2(t)] \, dt \qquad (4.3\text{-}15)$$

Even in the limit, $l(\mathbf{z})$ is a gaussian variable. Thus, the performance is specified by δ, the normalized distance between the means. For the vector case, δ^2 was

$$\delta^2 = \Delta \mathbf{s}^T \mathbf{V}^{-1} \Delta \mathbf{s} \qquad (4.3\text{-}16)$$

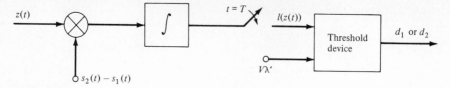

Figure 4.3-3 Integrating optimum receiver.

In the limit, δ^2 becomes

$$\lim_{\epsilon \to 0} \delta^2 = \lim_{\epsilon \to 0} \frac{\epsilon}{V} \sum_{i=0}^{l} (s_{2,i} - s_{1,i})^2$$

$$= \frac{1}{V} \int_0^T [s_2(t) - s_1(t)]^2 \, dt \tag{4.3-17}$$

Thus, the sequence of samples representation has let us reduce the waveform problem to a previously solved vector problem, and then, by passing to the limit, we have been able to express the decision variable, threshold, and performance measure in terms of the original waveforms.

Equation (4.3-13) suggests a very interesting implementation of the optimum receiver. The receiver must multiply the observation $z(t)$ by the difference between the two signals and integrate the product. The result of this integration can then be compared with the threshold $V\lambda'$. A block diagram of this operation is shown in Fig. 4.3-3.

The multiplier shown in Fig. 4.3-3 is not, in general, a very easy device to build. Note, however, that $l(z(t))$ as given in Eq. (4.3-13) can be written as the difference of two terms of the form $\int_0^T s_k(t)z(t) \, dt$.

This is almost the convolution of $s_k(t)$ and $z(t)$. In fact, a linear, time-invariant filter with impulse response

$$h_k(t) = s_k(T - t) \tag{4.3-18}$$

with input $z(t)$, will have as its output

$$y_k(t) = \int_0^t h_k(t - \tau)z(\tau) \, d\tau$$

$$= \int_0^t s_k(T - t + \tau)z(\tau) \, d\tau \tag{4.3-19}$$

The limits reflect the fact that $z(t)$ and both $s_k(t)$ are assumed to be nonzero only over the interval $[0, T]$. Noting that $y_k(T)$ is just the integral of the product $s_k(t)z(t)$, the sufficient statistic $l(z(t))$ can be written as

$$l(z(t)) = y_2(T) - y_1(T) \tag{4.3-20}$$

This leads to the optimum receiver implementation shown in Fig. 4.3-4. A filter whose impulse response is that given in Eq. (4.3-18) is said to be matched to the

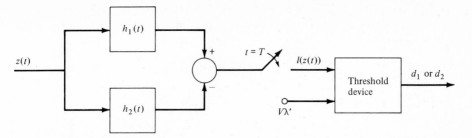

Figure 4.3-4 Matched-filter receiver.

signal $s_k(t)$. Thus the receiver shown in Fig. 4.3-4 is called a *matched-filter receiver*.

One further simplification is possible by noting that if a filter is matched to $s_2(t) - s_1(t)$, its output at $t = T$ will be $l(z(t))$. The receiver that results from this is illustrated in Fig. 4.3-5.

Example 4.3-1 Find a matched-filter receiver for the signal set in Fig. 4.3-6 and sketch the filter output when

$$z(t) = s_1(t) \tag{1}$$

$$z(t) = s_2(t) \tag{2}$$

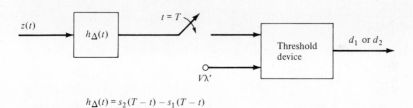

$h_\Delta(t) = s_2(T - t) - s_1(T - t)$

Figure 4.3-5 Simplified matched-filter receiver.

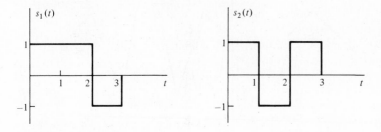

Figure 4.3-6 Signal set.

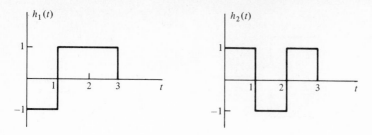

Figure 4.3-7 Matched-filter impulse responses.

The impulse response of the two filters are just the $s_k(t)$ turned around and delayed as shown in Fig. 4.3-7. To find the output when the input is $s_k(t)$, convolution can be used. The results are given in Fig. 4.3-8. For the case where $s_1(t)$ is the input, $y_1(T)$ is 3 and $y_2(T)$ is -1; whereas when $s_2(t)$

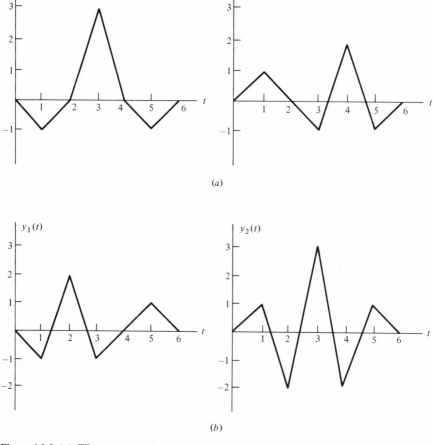

Figure 4.3-8 (*a*) Filter outputs when input is $s_1(t)$; (*b*) Filter outputs when input is $s_2(t)$.

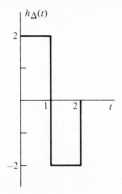

Figure 4.3-9 Simplified matched-filter impulse response.

is the input, $y_1(T)$ is -1 and $y_2(T)$ is 3. In both cases, this is the largest difference between the $y_k(t)$. Thus, sampling them at $t = T$ and comparing is intuitively pleasing, as well as correct.

A filter matched to $s_2(t) - s_1(t)$ would have impulse response $h_\Delta(t)$ as shown in Fig. 4.3-9. The associated outputs are shown in Fig. 4.3-10. The output of this filter at $t = T = 3$ when the input is $s_1(t)$ is -4; when the input is $s_2(t)$, the output is 4. If the input is $s_k(t) + n(t)$ where $n(t)$ is white gaussian noise with power spectral density V, the output will be the sum of ei-

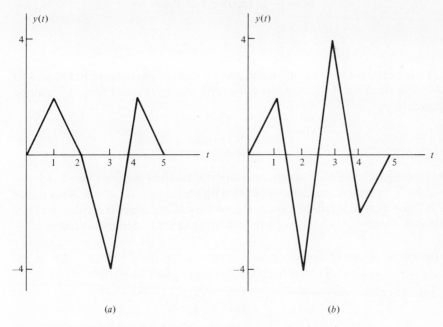

(a) (b)

Figure 4.3-10 (a) Output when input is $s_1(t)$; (b) output when input is $s_2(t)$.

ther 4 or −4 and the random variable

$$n = \int_0^T n(t - \tau) h_\Delta(\tau) \, d\tau$$

Since n is the result of a linear operation on a gaussian process, it is a gaussian random variable. It has a zero mean, and its variance is

$$\text{var } \{n\} = \int_0^T \int_0^T h_\Delta(\tau) h_\Delta(t) E\{n(t - \tau) n(t - \tau)\} \, dt \, d\tau$$

$$= V \int_0^T h_\Delta^2(\tau) \, d\tau$$

$$= 8V$$

Therefore, $l(z(t))$ is a gaussian variable with variance $8V$ and conditional mean

$$E\{l | m_k\} = \begin{cases} -4 & k=1 \\ 4 & k=2 \end{cases}$$

and its normalized distance should be

$$\delta^2 = \frac{8}{V}$$

Equation (4.3-16) says that δ^2 should be

$$\delta^2 = \frac{1}{V} \int_0^T (s_2(t) - s_1(t))^2 \, dt$$

$$= \frac{8}{V}$$

It was noted previously that the representation of white noise in Eq. (4.3-8) could be generalized. In fact, white noise with power spectral density V can be represented as

$$n(t) = \sum_{i=1}^\infty n_i \phi_i(t) \tag{4.3-21}$$

where the $\{\phi_i(t)\}$ is any *complete orthonormal set* over the interval $[0, T]$ and the n_i are independent random variables with variance V. It can be shown that this is equivalent to the definition in Eq. (4.3-8). If the n_i are gaussian, $n(t)$ is a white gaussian process. A complete orthonormal set is defined as follows.

Definition A set of functions is *complete* over $[0, T]$ if any square integrable function $z(t)$ [that is, $\int_0^T z^2(t) \, dt < \infty$] can be written

$$z(t) = \sum_{i=1}^\infty z_i \phi_i(t) \qquad \text{for } 0 \le t \le T$$

and is *orthonormal* over $0 \leq t \leq T$ if

$$\int_0^T \phi_i(t)\phi_j(t)\, dt = \delta_{ij}$$

It is clear, then, that we need not be restricted to a sampling approach to make the transition from a waveform to a vector problem. In fact, for white noise, we have considerable freedom in the selection of $\{\phi_i(t)\}$. For example, if $s_1(t)$ and $s_2(t)$ are orthogonal over $[0, T]$, that is, if

$$\int_0^T s_1(t)s_2(t)\, dt = 0 \qquad (4.3\text{-}22)$$

then the first members of the orthonormal set could be

$$\phi_1(t) = \frac{s_1(t)}{\sqrt{E_1}}$$

$$\phi_2(t) = \frac{s_2(t)}{\sqrt{E_2}}$$

where E_1 and E_2 are selected to normalize $\phi_1(t)$ and $\phi_2(t)$:

$$E_k = \int_0^T s_k{}^2(t)\, dt \qquad \text{for } k = 1,2 \qquad (4.3\text{-}23)$$

Then the rest of the set is filled with functions that are orthogonal to $s_1(t)$ and $s_2(t)$.

To find an equivalent vector problem, the time functions are expanded in terms of the orthogonal set

$$s_k(t) = \sum_{i=1}^{\infty} s_{k,i}\phi_i(t) \qquad (4.3\text{-}24)$$

$$z(t) = \sum_{i=1}^{\infty} (s_{k,i} + n_i)\phi_i(t) \qquad (4.3\text{-}25)$$

and the vectors, **s, n,** and **z** are simply the coefficients of the expansion. Because of the choice of the basis functions, the signal vectors are

$$\mathbf{s}_1 = \begin{bmatrix} \sqrt{E_1} \\ 0 \\ \vdots \\ 0 \end{bmatrix}$$

$$\mathbf{s}_2 = \begin{bmatrix} 0 \\ \sqrt{E_2} \\ 0 \\ \vdots \\ 0 \end{bmatrix}$$

Since the sufficient statistic for the vector problem is

$$l(\mathbf{z}) = \frac{1}{V} \sum_{i=1}^{\infty} \Delta s_i z_i$$

and since Δs_i is zero for all i greater than 2, all but the first two components of $\mathbf{z}$ are ignored. Thus, the waveform problem with two orthogonal time functions can be represented as a two-dimensional problem.

The signal space of this equivalent two-dimensional problem is shown in Fig. 4.3-11. The figure points out two interesting facts: Two time functions that are orthogonal in the sense of Eq. (4.3-22) are represented by vectors that are perpendicular, and the length of the vector is the square root of the energy in the time function as given in Eq. (4.3-23). The latter fact is a direct result of Parseval's theorem (Papoulis, 1962), which states that if $s_k(t)$ can be represented as in Eq. (4.3-24), then

$$\int_0^T s_k^2(t) \, dt = \sum_{i=1}^{\infty} s_{k,i}^2 \qquad (4.3\text{-}26)$$

This is easily proved by substituting the right-hand side of (4.3-24) for $s_k(t)$ and using the orthonormality of $\{\phi_i(t)\}$.

The preceding discussion applies only to the case of orthogonal signal vectors. However, with only slight modification, it can apply to any signal set. The procedure, known as the *Gram-Schmidt orthogonalization procedure* (Wozencraft and Jacobs, 1965), is to find a set of orthonormal functions such that only the first two components of the signal vectors are nonzero. As in the orthogonal case, the first step is to define the function $\phi_1(t)$:

$$\phi_1(t) = \frac{s_1(t)}{\sqrt{E_1}} \qquad (4.3\text{-}27)$$

Now, since in general $s_1(t)$ and $s_2(t)$ will not be orthogonal, the first component of $\mathbf{s}_2$ will not be zero. In fact, it will be

$$s_{2,1} = \int_0^T s_2(t)\phi_1(t) \, dt$$

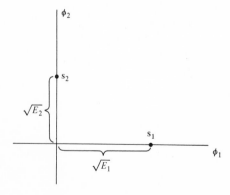

Figure 4.3-11 Signal space for orthogonal signals.

The integral of the product of $s_1(t)$ and $s_2(t)$ will appear frequently, and so it is given a special name:

$$\rho = \frac{1}{\sqrt{E_1 E_2}} \int_0^T s_1(t)s_2(t) \, dt \qquad (4.3\text{-}28)$$

Therefore, $s_{2,1}$ can be written as

$$s_{2,1} = \rho \sqrt{E_2}$$

Now, even though $s_2(t)$ is not necessarily orthogonal to $s_1(t)$, $s_2(t) - s_{2,1}\phi_1(t)$ will be and the second orthonormal function can be defined as

$$\phi_2(t) = \frac{s_2(t) - s_{2,1}\phi_1(t)}{\sqrt{\int_0^T (s_2(t) - s_{2,1}\phi_1(t))^2 \, dt}}$$

$$= \frac{[s_2(t)/\sqrt{E_2} - \rho\phi_1(t)]}{\sqrt{1 - \rho^2}} \qquad (4.3\text{-}29)$$

Using these as the first two elements of $\{\phi_i\}$:

$$\mathbf{s}_1 = \begin{bmatrix} \sqrt{E_1} \\ 0 \\ \vdots \\ 0 \end{bmatrix}$$

$$\mathbf{s}_2 = \begin{bmatrix} \rho\sqrt{E_2} \\ \sqrt{1-\rho^2}\,\sqrt{E_2} \\ 0 \\ \vdots \\ 0 \end{bmatrix}$$

which clearly satisfies Parseval's theorem. Since the vectors are zero after two components, all but the first two components of $\mathbf{z}$ are ignored. Thus, *any* binary decision problem with additive white gaussian noise can be reduced to a two-dimensional problem. Figure 4.3-12 illustrates the resulting signal space for nonorthogonal signal functions.

It was pointed out in Sec. 4.2 that for a gaussian vector problem, the decision-region boundary is always perpendicular to the difference vector $(\mathbf{s}_2 - \mathbf{s}_1)$. Therefore, if coordinates are chosen so that ϕ_1 parallels $(\mathbf{s}_2 - \mathbf{s}_1)$, only the first element of $\mathbf{z}$ would affect the decision. A similar result holds for waveform observation. If instead of using the Gram-Schmidt procedure, the first element of $\{\phi_i(t)\}$ is chosen to parallel $(s_2(t) - s_1(t))$, it is

$$\phi_1'(t) = \frac{s_2(t) - s_1(t)}{\sqrt{\int_0^T (s_2(t) - s_1(t))^2 \, dt}}$$

$$= \frac{s_2(t) - s_1(t)}{(E_1 + E_2 - 2\rho\sqrt{E_1 E_2})^{1/2}}$$

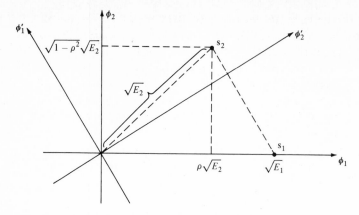

Figure 4.3-12 Signal space for nonorthogonal signals.

Then the first components of the signal vectors are

$$s'_{1,1} = \frac{E_1 - \rho\sqrt{E_1 E_2}}{(E_1 + E_2 - 2\rho\sqrt{E_1 E_2})^{1/2}}$$

and

$$s'_{2,1} = \frac{\rho\sqrt{E_1 E_2} - E_2}{(E_1 + E_2 - 2\rho\sqrt{E_1 E_2})^{1/2}}$$

If the second orthonormal function is selected to be

$$\phi'_2(t) = \frac{s_1(t) - s'_{1,1}\phi'_1(t)}{\sqrt{\int_0^T (s_1(t) - s'_{1,1}\phi'_1(t))^2 \, dt}}$$

then the second components of the signal vectors are

$$s'_{1,2} = s'_{2,2} = \sqrt{\frac{E_1 E_2 (1 - \rho^2)}{E_1 + E_2 - 2\rho\sqrt{E_1 E_2}}}$$

Therefore, the only nonzero component of $\Delta \mathbf{s}$ will be the first, and the problem is one-dimensional. The $\{\phi'_i(t)\}$ axes are also shown in Fig. 4.3-12.

4.4 SUMMARY

In this chapter we have shown that all the structure developed in Chap. 3 for analyzing binary decision problems with a scalar observation can be applied to problems where the observation is a vector or even a continuous function. We have seen that all the various decision criteria can be stated for multiple observations and that they all reduce to threshold tests of the form

$$l(\mathbf{z}) = \frac{p(\mathbf{z}|m_2)}{p(\mathbf{z}|m_1)} \begin{array}{c} d_2 \\ \gtrless \\ d_1 \end{array} \lambda \qquad (4.4\text{-}1)$$

The details of the particular criterion are then used to determine λ. We introduced the concept of sufficient statistic and saw that any multidimensional observation can always be characterized by a single variable. Frequently, this single variable is easier to compute than the likelihood ratio.

For an additive gaussian noise with independent components, the optimum decision can be implemented by a tapped delay line and a threshold device. The delay line is analogous to the matched filter in the optimum receiver for continuous waveforms.

In the general gaussian problem, the signal consists of the mean vector and variance matrix of the gaussian observation. In its most general form, the decision rule is

$$(\mathbf{z} - \mathbf{s}_1)^T \mathbf{V}_1^{-1} (\mathbf{z} - \mathbf{s}_1) - (\mathbf{z} - \mathbf{s}_2)^T \mathbf{V}_2^{-1} (\mathbf{z} - \mathbf{s}_2) \underset{d_1}{\overset{d_2}{\gtrless}} 2 \ln \lambda$$

For various special cases, this rule can be simplified, and it leads to some pleasing interpretations. By using the *theorem of reversibility*, any problem with nonwhite noise that is independent of the signal can make use of the white-noise result. The received signal $\mathbf{z}$ is linearly transformed to a new signal $\mathbf{z}'$ whose components are independent with unit variance. Since the transformation is reversible, it does not affect performance.

In the final section of this chapter, the problem of waveform signals corrupted by the addition of white gaussian noise was treated in some detail. We saw that the problem is analogous to a vector observation and additive noise. This lead to the various forms of correlation and matched-filter receivers. The sufficient statistic was again a simple gaussian variable whose mean depended on the message. The Gram-Schmidt procedure was used to show that an equivalent vector problem could be found that had only two dimensions. Finally, it was observed that this could be further reduced to a one-dimensional problem.

4.5 PROBLEMS

4.5-1 A simple binary decision problem has a two-dimensional signal space and a two-dimensional observation space. The signal vectors are:

$$\mathbf{s}_1 = \begin{bmatrix} 1 \\ 0 \end{bmatrix} \qquad \mathbf{s}_2 = \begin{bmatrix} 0 \\ 1 \end{bmatrix}$$

The observation vector is just the sum of the signal vector and a noise vector

$$\mathbf{z} = \mathbf{s} + \mathbf{n}$$

The noise vector is gaussian with

$$E\{n_1\} = E\{n_2\} = 0$$

$$\text{var}\{n_1\} = \text{var}\{n_2\} = 1$$

$$\text{cov}\{n_1, n_2\} = \tfrac{1}{2}$$

(*a*) Sketch the signal-space representation of the signals.

(b) Find the general expression for a likelihood-ratio decision rule.

(c) Find the decision rule that minimizes probability of error for equiprobable messages and the resulting P_e.

(d) Sketch a block diagram of the optimum receiver for part (c).

4.5-2 A two-dimensional binary decision problem with equiprobable messages has two signal vectors

$$\mathbf{s}_1 = \begin{bmatrix} 2 \\ 1 \end{bmatrix} \quad \mathbf{s}_2 = \begin{bmatrix} 1 \\ 2 \end{bmatrix}$$

The observation vector is

$$\mathbf{z} = \mathbf{s} + \mathbf{n}$$

where $\mathbf{n}$ is a random vector whose components are independent identically distributed random variables with densities:

$$p(n_i) = |n_i| \quad |n_i| \le 1 \quad i = 1, 2$$

Find the decision rule that minimizes P_e.

Note: It is easiest to express this rule by drawing the decision regions on the two-dimensional observation space.

4.5-3 For a multiple-observation problem, the signal vectors are

$$\mathbf{s}_1 = \begin{bmatrix} 1 \\ 1 \\ 1 \\ \vdots \\ 1 \end{bmatrix} \quad \mathbf{s}_2 = \begin{bmatrix} -1 \\ -1 \\ -1 \\ \vdots \\ -1 \end{bmatrix}$$

The observation is the sum of $\mathbf{s}$ and an I-dimensional gaussian vector with independent zero-mean, unit-variance components. For equiprobable signals, what is the smallest I such that $P_e \le 0.01$?

4.5-4 Find the maximum-likelihood decision rule if

$$m_1: z_i = n_i$$
$$i = 1, 2, \ldots, I$$
$$m_2: z_i = 1 + w_i$$

where $\{n_i\}$ and $\{w_i\}$ are independent white gaussian processes with zero mean and variances of v_n and v_w, respectively.

4.5-5 Consider the multiple-observation binary decision problem with

$$p(z_i|m_1) = \begin{cases} e^{-z_i} & z_i > 0 \\ 0 & \text{otherwise} \end{cases}$$

$$p(z_i|m_2) = \begin{cases} 2e^{-2z_i} & z_i > 0 \\ 0 & \text{otherwise} \end{cases}$$

for $i = 1, 2, \ldots, I$. The observations z_i are identically distributed and independent. Find the value of I such that the following constraints are met

$$P\{d_1|m_2\} \le 0.1$$

and

$$P\{d_2|m_1\} \le 0.1$$

4.5-6 Consider the multiple-observation binary decision problem with

$$p(z_i|m_1) = \begin{cases} 1 & -0.5 \leq z_i \leq 0.5 \\ 0 & \text{otherwise} \end{cases}$$

$$p(z_i|m_2) = \begin{cases} 0.5 & -1 \leq z_i \leq 1 \\ 0 & \text{otherwise} \end{cases}$$

I independent and identically distributed samples are taken. Determine the minimum probability-of-error test for $P\{m_1\} = 0.1$. What are $P\{d_2|m_1\}$ and $P\{d_1|m_2\}$ if $I = 5$?

4.5-7 Consider the multiple-observation binary decision problem with

$$m_1: p(z_i|m_1) = \begin{cases} e^{-z_i} & z_i > 0 \\ 0 & \text{otherwise} \end{cases}$$

$$m_2: p(z_i|m_2) = \begin{cases} 2e^{-2z_i} & z_i > 0 \\ 0 & \text{otherwise} \end{cases}$$

where $i = 1, 2$ (that is, two observations). Find the Neyman-Pearson decision rule such that $P\{d_2|m_1\} = 0.25$. The observations are identically distributed and independent.

4.5-8 Consider the two-dimensional additive gaussian noise problem where the signal space contains the two vectors s_1 and s_2, where the observation is

$$\mathbf{z} = \mathbf{s} + \mathbf{n}$$

and where the two components of $\mathbf{n}$ are independent zero-mean gaussian variables with variance v. Assume that the two messages are equiprobable and that probability of error is to be minimized.

(*a*) Find the optimum decision rule and resultant probability of error in terms of s_1, s_2, and v.

(*b*) Sketch the signal-space and decision regions for $s_1 = [1 \quad 0]^T$ and $s_2 = [0 \quad 1]^T$ and compute P_e.

(*c*) Show that the signal set $\{s_1 - \mathbf{a}, s_2 - \mathbf{a}\}$ has the same minimum probability of error for any constant vector $\mathbf{a}$. This implies that performance is determined by the relative positions of the signal points, not their absolute positions.

(*d*) Repeat part (*b*) for the signal set $\{s_1 - [\tfrac{1}{2} \ \tfrac{1}{2}]^T, s_2 - [\tfrac{1}{2} \ \tfrac{1}{2}]^T\}$.

4.5-9 In a communication problem, if the message is m_1, the signal is a zero-mean I-dimensional gaussian vector $\mathbf{s}$ and if the message is m_2, the signal is the all-zero vector. The observation $\mathbf{z}$ is the sum of the signal and a gaussian noise vector $\mathbf{n}$. It is known that

$$\text{var } \{\mathbf{n}\} = v_n \mathbf{I}$$

(*a*) Find a sufficient statistic if

$$\text{var } \{\mathbf{s}\} = v_s \mathbf{I}$$

(*b*) Find a sufficient statistic if

$$\text{var } \{\mathbf{s}\} = \begin{bmatrix} v_1 & & 0 \\ & v_2 & \\ & & \ddots \\ 0 & & v_I \end{bmatrix}$$

Explain why the weighting of the various components of $\mathbf{z}$ is reasonable. Suppose some of the v_i are very small, does your answer make sense?

4.5-10 For a binary decision problems, the observation is

$$\mathbf{z} = \begin{bmatrix} z_1 \\ z_2 \end{bmatrix}$$

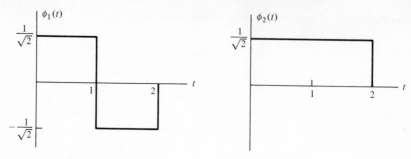

Figure 4.5-1 Problem 4.5-11.

where z_1 and z_2 are independent and

$$p(z_i|m_1) = \begin{cases} \frac{1}{2} & 0 \le z_i \le 2 \\ 0 & \text{otherwise} \end{cases} \quad i = 1, 2$$

$$p(z_i|m_2) = \begin{cases} e^{-z_i} & z_i \ge 0 \\ 0 & z_i < 0 \end{cases} \quad i = 1, 2$$

(*a*) What decision rule yields a

$$P\{d_2|m_1\} \le \tfrac{1}{8}$$

and minimizes $P\{d_1|m_2\}$? (Please sketch your decision rule.)

(*b*) If the messages are equiprobable, what assignment of Bayes cost would yield the same decision rule?

4.5-11 Suppose that you have two function generators that generate the two functions shown in Fig. 4.5-1. You are to use these to communicate over an additive white gaussian noise channel with noise-power spectral density of height 1. The total energy of each of the signals you can send is constrained to satisfy

$$\int_{-\infty}^{\infty} s^2(t)\, dt \le E$$

Use probability-of-error costs.

(*a*) If your signal set is

$$s_1(t) = \sqrt{E}\ \phi_1(t)$$
$$s_2(t) = \sqrt{E}\ \phi_2(t)$$

(i) Design a matched-filter receiver.

(ii) Find the distance parameter δ^2.

(iii) Find the probability of error as a function of $P\{m_1\}$.

(*b*) Find a better signal set and the resultant δ^2.

Hint: Draw the signal space.

4.5-12 For a binary waveform problem, the signals are as shown in Fig. 4.5-2. The received signal is the sum of the transmitted signal and white gaussian noise with power spectral density of height 2.

(*a*) Draw a signal-space representation of the problem.

(*b*) Sketch the probability-of-error decision regions and find the resulting probabilities of error if the signals are equiprobable.

(*c*) Describe a matched-filter receiver for part (*b*).

(*d*) It is desired to simulate the operation of your filter in part (*c*) with a digital filter approximation. The signals are to be represented as 10-dimensional vectors. Each component is to repre-

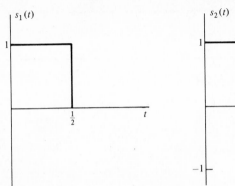

Figure 4.5-2 Problem 4.5-12.

sent a sample of the corresponding time waveform. Give a suitable definition of sample and describe fully s_1, s_2, and $\mathbf{n}$, including the mean vector and variance matrix of $\mathbf{n}$.

4.5-13 Consider the decision problem with

$$m_1: z_i = v_i$$
$$i = 1, 2, \ldots, I$$
$$m_2: z_i = 1 + v_i$$

where v_i are independent zero-mean gaussian samples with variance $\sigma^2 = 4$. Let $C_{00} = C_{11} = 0$ and $C_{12} = 2$, $C_{21} = 1$ and $P\{m_1\} = 0.4$.

(*a*) Determine the likelihood-ratio test.

(*b*) How large must I be to have the average cost decreased by a factor of 1000 from the value for $I = 1$?

4.5-14 For the function $x(t)$ shown in Fig. 4.5-3, find the signal-space representation and the probability of error for the observation

$$z(t) = s_k(t) + n(t)$$

If $n(t)$ is white gaussian noise with unit spectral density and if the two messages are equiprobable when the signals are

(*a*) $s_1(t) = 2x(t)$ $s_2(t) = 2x(t) + 2x(t-2)$
(*b*) $s_1(t) = 2x(t)$ $s_2(t) = 0$
(*c*) $s_1(t) = \sqrt{2}x(t)$ $s_2(t) = \sqrt{2}x(t-2)$
(*d*) $s_1(t) = x(t)$ $s_2(t) = -x(t)$

which signal set is best? Let $T = 4$.

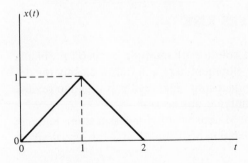

Figure 4.5-3 Signal for Prob. 4.5-14.

FIVE

MULTIPLE DECISIONS

In this chapter we consider another extension of the simple binary decision problem treated so far. Here, we shall consider problems for which the decision space has more than two elements. We begin with the general bayesian approach in Sec. 5.1 where we examine problems with multiple messages and decisions. Although the results of this general study are quite elegant, generally they are not very useful in practice.

Section 5.2 treats a simplified form of the multiple decision problem in which the number of messages and the number of decisions are equal and a probability-of-error criterion is used. This leads to a very general and powerful decision rule. The next section presents an in-depth discussion of the gaussian multiple decision problem using the probability-of-error criterion.

Section 5.4 treats another special case of the multiple decision problem. It is assumed that there are K messages and $K + 1$ decisions with decision d_{K+1} corresponding to an erasure or uncertain decision. In other words, we decide d_{K+1} when we are so uncertain of which message is true that we wish to make no decision. The results of Sec. 5.4 represent an important practical extension of the results of Sec. 5.2 and also serve as an introduction to the sequential decision techniques of Chap. 6.

5.1 MULTIPLE DECISIONS: BAYES RISK

In this section, we wish to study the solution of multiple decision problems using the Bayes risk criterion. The development here will follow closely the development given in Sec. 3.3 for binary decisions. The reader is urged to review the development in Sec. 3.3 before studying this section.

We assume that the message space $\mathbf{M}$ consists of K messages: $m_1, m_2, \ldots,$ m_K; as usual, there is a one-to-one mapping between $\mathbf{M}$ and the signal space

$\mathbf{S} = \{s_1, s_2, \ldots, s_K\}$. The decision space $\mathbf{D}$ consists of J elements: $d_1, d_2, \ldots, d_J$. Quite often $J = K$ and there is a logical pairing of messages and decisions; i.e., if m_i is sent, d_i is the correct decision. This pairing is *not* necessary and will not be assumed at this point. Associated with each message m_k and decision d_j is a unique cost C_{jk}:

$$C_{jk} = \text{Cost of deciding } d_j \text{ given } m_k \text{ was sent} \qquad (5.1\text{-}1)$$

In addition, there is a predetermined a priori probability $P\{m_k\}$ associated with each message m_k. Since one of the K messages must be sent, we know that

$$\sum_{k=1}^{K} P\{m_k\} = 1 \qquad (5.1\text{-}2)$$

The average risk (cost) for this problem is given by

$$B = \sum_{j=1}^{J} \sum_{k=1}^{K} C_{jk} P\{d_j, m_k\} \qquad (5.1\text{-}3)$$

and since $P\{d_j, m_k\} = P\{d_j | m_k\} P\{m_k\}$, the average cost becomes

$$B = \sum_{j=1}^{J} \sum_{k=1}^{K} P\{m_k\} C_{jk} P\{d_j | m_k\} \qquad (5.1\text{-}4)$$

The observation space $\mathbf{Z}$ is divided into J disjoint sets $\mathbf{Z}_1, \mathbf{Z}_2, \ldots, \mathbf{Z}_J$ which cover $\mathbf{Z}$, that is, $\mathbf{Z}_i \mathbf{Z}_j = \varnothing$ if $i \neq j$ and $\bigcup_{j=1}^{J} \mathbf{Z}_j = \mathbf{Z}$. If the observation $\mathbf{z} \in \mathbf{Z}_j$, then we decide d_j. Hence $P\{d_j | m_k\} = P\{\mathbf{z} \in \mathbf{Z}_j | m_k\}$ or

$$P\{d_j | m_k\} = \int_{\mathbf{Z}_j} p(\mathbf{z} | m_k) \, d\mathbf{z} \qquad (5.1\text{-}5)$$

Therefore the average risk of Eq. (5.1-4) becomes

$$B = \sum_{j=1}^{J} \sum_{k=1}^{K} P\{m_k\} C_{jk} \int_{\mathbf{Z}_j} p(\mathbf{z} | m_k) \, d\mathbf{z}$$

$$= \sum_{j=1}^{J} \int_{\mathbf{Z}_j} \sum_{k=1}^{K} P\{m_k\} C_{jk} p(\mathbf{z} | m_k) \, d\mathbf{z} \qquad (5.1\text{-}6)$$

As we recall from Sec. 3.3, the Bayes criterion is to select the decision regions $\mathbf{Z}_j$, $j = 1, 2, \ldots, J$, such that the average risk B is minimized. We can minimize B by selecting $\mathbf{Z}_j$, $j = 1, 2, \ldots, J$, such that $\mathbf{z} \in \mathbf{Z}_j$ if

$$\sum_{k=1}^{K} C_{jk} P\{m_k\} p(\mathbf{z} | m_k) < \sum_{k=1}^{K} C_{lk} P\{m_k\} p(\mathbf{z} | m_k) \qquad (5.1\text{-}7)$$

for all $l \neq j$. To understand why this procedure minimizes B, let us use $I_j(\mathbf{z})$ to represent the integrand in the jth term of Eq. (5.1-6), or

$$I_j(\mathbf{z}) = \sum_{k=1}^{K} C_{jk} P\{m_k\} p(\mathbf{z} | m_k) \qquad (5.1\text{-}8)$$

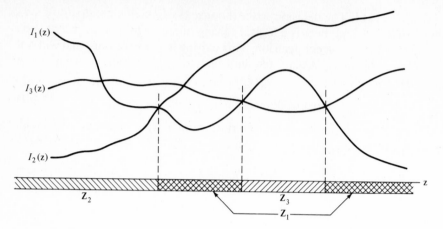

Figure 5.1-1 Design of a decision rule for a ternary decision problem.

Then Eq. (5.1-6) can be written as

$$B = \int_{Z_1} I_1(\mathbf{z}) \, d\mathbf{z} + \int_{Z_2} I_2(\mathbf{z}) \, d\mathbf{z} + \cdots + \int_{Z_J} I_J(\mathbf{z}) \, d\mathbf{z} \tag{5.1-9}$$

Now B will be minimized by selecting $\mathbf{Z}_j$ as the set of $\mathbf{z}$ for which $I_j(\mathbf{z}) < I_l(\mathbf{z})$ for all $l \neq j$ since in each case we shall be integrating with the smallest integrand. Hence $\mathbf{Z}_j = \{\mathbf{z}: I_j(\mathbf{z}) < I_l(\mathbf{z}), \, l \neq j\}$; this is identical to Eq. (5.1-7). The procedure of selecting the decision regions is shown symbolically in Fig. 5.1-1 for $J = 3$.

To illustrate the use of the decision rule of Eq. (5.1-7), let us consider the ternary case when $K = J = 3$. We use this simple case because it permits us to represent our results graphically. For the ternary case, the decision region $\mathbf{Z}_1$ is given by the set of $\mathbf{z}$ for which

$$\sum_{k=1}^{3} C_{1k} P\{m_k\} p(\mathbf{z}|m_k) < \sum_{k=1}^{3} C_{lk} P\{m_k\} p(\mathbf{z}|m_k) \tag{5.1-10}$$

for $l = 2$ and 3. Writing this result out gives

$$C_{11} P\{m_1\} p(\mathbf{z}|m_1) + C_{12} P\{m_2\} p(\mathbf{z}|m_2) + C_{13} P\{m_3\} p(\mathbf{z}|m_3)$$
$$< C_{21} P\{m_1\} p(\mathbf{z}|m_1) + C_{22} P\{m_2\} p(\mathbf{z}|m_2) + C_{23} P\{m_3\} p(\mathbf{z}|m_3) \tag{5.1-11}$$

and $\quad C_{11} P\{m_1\} p(\mathbf{z}|m_1) + C_{12} P\{m_2\} p(\mathbf{z}|m_2) + C_{13} P\{m_3\} p(\mathbf{z}|m_3)$
$$< C_{31} P\{m_1\} p(\mathbf{z}|m_1) + C_{32} P\{m_2\} p(\mathbf{z}|m_2) + C_{33} P\{m_3\} p(\mathbf{z}|m_3) \tag{5.1-12}$$

Now dividing both sides of both of these inequalities by $p(\mathbf{z}|m_1)$ and defining

$$\Lambda_2(\mathbf{z}) = \frac{p(\mathbf{z}|m_2)}{p(\mathbf{z}|m_1)} \tag{5.1-13}$$

$$\Lambda_3(\mathbf{z}) = \frac{p(\mathbf{z}\,|\,m_3)}{p(\mathbf{z}\,|\,m_1)} \qquad (5.1\text{-}14)$$

then Eqs. (5.1-11) and (5.1-12) can be written as

$$(C_{12} - C_{22})P\{m_2\}\Lambda_2(\mathbf{z}) + (C_{13} - C_{23})P\{m_3\}\Lambda_3(\mathbf{z}) < (C_{21} - C_{11})P\{m_1\} \quad (5.1\text{-}15)$$

and

$$(C_{12} - C_{32})P\{m_2\}\Lambda_2(\mathbf{z}) + (C_{13} - C_{33})P\{m_3\}\Lambda_3(\mathbf{z}) < (C_{31} - C_{11})P\{m_1\} \quad (5.1\text{-}16)$$

Now let us define the following constants:

$$A = (C_{12} - C_{22})P\{m_2\}$$
$$B = (C_{13} - C_{23})P\{m_3\}$$
$$C = (C_{21} - C_{11})P\{m_1\}$$
$$D = (C_{12} - C_{32})P\{m_2\}$$
$$E = (C_{13} - C_{33})P\{m_3\}$$
$$F = (C_{31} - C_{11})P\{m_1\}$$

Substituting these definitions into Eqs. (5.1-15) and (5.1-16), we find that $\mathbf{Z}_1$ is defined by

$$A\Lambda_2(\mathbf{z}) + B\Lambda_3(\mathbf{z}) < C \qquad (5.1\text{-}15)$$

$$D\Lambda_2(\mathbf{z}) + E\Lambda_3(\mathbf{z}) < F \qquad (5.1\text{-}16)$$

In a completely similar way it is possible to show that $\mathbf{Z}_2$ is given by the set of $\mathbf{z}$ for which

$$A\Lambda_2(\mathbf{z}) + B\Lambda_3(\mathbf{z}) > C \qquad (5.1\text{-}17)$$

and
$$(A - D)\Lambda_2(\mathbf{z}) + (B - E)\Lambda_3(\mathbf{z}) > C - F \qquad (5.1\text{-}18)$$

And $\mathbf{Z}_3$ is defined by

$$D\Lambda_2(\mathbf{z}) + E\Lambda_3(\mathbf{z}) > F \qquad (5.1\text{-}19)$$

$$(A - D)\Lambda_2(\mathbf{z}) + (B - E)\Lambda_3(\mathbf{z}) < C - F \qquad (5.1\text{-}20)$$

The following is an alternative form for representation of the decision rule:

$$A\Lambda_2(\mathbf{z}) + B\Lambda_3(\mathbf{z}) \underset{\text{not } d_2}{\overset{\text{not } d_1}{\gtrless}} C \qquad (5.1\text{-}21)$$

$$D\Lambda_2(\mathbf{z}) + E\Lambda_3(\mathbf{z}) \underset{\text{not } d_3}{\overset{\text{not } d_1}{\gtrless}} F \qquad (5.1\text{-}22)$$

$$(A - D)\Lambda_2(\mathbf{z}) + (B - E)\Lambda_3(\mathbf{z}) \underset{\text{not } d_2}{\overset{\text{not } d_3}{\gtrless}} C - F \qquad (5.1\text{-}23)$$

The boundaries between the decision regions consist of three lines in the Λ_2, Λ_3 plane obtained by changing Eqs. (5.1-21) to (5.1-23) to equalities.

$$A\Lambda_2(\mathbf{z}) + B\Lambda_3(\mathbf{z}) = C \qquad (5.1\text{-}24)$$

$$D\Lambda_2(\mathbf{z}) + E\Lambda_3(\mathbf{z}) = F \qquad (5.1\text{-}25)$$

$$(A - D)\Lambda_2(\mathbf{z}) + (B - E)\Lambda_3(\mathbf{z}) = C - F \qquad (5.1\text{-}26)$$

Because these three equations are *not* linearly independent, for example, Eq. (5.1-26) can be obtained by subtracting Eq. (5.1-25) from Eq. (5.1-24), the three lines must intersect at a single point in the Λ_2, Λ_3 plane and the associated decision regions are uniquely defined. A typical set of decision regions for a ternary decision problem is shown in Fig. 5.1-2.

We note that a ternary decision problem requires, in general, a two-dimensional decision space and hence a two-dimensional sufficient statistic of which

$$\mathbf{l}(\mathbf{z}) = \left[\begin{array}{c} \Lambda_2(\mathbf{z}) \\ \Lambda_3(\mathbf{z}) \end{array} \right]$$

is an obvious choice. Of course any invertible transformation of the elements of $\mathbf{l}(\mathbf{z})$ is acceptable. For the general problem with K messages, the sufficient statistic defined by

$$\mathbf{l}(\mathbf{z}) = \left[\begin{array}{c} \Lambda_2(\mathbf{z}) \\ \Lambda_3(\mathbf{z}) \\ \vdots \\ \Lambda_K(\mathbf{z}) \end{array} \right] \qquad (5.1\text{-}27)$$

has dimension $K - 1$.

Another method for defining a sufficient statistic involves the use of the integrand functions defined by Eq. (5.1-8). Obviously, if we knew $I_j(\mathbf{z})$ for $j = 1$, $2, \ldots, J$, then we could make the decision required by Eq. (5.1-7). Since only the relative values of the $I_j(\mathbf{z})$'s are important, we could normalize them by dividing by $I_1(\mathbf{z})$ to generate the $(J - 1)$-dimensional sufficient statistic:

$$\mathbf{l}'(\mathbf{z}) = \left[\begin{array}{c} I_2(\mathbf{z})/I_1(\mathbf{z}) \\ I_3(\mathbf{z})/I_1(\mathbf{z}) \\ \vdots \\ I_J(\mathbf{z})/I_1(\mathbf{z}) \end{array} \right] \qquad (5.1\text{-}28)$$

For our ternary example, the decision regions are defined in terms the integrand functions as

$$\mathbf{Z}_1 = \{\mathbf{z}: I_1(\mathbf{z}) < I_2(\mathbf{z}); I_1(\mathbf{z}) < I_3(\mathbf{z})\}$$

$$\mathbf{Z}_2 = \{\mathbf{z}: I_2(\mathbf{z}) < I_1(\mathbf{z}); I_2(\mathbf{z}) < I_3(\mathbf{z})\}$$

$$\mathbf{Z}_3 = \{\mathbf{z}: I_3(\mathbf{z}) < I_1(\mathbf{z}); I_3(\mathbf{z}) < I_2(\mathbf{z})\}$$

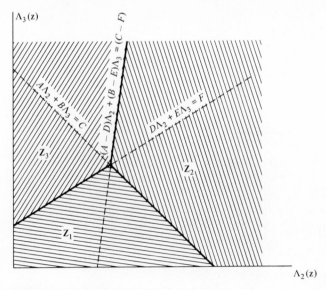

Figure 5.1-2 Decision regions in likelihood-ratio space for ternary decision problem.

Dividing† by $I_1(\mathbf{z})$, we can express the decision regions in terms of the sufficient statistic of Eq. (5.1-28) as

$$\mathbf{Z}_1 = \{\mathbf{z}: l'_1(\mathbf{z}) > 1; l'_2(\mathbf{z}) > 1\}$$

$$\mathbf{Z}_2 = \{\mathbf{z}: l'_1(\mathbf{z}) < 1, l'_1(\mathbf{z}) < l'_2(\mathbf{z})\}$$

$$\mathbf{Z}_3 = \{\mathbf{z}: l'_2(\mathbf{z}) < 1, l'_2(\mathbf{z}) < l'_1(\mathbf{z})\}$$

This result is shown graphically in Fig. 5.1-3.

Since we can also always make the decision the Ith-dimensional observation space, we see that a sufficient statistic need not have a dimension greater than the minimum of $J - 1$, $K - 1$, and I. Of course we can always use a sufficient statistic of higher dimension if we wish, and there are also degenerate problems for which a sufficient statistic of lower dimension may be possible.

We note that the computation of the Bayes cost B as given by Eq. (5.1-6), in general, will be a tedious process. Equation (5.1-6) requires the computation of $K(J - 1)$ I-fold integrals where I is the dimension of the observation vector $\mathbf{z}$. If, however, we express the conditional probabilities $P\{d_j|m_k\}$ in terms of a $(J - 1)$-dimensional sufficient statistic, then the determination of B requires $K(J - 1)$ $(J - 1)$-fold integrals. If $J - 1 < I$, then this approach may be simpler if the probability densities for the sufficient statistic can be found.

Let us consider the ternary problem treated previously. We define a two-

---

†$l_j(\mathbf{z})$ will be positive for all $\mathbf{z} \in \mathbf{Z}$ and for all j if the C_{jk} are all positive.

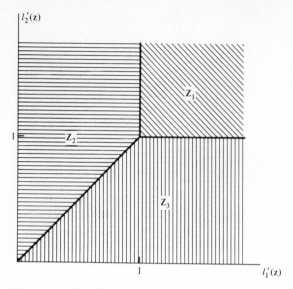

Figure 5.1-3 Decision regions in terms of sufficient statistic of Eq. (5.1-28).

dimensional sufficient statistic by

$$l_1(\mathbf{z}) = A\Lambda_2(\mathbf{z}) + B\Lambda_3(\mathbf{z})$$
$$l_2(\mathbf{z}) = D\Lambda_2(\mathbf{z}) + E\Lambda_3(\mathbf{z})$$

In terms of this sufficient statistic, the decision regions can be expressed as

$$\mathbf{Z}_1 = \{\mathbf{z}\colon l_1(\mathbf{z}) < C,\ l_2(\mathbf{z}) < F\}$$
$$\mathbf{Z}_2 = \{\mathbf{z}\colon l_1(\mathbf{z}) > C,\ l_1(\mathbf{z}) - l_2(\mathbf{z}) > C - F\}$$
$$\mathbf{Z}_3 = \{\mathbf{z}\colon l_2(\mathbf{z}) > F,\ l_1(\mathbf{z}) - l_2(\mathbf{z}) < C - F\}$$

These decision regions are shown graphically in Fig. 5.1-4.
The conditional probabilities $P\{d_j|m_k\}$ are therefore

$$P\{d_1|m_k\} = \int_{-\infty}^{C} dl_1 \int_{-\infty}^{F} p(l_1, l_2|m_k)\, dl_2 \qquad (5.1\text{-}29)$$

and

$$P\{d_2|m_k\} = \int_{C}^{\infty} dl_1 \int_{-\infty}^{l_1 - C + F} p(l_1, l_2|m_k)\, dl_2 \qquad (5.1\text{-}30)$$

while

$$P\{d_3|m_k\} = \int_{F}^{\infty} dl_2 \int_{-\infty}^{l_2 + C - F} p(l_1, l_2|m_k)\, dl_1 \qquad (5.1\text{-}31)$$

Example 5.1-1 Let us determine the decision regions in likelihood-ratio space for a ternary problem for which the cost matrix is given by

$$\mathbf{C} = \begin{bmatrix} 0 & 2 & 4 \\ 1 & 1 & 1 \\ 3 & 4 & 0 \end{bmatrix}$$

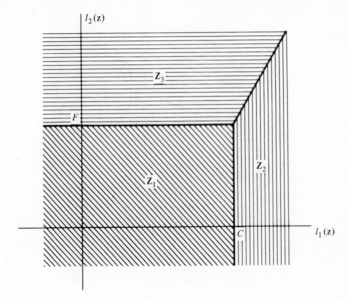

Figure 5.1-4 Decision regions in sufficient statistic space.

and $P\{m_1\} = \frac{1}{4}$, $P\{m_2\} = \frac{1}{2}$, and $P\{m_3\} = \frac{1}{4}$. Substituting into the definitions for A, B, C, D, E, and F gives

$$A = (2 - 1)\,(\tfrac{1}{2}) = \tfrac{1}{2}$$

$$B = (4 - 1)\,(\tfrac{1}{4}) = \tfrac{3}{4}$$

$$C = (1 - 0)\,(\tfrac{1}{4}) = \tfrac{1}{4}$$

$$D = (2 - 4)\,(\tfrac{1}{2}) = -1$$

$$E = (4 - 0)\,(\tfrac{1}{4}) = 1$$

$$F = (3 - 0)\,(\tfrac{1}{4}) = \tfrac{3}{4}$$

The decision regions are shown graphically in Fig. 5.1-5. The reason that Z_2 contains so much area is the small cost associated with incorrectly deciding d_2 if m_1 or m_3 are true compared with the higher cost of incorrectly deciding d_1 or d_3.

Example 5.1-2 Let us suppose that our decision problem has three decisions d_1, d_2, and d_3 and only two equally likely messages m_1 and m_2. The conditional probability densities for the scalar observation z are

$$p(z|m_1) = \frac{1}{\sqrt{2\pi}} \exp \frac{-z^2}{2}$$

$$p(z|m_2) = \frac{1}{\sqrt{2\pi}} \exp \frac{-(z - 1)^2}{2}$$

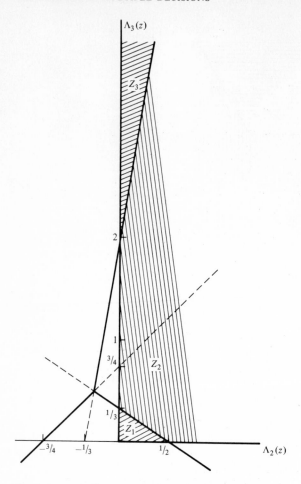

Figure 5.1-5 Decision regions for Example 5.1-1.

The cost matrix is given by

$$\mathbf{C} = \begin{bmatrix} 0 & 1 \\ 2 & 0 \\ 0.2 & 0.2 \end{bmatrix}$$

From Eq. (5.1-7), the decision region Z_1 is given by

$$\sum_{k=1}^{2} C_{1k}P\{m_k\}p(z|m_k) < \sum_{k=1}^{2} C_{lk}P\{m_k\}p(z|m_k)$$

for $l = 2$ and 3. Using the **C** matrix given previously, this becomes

$$(1)(\tfrac{1}{2})p(z|m_2) < (2)(\tfrac{1}{2})p(z|m_1)$$

and $\quad (2)(\tfrac{1}{2})p(z|m_2) < (0.2)(\tfrac{1}{2})p(z|m_1) + (0.2)(\tfrac{1}{2})p(z|m_2)$

In terms of the likelihood ratio, the decision region Z_1 is defined by

$$\Lambda(z) < 2$$

and
$$\Lambda(z) < \tfrac{1}{4}$$

The second expression is obviously the dominant one. In a similar fashion one can find that Z_2 is defined by

$$\Lambda(z) > 11$$

while Z_3 is defined by

$$11 > \Lambda(z) > \tfrac{1}{4}$$

The likelihood ratio is given by

$$\Lambda(z) = \exp\,(z - \tfrac{1}{2})$$

Therefore in terms of z, Z_1 is

$$\exp\,(z - \tfrac{1}{2}) < \tfrac{1}{4}$$

or
$$z < -0.89$$

In a similar fashion, we can show that Z_2 is defined by

$$z > 2.9$$

while Z_3 becomes

$$-0.89 < z < 2.9$$

5.2 PROBABILITY OF ERROR: GENERAL CASE

The general Bayes risk solution to the multiple decision problem presented in the preceding section unfortunately is difficult to apply. In this section, we assume probability-of-error costs and show that considerable simplification of the decision rule can be achieved. Here we shall require that the number of messages be equal to the number of decisions and that there is the logical pairing of message m_i and decision d_i.

The Bayes cost matrix **C** is defined by

$$C_{jk} = \begin{cases} 0 & \text{if } j = k \\ 1 & \text{if } j \neq k \end{cases} \tag{5.2-1}$$

If we substitute this cost matrix into the general decision rule given by Eq. (5.1-7), then we find that $\mathbf{z} \in \mathbf{Z}_j$ if

$$\sum_{\substack{k=1 \\ k \neq j}}^{K} P\{m_k\} p(\mathbf{z}|m_k) < \sum_{\substack{k=1 \\ k \neq l}}^{K} P\{m_k\} p(\mathbf{z}|m_k) \tag{5.2-2}$$

for all $l \neq j$. We note that the sums on both sides of Eq. (5.2-2) are identical except that a different term is missing. Let us add and subtract $P\{m_j\}\,p(\mathbf{z}|m_j)$ on the left-hand side of Eq. (5.2-2) and add and subtract $P\{m_l\}p(\mathbf{z}|m_l)$ on the right-hand side. Then we have

$$\sum_{k=1}^{K} P\{m_k\}p(\mathbf{z}|m_k) - P\{m_j\}p(\mathbf{z}|m_j)$$

$$< \sum_{k=1}^{K} P\{m_k\}p(\mathbf{z}|m_k) - P\{m_l\}p(\mathbf{z}|m_l) \quad (5.2\text{-}3)$$

Now canceling the common term and changing signs yields the following definition of the decision region $\mathbf{Z}_j$:

$$P\{m_j\}p(\mathbf{z}|m_j) > P\{m_l\}p(\mathbf{z}|m_l) \quad (5.2\text{-}4)$$

for all $l \neq j$.

Equation (5.2-4) indicates that we should compute $P\{m_k\}p(\mathbf{z}|m_k)$ for $k = 1$, $2, \ldots, K$ and then select the decision corresponding to the value of k for which $P\{m_k\}p(\mathbf{z}|m_k)$ is maximum. In other words, $\mathbf{z} \in \mathbf{Z}_j$ if

$$P\{m_j\}p(\mathbf{z}|m_j) = \max_{k} P\{m_k\}p(\mathbf{z}|m_k) \quad (5.2\text{-}5)$$

The decision rule is shown schematically in Fig. 5.2-1.

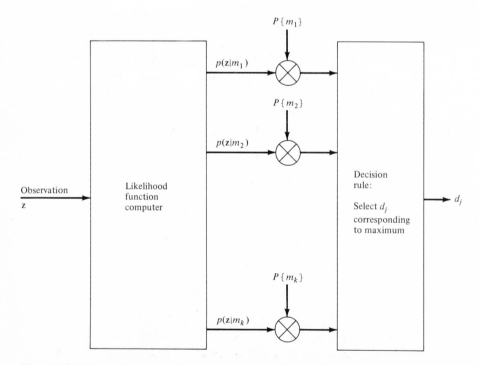

Figure 5.2-1 Schematic representation of the probability-of-error decision rule.

Example 5.2-1 Let us consider a simple illustration of the use of the preceding result. We shall treat a ternary problem with the conditional probabilities given by (we assume $z \geq 0$):

$$p(z|m_k) = \begin{cases} 4e^{-4z} & \text{for } k = 1 \\ 2e^{-2z} & \text{for } k = 2 \\ 0.5e^{-z/2} & \text{for } k = 3 \end{cases}$$

We shall assume the following a priori probabilities:

$$P\{m_1\} = 0.5 \qquad P\{m_2\} = P\{m_3\} = 0.25$$

Therefore $P\{m_k\}p(z|m_k)$ is given by

$$P\{m_k\}p(z|m_k) = \begin{cases} 2e^{-4z} & \text{for } k = 1 \\ 0.5e^{-2z} & \text{for } k = 2 \\ 0.125e^{-z/2} & \text{for } k = 3 \end{cases}$$

The problem now is to find the value of k corresponding to the maximum for each value of z. We can simplify this process if we take the natural logarithm so that we have

$$\ln\left[P\{m_k\}p(z|m_k)\right] = \begin{cases} \ln 2 - 4z & \text{for } k = 1 \\ \ln 0.5 - 2z & \text{for } k = 2 \\ \ln 0.125 - \dfrac{z}{2} & \text{for } k = 3 \end{cases}$$

Now it is easy to show that $P\{m_1\}p(z|m_1)$ is the maximum for $0 \leq z \leq 0.69$, that $P\{m_2\}p(z|m_2)$ is the maximum for $0.69 \leq z \leq 0.92$, and that $P\{m_3\}p(z|m_3)$ is the maximum for $0.92 \leq z$. Hence the decision rule becomes

$$d(z) = \begin{cases} d_1 & \text{for } 0 \leq z < 0.69 \\ d_2 & \text{for } 0.69 \leq z < 0.92 \\ d_3 & \text{for } 0.92 \leq z \end{cases}$$

The probability of error associated with a given set of decision regions $\mathbf{Z}_1$, $\mathbf{Z}_2, \ldots, \mathbf{Z}_K$ is 1 minus the probability of a correct decision. Therefore P_e is given by

$$P_e = 1 - P\{\text{correct decision}\}$$

$$= 1 - \sum_{k=1}^{K} P\{d_k|m_k\}P\{m_k\} \tag{5.2-6}$$

Now since we know that

$$P\{d_k|m_k\} = \int_{\mathbf{z}_k} p(\mathbf{z}|m_k)\, d\mathbf{z} \qquad (5.2\text{-}7)$$

we can write P_e as

$$P_e = 1 - \sum_{k=1}^{K} P\{m_k\} \int_{\mathbf{z}_k} p(\mathbf{z}|m_k)\, d\mathbf{z} \qquad (5.2\text{-}8)$$

The simplicity of Eq. (5.2-8) is deceiving; we note that in general it will require K I-fold integrals. For some problems, this is acceptable and Eq. (5.2-8) can be used to find P_e.

We know from the previous section that the decision can be made in a $(K-1)$-dimensional sufficient statistic space. If $K << I$, then an expression for P_e in terms of sufficient statistic decision regions would require only K $(K-1)$-dimensional integrals and may be computationally superior to Eq. (5.2-8). Unfortunately, the usual $(K-1)$-dimensional sufficient statistic defined by

$$\mathbf{l}(\mathbf{z}) = \begin{bmatrix} p(\mathbf{z}|m_2)/p(\mathbf{z}|m_1) \\ p(\mathbf{z}|m_3)/p(\mathbf{z}|m_1) \\ \vdots \\ p(\mathbf{z}|m_K)/p(\mathbf{z}|m_1) \end{bmatrix}$$

is not very useful since it is very difficult to express the decision region in terms of this sufficient statistic. However, the K-dimensional sufficient statistic defined by

$$\mathbf{l}(\mathbf{z}) = \begin{bmatrix} p(\mathbf{z}|m_1) \\ p(\mathbf{z}|m_2) \\ \vdots \\ p(\mathbf{z}|m_K) \end{bmatrix} = \begin{bmatrix} l_1(\mathbf{z}) \\ l_2(\mathbf{z}) \\ \vdots \\ l_K(\mathbf{z}) \end{bmatrix}$$

can be used to express P_e as

$$P_e = 1 - \sum_{k=1}^{K} P\{m_k\} \int_{\substack{l_k > l_i \\ i \neq k}} p(\mathbf{l}|m_k)\, d\mathbf{l} \qquad (5.2\text{-}10)$$

Here we have K K-fold integrals to evaluate. Unfortunately, even though the integrals are easy, the determination of $p(\mathbf{l}|m_k)$ may not be easy. The basic point is that there is really no computationally easy way to calculate P_e in general.

Example 5.2-2 Let us determine the probability of error for the decision problem of Example 5.2-1. For this problem, Eq. (5.2-8) is the simplest expression to use since the decision space is one-dimensional.

We begin by calculating the three conditional probabilities of a correct decision:

$$P\{d_1|m_1\} = \int_0^{0.69} 4e^{-4z}\,dz = -e^{-4z}\Big|_0^{0.69} = 0.94$$

$$P\{d_2|m_2\} = \int_{0.69}^{0.92} 2e^{-2z}\,dz = -e^{-2z}\Big|_{0.69}^{0.92} = 0.09$$

$$P\{d_3|m_3\} = \int_{0.92}^{\infty} 0.5e^{-z/2}\,dz = -e^{-z/2}\Big|_{0.92}^{\infty} = 0.63$$

Therefore P_e is given by

$$P_e = 1 - 0.5(0.94) - 0.25(0.09) - 0.25(0.63) = 0.35$$

In Sec. 3.3 we showed that the minimum probability-of-error decision rule was identical to the maximum a posteriori (MAP) decision rule. We want to show that this property is also true for the M-ary case we have examined in this section. Consider the decision rule given by Eq. (5.2-5). If we divide both sides of this equation by $p(\mathbf{z})$, we find that $\mathbf{z} \in \mathbf{Z}_j$ if

$$\frac{P\{m_j\}p(\mathbf{z}|m_j)}{p(\mathbf{z})} = \max_k \frac{P\{m_k\}p(\mathbf{z}|m_k)}{p(\mathbf{z})} \qquad (5.2\text{-}11)$$

The mixed Bayes rule indicates that

$$\frac{P\{m_i\}p(\mathbf{z}|m_i)}{p(\mathbf{z})} = P\{m_i|\mathbf{z}\} \qquad (5.2\text{-}12)$$

Therefore the decision region $\mathbf{Z}_j$ is given by the values of $\mathbf{z}$ for which

$$P\{m_j|\mathbf{z}\} = \max_k P\{m_k|\mathbf{z}\} \qquad (5.2\text{-}13)$$

In other words we select decision d_j if the message m_j has the maximum a posteriori probability. Since it is generally easier to compute $p(\mathbf{z}|m_k)$ than $P\{m_k|\mathbf{z}\}$, Eq. (5.2-5) is generally computationally more feasible to use than Eq. (5.2-13).

Example 5.2-3 As a final example let us consider the general ternary decision problem with probability-of-error costs. The region $\mathbf{Z}_1$ is given by Eq. (5.2-4) as the values of $\mathbf{z}$ for which

$$P\{m_1\}p(\mathbf{z}|m_1) > P\{m_2\}p(\mathbf{z}|m_2)$$

and

$$P\{m_1\}p(\mathbf{z}|m_1) > P\{m_3\}p(\mathbf{z}|m_3)$$

Dividing by $p(\mathbf{z}|m_1)$, the decision region $\mathbf{z}_1$ can be written as

$$\Lambda_2(\mathbf{z}) < \frac{P\{m_1\}}{P\{m_2\}}$$

$$\Lambda_3(\mathbf{z}) < \frac{P\{m_1\}}{P\{m_3\}}$$

From Eq. (5.2-4), the decision $\mathbf{Z}_2$ is defined by

$$P\{m_2\}p(\mathbf{z}|m_2) > P\{m_1\}p(\mathbf{z}|m_1)$$

$$P\{m_2\}p(\mathbf{z}|m_2) > P\{m_3\}p(\mathbf{z}|m_3)$$

or in terms of the likelihood ratios

$$\Lambda_2(\mathbf{z}) > \frac{P\{m_1\}}{P\{m_2\}}$$

$$\Lambda_2(\mathbf{z}) > \frac{P\{m_3\}}{P\{m_2\}} \Lambda_3(\mathbf{z})$$

In a similar fashion, we can show that $\mathbf{Z}_3$ is defined by

$$\Lambda_3(\mathbf{z}) > \frac{P\{m_1\}}{P\{m_3\}}$$

$$\Lambda_2(\mathbf{z}) < \frac{P\{m_3\}}{P\{m_2\}} \Lambda_3(\mathbf{z})$$

The decision regions are shown graphically in Fig. 5.2-2.

5.3 PROBABILITY OF ERROR: GAUSSIAN CASE

In Sec. 5-2 we established the general decision rule for probability of error and multiple decisions. In this section we shall specialize the result further: We shall assume that the signal is corrupted by the addition of white gaussian noise. Although we shall treat the waveform case, most of our attention will be focused on the vector case. We shall see that just as for binary message spaces, waveform signals and observations can be reduced to equivalent vector quantities.

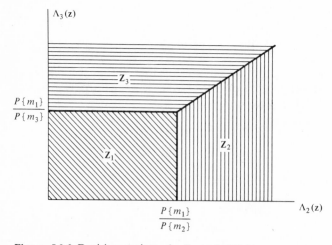

Figure 5.2-2 Decision regions for Example 5.2-3.

For an additive-noise problem, the observation is just the sum of the signal vector and a noise vector:

$$\mathbf{z} = \mathbf{s}_k + \mathbf{n} \tag{5.3-1}$$

Therefore the conditional probability density function of $\mathbf{z}$ is the density of $\mathbf{n}$ shifted to be centered at $\mathbf{s}_k$:

$$p(\mathbf{z}|m_k) = p_\mathbf{n}(\mathbf{z} - \mathbf{s}_k) \tag{5.3-2}$$

Now, if the noise is white and gaussian, the conditional density can be written as

$$p(\mathbf{z}|m_k) = (2\pi\sigma^2)^{-1/2} \exp -\frac{\|\mathbf{z} - \mathbf{s}_k\|^2}{2\sigma^2} \tag{5.3-3}$$

where $\|\mathbf{x}\|^2$ is used to indicate the squared length of the vector $\mathbf{x}$ and can be written as

$$\|\mathbf{x}\|^2 = \sum_{i=1}^{l} x_i^2$$

The decision rule developed in Sec. 5.2 that minimizes the probability of error is to let $\mathbf{z} \in \mathbf{Z}_j$ if

$$P\{m_j\}p(\mathbf{z}|m_j) = \max_k \ P\{m_k\}p(\mathbf{z}|m_k) \tag{5.3-4}$$

Initially we shall assume that all messages are equiprobable. Therefore, canceling common terms, Eq. (5.3-4) can be written as

$$\exp \frac{-\|\mathbf{z} - \mathbf{s}_j\|^2}{2\sigma^2} = \max_k \ \exp \frac{-\|\mathbf{z} - \mathbf{s}_k\|^2}{2\sigma^2}$$

Then, taking logs and again canceling common terms (*note*: when canceling the minus sign, the maximum becomes a minimum) the rule becomes $\mathbf{z} \in \mathbf{Z}_j$ if

$$\|\mathbf{z} - \mathbf{s}_j\|^2 = \min_k \ \|\mathbf{z} - \mathbf{s}_k\|^2 \tag{5.3-5}$$

In other words, if we picture the messages as points in an l-dimensional space, the region $\mathbf{Z}_j$ is the set of all points that are closer to $\mathbf{s}_j$ than to any other signal point. This concept is illustrated in the following example.

Example 5.3-1 In a problem with equiprobable messages and with signal vectors

$$\mathbf{s}_1 = \begin{bmatrix} 2 \\ 2 \end{bmatrix}$$

$$\mathbf{s}_2 = \begin{bmatrix} 2 \\ 0 \end{bmatrix}$$

$$\mathbf{s}_3 = \begin{bmatrix} 0 \\ 2 \end{bmatrix}$$

find the decision regions $\mathbf{Z}_j$. According to Eq. (5.3-5), the region $\mathbf{Z}_1$ is defined as the set of $\mathbf{z}$ such that $\|\mathbf{z} - \mathbf{s}_1\|^2$ is smaller than $\|\mathbf{z} - \mathbf{s}_2\|^2$ and smaller than $\|\mathbf{z} - \mathbf{s}_3\|^2$. In other words each $\mathbf{z}$ in $\mathbf{Z}_1$ must satisfy

$$(z_1 - 2)^2 + (z_2 - 2)^2 < (z_1 - 2)^2 + z_2^2$$

and
$$(z_1 - 2)^2 + (z_2 - 2)^2 < z_1^2 + (z_2 - 2)^2$$

Carrying out the squaring operations and canceling common terms, these two constraints become

$$z_2 > 1$$

and
$$z_1 > 1$$

This region is indicated in Fig. 5.3-1.

For $\mathbf{z}$ to be in $\mathbf{Z}_2$, we require that $\|\mathbf{z} - \mathbf{s}_2\|^2$ be smaller than $\|\mathbf{z} - \mathbf{s}_1\|^2$ and $\|\mathbf{z} - \mathbf{s}_3\|^2$. In other words, $\mathbf{Z}_2$ in all those $\mathbf{z}$ for which

$$(z_1 - 2)^2 + z_2^2 < (z_1 - 2)^2 + (z_2 - 2)^2$$

and
$$(z_1 - 2)^2 + z_2^2 < z_1^2 + (z_2 - 2)^2$$

Again these can be simplified and $\mathbf{Z}_2$ is

$$\mathbf{Z}_2 = \{\mathbf{z}: z_2 < 1 \text{ and } z_1 > z_2\}$$

In a completely analogous way it is easy to show that

$$\mathbf{Z}_3 = \{\mathbf{z}: z_1 < 1 \text{ and } z_2 < z_1\}$$

All three regions are shown in the figure.

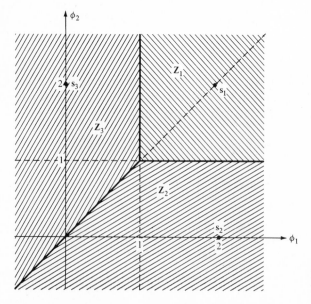

Figure 5.3-1 Decision regions for Example 5.3-1.

We have not specified which regions the boundaries themselves are in. Typically they will be assigned to one of the adjacent regions. However, since the probability of actually landing on a boundary is zero, they can be assigned anywhere without altering the probability of error.

It is interesting to note in the preceding example that the boundary lines are actually segments of the perpendicular bisectors of the lines that join the signal points. In fact, for any two-dimensional signal space, all the decision regions will be bounded by such segments. For three-dimensional problems, the boundaries will be the planes that perpendicularly bisect these lines, and for more than three dimensions, they will be the hyperplanes.

Another point to note is that we have been able to completely specify the decision rule without using the variance of the noise. This fact is somewhat unusual and, as we shall see, applies here only because the signals are equiprobable.

Although finding the decision regions for equiprobable signals is straightfoward, the probability of error can be more complex. Let us return to the preceding example.

Example 5.3-2 We are now to compute the probability of error for the structure of Example 5.3-1. To do so, we shall compute the conditional error probabilities for each of the messages and combine the results. When the message is m_1, an error will occur if z is not in Z_1. Therefore the conditional error probability is

$$P\{e|m_1\} = P\{z \notin Z_1|m_1\} = P\{z_1 < 1 \text{ or } z_2 < 1|m_1\}$$

But when the message is m_1, z_1 is just $2 + n_1$ and z_2 is $2 + n_2$.

Since we have assumed that n_1 and n_2 are independent, the error event is the union of two independent events and the conditional error probability becomes

$$P\{e|m_1\} = P\{n_1 < -1\} + P\{n_2 < -1\} - P\{n_1 < -1\}P\{n_2 < -1\}$$

Now, for each n_i, the probability that it is smaller than -1 is just

$$P\{n_i < -1\} = \int_{-\infty}^{-1} \frac{1}{\sqrt{2\pi\sigma^2}} \exp \frac{-\eta^2}{2\sigma^2} \, d\eta = Q\left(\frac{1}{\sigma}\right)$$

So the conditional error probability is

$$P\{e|m_1\} = 2Q\left(\frac{1}{\sigma}\right) - Q^2\left(\frac{1}{\sigma}\right)$$

Unfortunately the error probabilities for m_2 and m_3 are not as neat. As before, the error event can be written as an event on z_1 and z_2. Thus the conditional error probability is

$$P\{e|m_2\} = P\{z \notin Z_2|m_2\} = P\{z_2 > 1 \text{ or } z_2 > z_1|m_2\}$$

Since z is just the sum of s_2 and n, the error probability can be written as

$$P\{e|m_2\} = P\{n_2 > 1 \text{ or } n_2 > n_1 + 2\}$$

Unfortunately, since these two events are not independent, we cannot simplify this expression. Of course, it is possible to write it as an integral on the joint probability density. Rewriting the expression gives

$$P\{e|m_2\} = P\{n_2 > \min(1, n_1 + 2)\}$$

Thus, the integral is

$$P\{e|m_2\} = \int_{-\infty}^{\infty} d\eta_1 \int_{\min(1,\eta_1+2)}^{\infty} \frac{1}{2\pi\sigma^2} \exp -\frac{\eta_1^2 + \eta_2^2}{2\sigma^2} d\eta_2$$

A similar expression can be found for $P\{e|m_3\}$. Therefore, the overall average probability is

$$P_e = \tfrac{1}{3}Q\left(\frac{1}{\sigma}\right)\left[2 - Q\left(\frac{1}{\sigma}\right)\right] + \tfrac{2}{3}\int_{-\infty}^{\infty} d\eta_1 \int_{\min(1,\eta_1+2)}^{\infty} \frac{1}{2\pi\sigma^2} \exp -\frac{\eta_1^2 + \eta_2^2}{2\sigma^2} d\eta_2$$

Although this expression is exact, it does not provide much insight into how the system actually performs. A more useful approach is to find an upper bound on the error probability that is simple and that is also a good approximation. We shall start with $P\{e|m_2\}$. It can be written as the probability that $n_2 > 1$ plus the probability that $n_2 > n_1 + 2$ minus the joint probability of these two events:

$$P\{e|m_2\} = P\{n_2 > 1\} + P\{n_2 > n_1 + 2\} - P\{n_2 > 1 \text{ and } n_2 > n_1 + 2\}$$

Now only the third term is difficult to compute. However, this term is always negative, and the error probability can be overbounded by the sum of the other two terms:

$$P\{e|m_2\} \leq P\{n_2 > 1\} + P\{n_2 > n_1 + 2\}$$

Figure 5.3-2 illustrates these two events and shows how the sum overbounds the error probability.

The first term in the sum is clearly just $Q(1/\sigma)$ as before. If the second term is written as $P\{n_2 - n_1 > 2\}$ and if it is noted that $(n_2 - n_1)$ is a zero-mean qaussian random variable with variance $2\sigma^2$, then it is clear that the bound is

$$P\{e|m_2\} \leq Q\left(\frac{1}{\sigma}\right) + Q\left(\frac{2}{\sqrt{2}\sigma}\right)$$

The third error probability $P\{e|m_3\}$ can be bounded by the same expression, and the average error probability can be bounded by

$$P_e \leq \frac{4}{3}Q\left(\frac{1}{\sigma}\right) + \frac{2}{3}Q\left(\frac{\sqrt{2}}{\sigma}\right) - \frac{1}{3}Q^2\left(\frac{1}{\sigma}\right)$$

As the preceding example illustrates, it is not always possible to obtain meaningful exact expressions for error probabilities. Frequently we must settle for bounds. However, if we can find simple *upper* bounds that are tight, we

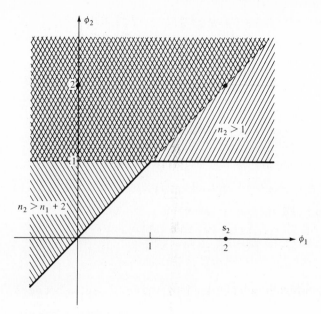

Figure 5.3-2 Bound on $P\{e|m_2\}$

should be satisfied. Why the emphasis on *upper* bounds rather than simply good approximations? The answer is that frequently a system must be designed to satisfy some minimum performance standard. That is, the designer must be certain that an error probability, for example, is no larger than some given number. If it can be guaranteed that an upper bound on the error probability is lower then this number, then the designer knows that the requirement has been met. The designer who is forced to work with an approximation cannot be sure.

Happily, the approach to finding an upper bound that was used in the Example 5.3-2 can be generalized quite easily. It is called the *union bound* and is stated in the following theorem.

Theorem 5.3-1 If the event A is the union of K events

$$A = \bigcup_{k=1}^{K} E_k$$

then the probability of A is bounded by

$$P\{A\} \le \sum_{k=1}^{K} P\{E_k\}$$

The proof is a simple induction on K. For $K = 2$, it is known [see Eq. (2.1-4)] that

$$P\{A\} = P\{E_1 \cup E_2\} = P\{E_1\} + P\{E_2\} - P\{E_1 E_2\} \le P\{E_1\} + P\{E_2\}$$

If the theorem is true for $K - 1$, then for K

$$P\{A\} = P\{(E_1 \cup E_2 \cup \cdots \cup E_{K-1}) \cup E_K\}$$
$$= P\{E_1 \cup E_2 \cup \cdots \cup E_{K-1}\} + P\{E_K\}$$
$$- P\{(E_1 \cup E_2 \cup \cdots \cup E_{K-1}) E_K\}$$
$$\leq \sum_{k=1}^{K-1} P\{E_k\} + P\{E_K\}$$

Using Eq. (5.3-5), we can write the decision region $\mathbf{Z}_j$ as

$$\mathbf{Z}_j = \{\mathbf{z}: \|\mathbf{z} - \mathbf{s}_j\|^2 \leq \|\mathbf{z} - \mathbf{s}_l\|^2 \text{ for all } l \neq j\} \tag{5.3-6}$$

Therefore the complement of $\mathbf{Z}_j$ is a union of regions

$$\mathbf{Z}_j^c = \bigcup_{\substack{l=1 \\ l \neq j}}^{K} \{\mathbf{z}: \|\mathbf{z} - \mathbf{s}_j\|^2 \geq \|\mathbf{z} - \mathbf{s}_l\|^2\}$$

and the conditional error probability when the message m_k is sent is bounded by

$$P\{e|m_k\} = P\{\mathbf{z} \in \mathbf{Z}_k^c | m_k\} \leq \sum_{\substack{l=1 \\ l \neq k}}^{K} P\{\|\mathbf{z} - \mathbf{s}_k\|^2 > \|\mathbf{z} - \mathbf{s}_l\|^2 | m_k\} \tag{5.3-7}$$

Each term in the sum can be simplified further. When the message is m_k, $\mathbf{z}$ is $\mathbf{s}_k + \mathbf{n}$ and, as in Chap. 4, the expression for each l becomes

$$P\{\|\mathbf{z} - \mathbf{s}_k\|^2 > \|\mathbf{z} - \mathbf{s}_l\|^2 | m_k\} = P\{\|\mathbf{n}\|^2 > \|\mathbf{n} + \mathbf{s}_k - \mathbf{s}_l\|^2\}$$
$$= P\{2\mathbf{n}^T(\mathbf{s}_l - \mathbf{s}_k) > \|\mathbf{s}_l - \mathbf{s}_k\|^2\}$$

Then, since $2\mathbf{n}^T(\mathbf{s}_l - \mathbf{s}_k)$ is a zero-mean gaussian random variable with variance $4\sigma^2\|\mathbf{s}_l - \mathbf{s}_k\|^2$, the probability is

$$P\{\|\mathbf{z} - \mathbf{s}_k\|^2 > \|\mathbf{z} - \mathbf{s}_l\|^2 | m_k\} = Q\left(\frac{d_{lk}}{2\sigma}\right)$$

where d_{lk} is the distance between the two message vectors $\mathbf{s}_l$ and $\mathbf{s}_k$

$$d_{lk} = \|\mathbf{s}_l - \mathbf{s}_k\| \tag{5.3-8}$$

Therefore we can bound the conditional probability of error with

$$P\{e|m_k\} \leq \sum_{\substack{l=1 \\ l \neq k}}^{K} Q\left(\frac{d_{lk}}{2\sigma}\right) \tag{5.3-9}$$

To bound the overall average probability of error, Eq. (5.3-9) is averaged over all k so that the *Union Bound* becomes

$$P_e \leq \sum_{k=1}^{K} \frac{1}{K} \sum_{\substack{l=1 \\ l \neq k}}^{K} Q\left(\frac{d_{lk}}{2\sigma}\right) \tag{5.3-10}$$

The use of this bound is illustrated by the following example.

Example 5.3-3 In a 4-ary communication problem, the four signal vectors are

$$\mathbf{s}_1 = [2 \quad 2]^T \qquad \mathbf{s}_3 = [-2 \quad -2]^T$$
$$\mathbf{s}_2 = [-2 \quad 2]^T \qquad \mathbf{s}_4 = [2 \quad -2]^T$$

For equiprobable signals and for noise of unit variance, we are to upper bound the probability of error.

To use the union bound, first we must find all the distances d_{lk}. Either by direct computation from Eq. (5.3-8) or by inspection of Fig. 5.3-3, it is easy to establish that the distances are as given in the following table.

Table 5.3-1 Distances

k	l 1	2	3	4
1	$\cdots$	4	$4\sqrt{2}$	4
2	4	$\cdots$	4	$4\sqrt{2}$
3	$4\sqrt{2}$	4	$\cdots$	4
4	4	$4\sqrt{2}$	4	$\cdots$

Using these in Eq. (5.3-10) to bound the probability of error yields

$$P_e \le 2Q(2) + Q(2\sqrt{2}) = 0.0477$$

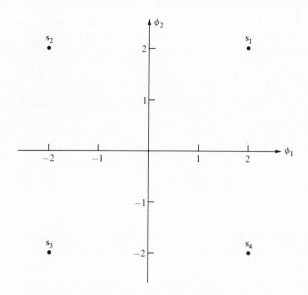

Figure 5.3-3 Signal set for Example 5.3-3.

For this particular example, it is possible to compute the exact value of probability of error. For example, if message m_1 is sent, no error will be made unless n_1 or n_2 is less than 2. Therefore,

$$P\{e|m_1\} = 2Q(2) - Q^2(2)$$

But from the symmetry of the signal space, all messages in the space have the same probability of error. Therefore

$$P_e = 2Q(2) - Q^2(2) = 0.0449$$

It is interesting to note that for this particular case, the union bound is within 6 percent of the correct answer.

The bound given in Eq. (5.3-10) may appear somewhat complex, and often it is desirable to obtain a rough estimate of the performance of several similar signal sets. Since the function $Q(\alpha)$ decreases as $\exp -\alpha^2/2$, those terms with the smallest values of d_{lk} clearly will dominate the bound. In fact, if we define $d_{\min}$ as the *minimum distance* of a signal set

$$d_{\min} = \min_k \left[\min_{l \neq k} d_{lk} \right]$$

we shall have a fairly efficient yardstick with which to measure the effectiveness of the set. We can demonstrate this formally by noting that the union bound can be further upper-bounded by

$$\sum_{k=1}^{K} \frac{1}{K} \sum_{\substack{l=1 \\ l \neq k}}^{K} Q\left(\frac{d_{lk}}{2\sigma}\right) \leq (K-1)Q\left(\frac{d_{\min}}{2\sigma}\right) \tag{5.3-11}$$

Thus we have an upper bound on P_e that depends only on $d_{\min}$.

If the signal set is symmetric, we can find a lower bound in terms of $d_{\min}$; we must note only that the probability of a union of events is always larger than the probability of a single event in the union. Therefore, for each m_k,

$$P\{e|m_k\} \geq Q\left(\frac{d_{lk}}{2\sigma}\right) \qquad \text{for each } l \neq k$$

$$\geq Q\left(\frac{d_{\min}}{2\sigma}\right) \tag{5.3-12}$$

Combining Eqs. (5.3-11) and (5.3-12) gives

$$Q\left(\frac{d_{\min}}{2\sigma}\right) \leq P\{e\} \leq (K-1)Q\left(\frac{d_{\min}}{2\sigma}\right) \tag{5.3-13}$$

Therefore, since the upper and lower bounds differ only by $(K-1)$, it is clear how close they are. Even if the signal set is not symmetric, P_e can be lower-bounded by $2Q(d_{\min}/2\sigma)/K$ by lower bounding most of the $P\{e|m_k\}$ terms by zero. Note that if we are interested in describing the behavior of the system over a range of signal-to-noise ratios, we need look only at $Q(d_{\min}/2\sigma)$ since $(K-1)$ does not depend on SNR. Typically the union bound will be much tighter than the right-hand side of Eq. (5.3-13), and P_e will be quite close to the lower bound.

So far we have treated only those cases for which the messages are equiprobable. The more general case is quite similar and almost as easy to handle. The general decision rule in Eq. (5.3-4) says to select the message for which $P\{m_j\}p(\mathbf{z}|m_j)$ is a maximum. If we do not assume that all the $P\{m_j\}$ are the same, they will not cancel and will appear in the final definition of the decision region $\mathbf{Z}_j$.

If $P\{m_j\}p(\mathbf{z}|m_j)$ is to be the maximum of a set, clearly it must be larger than every other element in the set. Therefore the set of $\mathbf{z}$ for which $P\{m_j\}p(\mathbf{z}|m_j)$ is the maximum can be written as the joint intersection of those regions of $\mathbf{Z}$ for which it is larger than $P\{m_l\}p(\mathbf{z}|m_l)$ for each $l \neq j$. In other words,

$$\mathbf{Z}_j = \bigcap_{\substack{l=1 \\ l \neq j}}^{K} \{\mathbf{z}: P\{m_j\}p(\mathbf{z}|m_j) > P\{m_l\}p(\mathbf{z}|m_l)\} \tag{5.3-14}$$

Let us examine one of these regions in detail. Using $\mathbf{Z}_{jl}$ to denote the lth term on the right of Eq. (5.3-14), it is clear that for the gaussian case

$$\mathbf{Z}_{jl} = \left\{\mathbf{z}: P\{m_j\} \exp \frac{-\|\mathbf{z}-\mathbf{s}_j\|^2}{2\sigma^2} > P\{m_l\} \exp \frac{-\|\mathbf{z}-\mathbf{s}_l\|^2}{2\sigma^2}\right\} \tag{5.3-15}$$

Taking logs and canceling common terms simplifies the expression somewhat, and it becomes

$$\mathbf{Z}_{jl} = \left\{\mathbf{z}: \|\mathbf{z}-\mathbf{s}_j\|^2 < \|\mathbf{z}-\mathbf{s}_l\|^2 + 2\sigma^2 \ln \frac{P\{m_j\}}{P\{m_l\}}\right\} \tag{5.3-16}$$

If $P\{m_l\}$ and $P\{m_j\}$ are equal, then $\mathbf{Z}_{jl}$ is just the set of points that are closer to $\mathbf{s}_j$ than to $\mathbf{s}_l$. If $P\{m_l\}$ is smaller than $P\{m_j\}$, some points that are closer to $\mathbf{s}_l$ will be included in $\mathbf{Z}_{jl}$.

We know that for equal probabilities the boundary of $\mathbf{Z}_{jl}$ is the hyperplane that is the perpendicular bisector of the line that joins $\mathbf{s}_l$ and $\mathbf{s}_j$. Even if the probabilities are not equal, the boundary is still a hyperplane that is perpendicular to $(\mathbf{s}_l - \mathbf{s}_j)$. To show this, Eq. (5.3-16) is rewritten by writing out the squared vector lengths and collecting similar terms:

$$\mathbf{Z}_{jl} = \left\{\mathbf{z}: 2\mathbf{z}^T\mathbf{s}_l - 2\mathbf{z}^T\mathbf{s}_j < \|\mathbf{s}_l\|^2 - \|\mathbf{s}_j\|^2 + 2\sigma^2 \ln \frac{P\{m_j\}}{P\{m_l\}}\right\}$$

It is clear, then, that the boundary of the region is the set of $\mathbf{z}$ for which

$$\mathbf{z}^T(\mathbf{s}_l - \mathbf{s}_j) = \frac{1}{2}\|\mathbf{s}_l\|^2 - \frac{1}{2}\|\mathbf{s}_j\|^2 + \sigma^2 \ln \frac{P\{m_j\}}{P\{m_l\}} \tag{5.3-17}$$

However, the set of $\mathbf{z}$ for which $\mathbf{z}^T(\mathbf{s}_l - \mathbf{s}_j)$ is a constant is a hyperplane that is perpendicular to $(\mathbf{s}_l - \mathbf{s}_j)$.

As noted previously, it is not possible to fully specify the decision regions without knowing σ^2. If σ^2 is large, the decision will be highly biased in favor of the more probable messages. This is reasonable since for large σ^2 the received signal is not very reliable. On the other hand, if σ^2 is small, the a priori probabilities do not affect the decision regions very much.

As for the equiprobable case, the probability of error typically is not easy to calculate. However, the union bound can be used on $\mathbf{Z}_{ji}^c$, and the error probability can be bounded by

$$P_e \leq \sum_{j=1}^{K} \frac{1}{K} \sum_{\substack{l=1 \\ l \neq j}}^{K} P\left\{\|\mathbf{n}\|^2 > \|\mathbf{n} + \mathbf{s}_j - \mathbf{s}_l\|^2 + 2\sigma^2 \ln \frac{P\{m_j\}}{P\{m_l\}}\right\} \qquad (5.3\text{-}18)$$

Using the same logic as in the equiprobable case, this becomes

$$P_e \leq \sum_{j=1}^{K} \frac{1}{K} \sum_{\substack{l=1 \\ l \neq j}}^{K} Q\left(\frac{d_{lj}}{2\sigma} - \frac{\sigma}{d_{lj}} \ln \left[\frac{P\{m_j\}}{P\{m_l\}}\right]\right) \qquad (5.3\text{-}19)$$

Unfortunately the concept of the minimum distance is no longer useful since the relative size of the terms in the sum will depend on σ and the a priori probabilities as well as on d_{lj}.

In Chap. 4 we saw that when we had a binary message set all the results that we developed for vector problems could be used when the observation was a known waveform corrupted by additive white gaussian noise. It should not be surprising that the same is true for a K-ary message space. For the binary messages, we first showed that an equivalent vector problem existed and then we used the Gram-Schmidt procedure to find a convenient equivalent vector problem.

The arguments for the existence of an equivalent vector problem for K messages are exactly analogous to those of Chap. 4, and they will not be repeated here. Instead, we shall concentrate on finding a way to handle the problem of K signal waveforms. For the problem that we shall be concerned with, the observation $z(t)$ is given by

$$z(t) = s_k(t) + n(t) \qquad 0 \leq t \leq T \qquad (5.3\text{-}20)$$

where $n(t)$ is white gaussian noise. We wish to find an orthonormal set of functions $\{\phi_i(t), i = 1, 2, \ldots, I\}$ such that we can exactly represent each of the messages as

$$s_k(t) = \sum_{i=1}^{I} s_{k,i}\phi_i(t) \qquad 0 \leq t \leq T$$

where the coefficients are given by

$$s_{k,i} = \int_0^T s_k(t)\phi_i(t) \, dt \qquad (5.3\text{-}21)$$

Once we have found such a set, the arguments of Chap. 4 show that the vector problem with observations

$$z_i = s_{k,i} + n_i \qquad i = 1, 2, \ldots, I$$

where the noise is given by

$$n_i = \int_0^T n(t)\phi_i(t)\ dt$$

is equivalent to the waveform problem.

To find one acceptable signal set, we can generalize the Gram-Schmidt procedure. For the first element of the set, we let

$$\phi_1(t) = \frac{s_1(t)}{\sqrt{\int_0^T s_1^2(t)\ dt}} \qquad (5.3\text{-}22)$$

We must assume, of course, that $s_1(t)$ is not zero over the entire interval $(0,\ T)$. If it is, we would use $s_2(t)$ instead. Assuming that we have used $s_1(t)$, we proceed to compute $s_{2,1}$ according to Eq. (5.3-21). If $s_2(t)$ is not equal to $s_{2,1}\phi_1(t)$, we can define $\phi_2(t)$ as

$$\phi_2(t) = \frac{s_2(t) - s_{2,1}\phi_1(t)}{\sqrt{\int_0^T [s_2(t) - s_{2,1}\phi_1(t)]^2\ dt}} \qquad (5.3\text{-}23)$$

So far, this is exactly the same as for two messages. If $s_2(t)$ is equal to $s_{2,1}\phi_1(t)$, we use $s_3(t)$ in its place. If $s_3(t)$ is also completely represented by $s_{3,1}\phi_1(t)$, we use the next $s_k(t)$ that is not. If there is no such $s_k(t)$, then we can stop since we have been able to represent all signals with just $\phi_1(t)$.

The procedure is easy to generalize. Suppose that we have found I' functions $\phi_i(t)$, and suppose they can be used to exactly represent the first K' signal functions. To find $\phi_{I'+1}(t)$, we compute $s_{K'+1,i}$ for i from 1 to I' and then define $\phi_{I'+1}(t)$ as

$$\phi_{I'+1}(t) = \frac{s_{K'+1}(t) - \sum\limits_{i=1}^{I'} s_{K'+1,i}\phi_i(t)}{\sqrt{\int_0^T [s_{K'+1}(t) - \sum\limits_{i=1}^{I'} s_{K'+1,i}\ \phi_i(t)]^2\ dt}} \qquad (5.3\text{-}24)$$

If K' is equal to K, then all the signals can be represented in terms of $\{\phi_i : i = 1, 2, \ldots, I'\}$, and so I' is I. It is interesting to note that I need never be larger than K since every time a $\phi_i(t)$ is added to the basis set, at least one more signal can be exactly represented. The following examples illustrate the use of this procedure.

Example 5.3-4 Consider the 4-ary signal set described by

$$s_1(t) = x(t)$$
$$s_2(t) = y(t)$$
$$s_3(t) = -x(t)$$
$$s_4(t) = -y(t)$$

where $x(t)$ and $y(t)$ are shown in Fig. 5.3-4. For equiprobable messages, we are to find the decision rule and the probability of error.

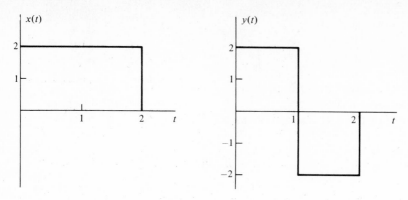

Figure 5.3-4 Waveforms for Example 5.3-4.

Using the Gram-Schmidt procedure, we define $\phi_1(t)$ as

$$\phi_1(t) = \frac{s_1(t)}{\sqrt{\int_0^2 s_1^2(t)\ dt}}$$

$$= \frac{1}{2\sqrt{2}}\ x(t)$$

The second orthonormal function is

$$\phi_2(t) = \frac{s_2(t) - s_{2,1}\phi_1(t)}{\sqrt{\int_0^2 (s_2(t) - s_{2,1}\phi_1(t))^2\ dt}}$$

But $\phi_1(t)$ is orthogonal to $s_2(t)$, and so $s_{2,1}$ is zero and $\phi_2(t)$ is

$$\phi_2(t) = \frac{1}{2\sqrt{2}}\ y(t)$$

This particular signal set obviously can be completely represented by $\phi_1(t)$ and $\phi_2(t)$, and the equivalent vector problem has signal vectors

$$\mathbf{s_1} = \begin{bmatrix} 2\sqrt{2} \\ 0 \end{bmatrix}$$

$$\mathbf{s_2} = \begin{bmatrix} 0 \\ 2\sqrt{2} \end{bmatrix}$$

$$\mathbf{s_3} = \begin{bmatrix} -2\sqrt{2} \\ 0 \end{bmatrix}$$

$$\mathbf{s_4} = \begin{bmatrix} 0 \\ -2\sqrt{2} \end{bmatrix}$$

These signal points are plotted in Fig. 5.3-5. Note that except for a rotation of axes, this is the same signal-space picture as for Example 5.3-3. If we

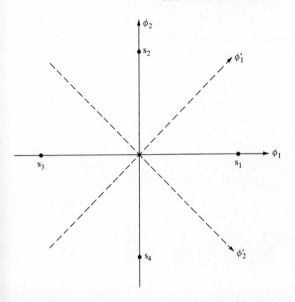

Figure 5.3-5 Signal space for Example 5.3-4.

define a new set of orthonormal functions

$$\phi_1'(t) = \frac{1}{\sqrt{2}}\left(\phi_1(t) + \phi_2(t)\right)$$

$$\phi_2'(t) = \frac{1}{\sqrt{2}}\left(\phi_1(t) - \phi_2(t)\right)$$

then the two representations are identical and the problem is completely solved in Example 5.3-3.

Example 5.3-5 A standard digital communication technique is to use the phase of a sinusoidal carrier to transmit information. If one of K messages is to be sent, the signal is

$$s_k(t) = A \cos\left(\omega t - 2\pi \frac{k-1}{K}\right) \qquad 0 \le t \le T$$

For simplicity, we shall assume that ω is an integer multiple of $2\pi/T$. This will assure that there are integer number of periods of the sinusoid in the interval $(0, T)$.

To find an equivalent problem, we use the Gram-Schmidt procedure to write that $\phi_1(t)$ is

$$\phi_1(t) = \frac{A \cos \omega t}{\sqrt{\int_0^T A^2 \cos^2 \omega t \, dt}} \qquad 0 \le t \le T$$

$$= \sqrt{\frac{2}{T}} \cos \omega t \qquad 0 \le t \le T$$

To find $s_{2,1}$ we must write

$$s_{2,1} = A \sqrt{\frac{2}{T}} \int_0^T \cos\left(\omega t - \frac{2\pi}{K}\right) \cos \omega t \, dt$$

$$= A \sqrt{\frac{T}{2}} \cos \frac{2\pi}{K}$$

Therefore, $\phi_2(t)$ is

$$\phi_2(t) = \frac{A \cos(\omega t - 2\pi/K) - A \cos(2\pi/K)\cos \omega t}{\sqrt{\int_0^T [A \cos(\omega t - 2\pi/K) - A \cos(2\pi/K)\cos \omega t]^2 \, dt}} \quad 0 \le t \le T$$

$$= \sqrt{\frac{2}{T}} \sin \omega t \qquad\qquad\qquad 0 \le t \le T$$

To show that this is a large enough basis set, we need write only

$$s_k(t) = A \cos 2\pi \frac{k-1}{K} \cos \omega t + A \sin 2\pi \frac{k-1}{K} \sin \omega t \qquad 0 \le t \le T$$

Therefore, the equivalent vector problem has the signal vectors

$$\mathbf{s}_k = \left[A\sqrt{\frac{T}{2}} \cos 2\pi \frac{k-1}{K} \quad A\sqrt{\frac{T}{2}} \sin 2\pi \frac{k-1}{K} \right]^T \qquad k = 1, 2, \ldots, K$$

The signal-space plot of this set is shown in Fig. 5.3-6 for $K = 7$. It is always a set of K points equally spaced about a circle of radius $A\sqrt{T/2}$.

It is interesting to note that for $K = 4$ and for $A = 4/\sqrt{T}$, the signal space is exactly the same as for Example 5.3-4. Thus, even though the

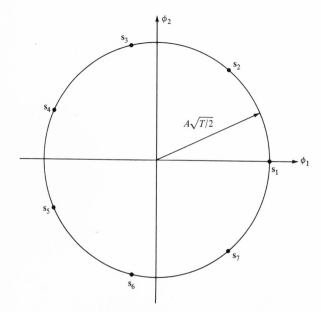

Figure 5.3-6 Signal space for Example 5.3-5.

time-domain representation of the two signal sets is radically different, their performance will be identical.

5.4 ERASURE DECISION PROBLEMS

In this section we shall consider a special class of multiple decision problems in which there are K messages and $K + 1$ decisions. We assume a natural pairing of the first K decisions and the K messages; that is, if m_k is true, then d_k is the correct decision. The decision d_{K+1} will be referred to as the *erasure decision*. When we decide d_{K+1}, we are indicating that we are so uncertain of which message is true that we wish to make no decision. There are many practical problems for which this model is appropriate and useful. For example, the doctor who has performed a series of diagnostic tests but does not feel that the tests are conclusive, may decide to ignore the first results and repeat the tests.

The following Bayes cost assignment will be used for the erasure decision problem.

$$C_{jk} = \begin{cases} 0 & \text{if } j = k \\ 1 & \text{if } j \neq k \text{ and } j < K + 1 \\ \alpha & \text{if } j = K + 1 \end{cases} \tag{5.4-1}$$

for $j = 1, 2, \ldots, K + 1$; $k = 1, 2, \ldots, K$. Here we assume zero cost for correct decisions, unity cost for incorrect decisions, and α cost for the erasure decision. Hence we have a probability of error-cost assignment with the addition of the erasure decision. As the cost of an erasure is increased, the probability of making the erasure decision will decrease. In particular, if $\alpha > 1$, then we would never decide d_{K+1} since the probability of an error is always less than or equal to 1.

If we substitute this cost assignment into the general Bayes criterion of Eq. (5.1-7), then we find that the decision region $\mathbf{Z}_j, j = 1, 2, \ldots, K$ is defined by

$$\sum_{\substack{k=1 \\ k \neq j}}^{K} P\{m_k\} p(\mathbf{z} | m_k) < \sum_{\substack{k=1 \\ k \neq l}}^{K} P\{m_k\} p(\mathbf{z} | m_k) \tag{5.4-2}$$

for all $l \neq j$ and

$$\sum_{\substack{k=1 \\ k \neq j}}^{K} P\{m_k\} p(\mathbf{z} | m_k) < \alpha \sum_{k=1}^{K} P\{m_k\} p(\mathbf{z} | m_k) \tag{5.4-3}$$

If we add and subtract $P\{m_j\} p(\mathbf{z} | m_j)$ on the left side of Eq. (5.4-2) and $P\{m_l\} p(\mathbf{z} | m_l)$ on the right side, then Eq. (5.4-2) becomes

$$-P\{m_j\} p(\mathbf{z} | m_j) < -P\{m_l\} p(\mathbf{z} | m_l) \tag{5.4-4}$$

Now we add and subtract $P\{m_j\}p(\mathbf{z}|m_j)$ on the left side of Eq. (5.4-3); then Eq. (5.4-3) can be written as

$$-P\{m_j\}p(\mathbf{z}|m_j) < (\alpha - 1) \sum_{k=1}^{K} P\{m_k\}p(\mathbf{z}|m_k) \tag{5.4-5}$$

Multiplying both sides of Eqs. (5.4-4) and (5.4-5) by -1 and reversing the inequalities yields the following definition for $\mathbf{Z}_j$, $j = 1, 2, \ldots, K$:

$$P\{m_j\}p(\mathbf{z}|m_j) > P\{m_l\}p(\mathbf{z}|m_l) \tag{5.4-6}$$

for $l \neq j$ and

$$P\{m_j\}p(\mathbf{z}|m_j) > (1 - \alpha) \sum_{k=1}^{K} P\{m_l\}p(\mathbf{z}|m_l) \tag{5.4-7}$$

If we divide both sides of Eqs. (5.4-6) and (5.4-7) by $p(\mathbf{z})$ and note that

$$p(\mathbf{z}) = \sum_{k=1}^{K} P\{m_l\}p(\mathbf{z}|m_l)$$

then $\mathbf{Z}_j$ is defined by

$$P\{m_j|\mathbf{z}\} > P\{m_l|\mathbf{z}\} \tag{5.4-8}$$

for $l \neq j$ and

$$P\{m_j|\mathbf{z}\} > 1 - \alpha \tag{5.4-9}$$

Equation (5.4-8) is identical to the probability-of-error (MAP) criterion developed in the Sec. 5.2. Equation (5.4-9), however, requires that the maximum a posteriori probability must exceed $1 - \alpha$ before the decision d_j can be made.
The erasure decision region $\mathbf{Z}_{K+1}$ is given by

$$\alpha \sum_{k=1}^{K} P\{m_k\}p(\mathbf{z}|m_k) < \sum_{\substack{k=1 \\ k \neq l}}^{K} P\{m_k\}p(\mathbf{z}|m_k) \tag{5.4-10}$$

for $l = 1, 2, \ldots, K$. Now adding and subtracting $P\{m_l\}p(\mathbf{z}|m_l)$ on the right side of Eq. (5.4-10) and rearranging slightly yields

$$P\{m_l\}p(\mathbf{z}|m_l) < (1 - \alpha) \sum_{k=1}^{K} P\{m_k\}p(\mathbf{z}|m_k) \tag{5.4-11}$$

If we divide both sides of this equation by $p(\mathbf{z})$, then the decision region $\mathbf{Z}_{K+1}$ can be defined by

$$P\{m_l|\mathbf{z}\} < 1 - \alpha \tag{5.4-12}$$

for $l = 1, 2, \ldots, K$. In other words, we decide d_{K+1} if none of the a posteriori probabilities exceed $1 - \alpha$. Equation (5.4-12) can also be written as

$$\max_{k} P\{m_k|\mathbf{z}\} < 1 - \alpha \tag{5.4-13}$$

Example 5.4-1 Let us consider the binary erasure problem in which we have two messages and three decisions. A direct application of Eq. (5.4-6) and (5.4-7) can be used to define $\mathbf{Z}_1$ as the set of $\mathbf{z}$ for which

$$P\{m_1\}p(\mathbf{z}|m_1) > P\{m_2\}p(\mathbf{z}|m_2)$$

and $\qquad P\{m_1\}p(\mathbf{z}|m_1) > (1-\alpha)[P\{m_1\}p(\mathbf{z}|m_1) + P\{m_2\}p(\mathbf{z}|m_2)]$

If we divide both sides of these equations by $p(\mathbf{z}|m_1)$ and use the usual definition of $\Lambda(\mathbf{z})$, then $\mathbf{Z}_1$ is defined by

$$\Lambda(\mathbf{z}) < \frac{P\{m_1\}}{P\{m_2\}}$$

and $\qquad\qquad \Lambda(\mathbf{z}) < \frac{\alpha}{1-\alpha}\frac{P\{m_1\}}{P\{m_2\}}$

In a similar manner we can show that $\mathbf{Z}_2$ is defined by

$$\Lambda(\mathbf{z}) > \frac{P\{m_1\}}{P\{m_2\}}$$

$$\Lambda(\mathbf{z}) > \frac{1-\alpha}{\alpha}\frac{P\{m_1\}}{P\{m_2\}}$$

and $\mathbf{Z}_3$ obviously is given by

$$\frac{P\{m_1\}}{P\{m_2\}}\frac{\alpha}{1-\alpha} < \Lambda(\mathbf{z}) < \frac{1-\alpha}{\alpha}\frac{P\{m_1\}}{P\{m_2\}}$$

We note, for $\alpha > 0.5$, that $\mathbf{Z}_3$ vanishes since $\alpha/(1-\alpha) > (1-\alpha)/\alpha$. The three decision regions are shown graphically in Fig. 5.4-1.

We can represent this result in a slightly different form if we begin with Eqs. (5.4-8) and (5.4-9). In this case, $\mathbf{Z}_1$ is given by the set of $\mathbf{z}$ such that

$$P\{m_1|\mathbf{z}\} > P\{m_2|\mathbf{z}\}$$

and $\qquad\qquad P\{m_1|\mathbf{z}\} > 1-\alpha$

while $\mathbf{Z}_2$ is defined by

$$P\{m_2|\mathbf{z}\} > P\{m_1|\mathbf{z}\}$$

$$P\{m_2|\mathbf{z}\} > 1-\alpha$$

Hence we select the decision corresponding to the message with the larger a posteriori probability as long as that probability is greater than

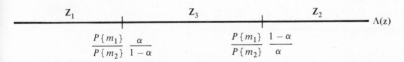

Figure 5.4-1 Result for general binary erasure problem.

$1 - \alpha$. The erasure decision region is given by

$$\max_{k} P\{m_k|\mathbf{z}\} < 1 - \alpha$$

We note that if $\alpha > \frac{1}{2}$, then $\mathbf{Z}_3 = \varnothing$ since the maximum a posteriori density will always be greater than $\frac{1}{2}$.

Example 5.4-2 As another example, let us consider a ternary erasure problem. For simplicity in obtaining our results, we shall assume that each of the three messages are equally likely so that $P\{m_k\} = \frac{1}{3}$ for $k = 1, 2, 3$. The use of Eqs. (5.4-6) and (5.4-7) yields the following definition of $\mathbf{Z}_1$:

$$p(\mathbf{z}|m_1) > p(\mathbf{z}|m_2)$$

$$p(\mathbf{z}|m_1) > p(\mathbf{z}|m_3)$$

$$p(\mathbf{z}|m_1) > (1 - \alpha)[p(\mathbf{z}|m_1) + p(\mathbf{z}|m_2) + p(\mathbf{z}|m_3)]$$

Now let us divide both sides of all these inequalities by $p(\mathbf{z}|m_1)$ and use the usual definitions:

$$\Lambda_2(\mathbf{z}) = \frac{p(\mathbf{z}|m_2)}{p(\mathbf{z}|m_1)}$$

$$\Lambda_3(\mathbf{z}) = \frac{p(\mathbf{z}|m_3)}{p(\mathbf{z}|m_1)}$$

Then $\mathbf{Z}_1$ can be expressed as

$$\Lambda_2(\mathbf{z}) < 1$$

$$\Lambda_3(\mathbf{z}) < 1$$

$$\Lambda_2(\mathbf{z}) + \Lambda_3(\mathbf{z}) < \frac{\alpha}{1 - \alpha}$$

In a similar manner, we can show that $\mathbf{Z}_2$ is given by

$$\Lambda_2(\mathbf{z}) > 1$$

$$\Lambda_2(\mathbf{z}) > \Lambda_3(\mathbf{z})$$

$$\frac{\alpha}{1 - \alpha}\Lambda_2(\mathbf{z}) - \Lambda_3(\mathbf{z}) > 1$$

while $\mathbf{Z}_3$ is defined by

$$\Lambda_3(\mathbf{z}) > 1$$

$$\Lambda_3(\mathbf{z}) > \Lambda_2(\mathbf{z})$$

$$-\Lambda_2(\mathbf{z}) + \frac{\alpha}{1 - \alpha}\Lambda_3(\mathbf{z}) > 1$$

The decision regions are shown graphically in Fig. 5.4-2. For $\alpha > \frac{2}{3}$,

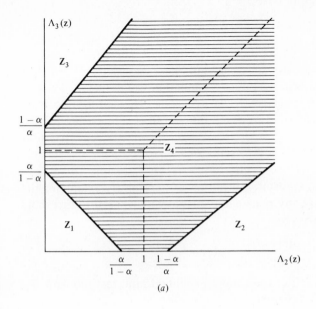

(a)

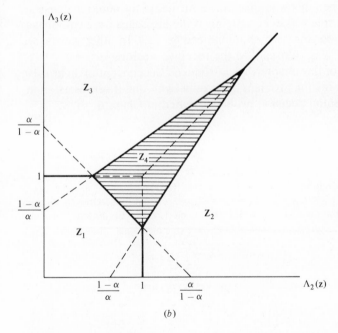

(b)

Figure 5.4-2 Decision regions for ternary erasure problem (a) with $0 < \alpha < \frac{1}{2}$; (b) with $\frac{1}{2} < \alpha < \frac{2}{3}$.

the erasure region Z_4 vanishes. The standard probability of error boundaries are marked on Fig. 5.4-2 for reference.

5.5 SUMMARY

We have now seen how the results derived in Chaps. 3 and 4 for binary decisions can be extended to the case of multiple messages and multiple decisions. We began with a general Bayes formulation which included essentially all possible combinations of costs and decisions. This led to a decision rule that said to select the decision d_j which minimized

$$\sum_{k=1}^{K} C_{jk} P\{m_k\} p(\mathbf{z}|m_k)$$

Although this is a nice-looking result, it is not always useful. By examining the $K = J = 3$ case, we saw that any reasonable cost assignment led to threshold tests on the likelihood ratios

$$\Lambda_2(z) = \frac{p(\mathbf{z}|m_2)}{p(\mathbf{z}|m_1)} \qquad \Lambda_3(\mathbf{z}) = \frac{p(\mathbf{z}|m_3)}{p(\mathbf{z}|m_1)}$$

This is clearly a generalization of the simple likelihood-ratio test of Chap. 3.

By specializing the cost assignment to probability-of-error costs, we were able to derive a much simpler decision rule. Here we just had to pick d_j to maximize $p(\mathbf{z}|m_j)P\{m_j\}$. When this was specialized further to the additive gaussian noise case, the decision rule was even simpler. If the messages were equiprobable, we would select d_j for the j which minimized $\|\mathbf{z} - \mathbf{s}_j\|$. In other words, we selected the signal that was "closest" to the received vector.

In the final section of this chapter, we introduced the concept of an erasure decision. This is an interesting problem in its own right, and it serves as an introduction to the sequential decision problem treated in Chap. 6.

5.6 PROBLEMS

5.6-1 Consider the ternary decision problem with $P\{m_1\} = P\{m_2\} = P\{m_3\} = \frac{1}{3}$ and the Bayes costs: $C_{11} = C_{22} = C_{33} = 0$, $C_{12} = C_{32} = 2$, $C_{13} = C_{21} = C_{31} = 3$ and $C_{23} = 1$. Draw a diagram showing the decision regions in the $\Lambda_2(\mathbf{z}) = p(\mathbf{z}|m_2)/p(\mathbf{z}|m_1)$ and $\Lambda_3(\mathbf{z}) = p(\mathbf{z}|m_3)/p(\mathbf{z}|m_1)$ plane.

5.6-2 Consider the quadriary decision problem with a two-dimensional observation space $\mathbf{z} = [z_1 \quad z_2]^T$ in which

$$m_i: \mathbf{z} = \mathbf{s}_i + \mathbf{v} \qquad i = 1, 2, 3, 4$$

Here $\mathbf{v}$ is a gaussian random vector with $E\{\mathbf{v}\} = \mathbf{0}$ and var $\{\mathbf{v}\} = \mathbf{I}$ and

$$\mathbf{s}_1 = \begin{bmatrix} -1 \\ -1 \end{bmatrix} \qquad \mathbf{s}_2 = \begin{bmatrix} -1 \\ 1 \end{bmatrix} \qquad \mathbf{s}_3 = \begin{bmatrix} 1 \\ -1 \end{bmatrix} \quad \text{and} \quad \mathbf{s}_4 = \begin{bmatrix} 1 \\ 1 \end{bmatrix}$$

Assume all messages are equally likely and $C_{ii} = 0$ for all $i = 1, 2, 3, 4$ and $C_{ij} = 1$ for $i \neq j$. Show the decision regions in the observation space. Find an expression for the probability of error.

5.6-3 The observations for a ternary decision problem are given by

$$m_i: \mathbf{z} = \mathbf{s}_i + \mathbf{v}$$

where **v** is a zero-mean gaussian random vector with var $\{\mathbf{v}\} = \sigma^2\mathbf{I}$. The Bayes costs are given by $C_{ii} = 0$, $i = 1, 2, 3$, and $C_{ij} = 1$, $i \neq j$. The three messages are equally probable. The signal s_i are orthogonal and of equal energy so that

$$\mathbf{s}_i^T\mathbf{s}_j = \begin{cases} E^2 & i = j \\ 0 & i \neq j \end{cases}$$

Develop the optimal decision rule and find union bound for the total probability of error in terms of σ^2 and E^2.

5.6-4 Consider an erasure decision problem with K messages and $K + 1$ decisions. The following cost assignment is made:

$$C_{jk} = \begin{cases} 1 & \text{if } j \neq K + 1, j \neq k \\ 0 & \text{if } j = k \\ \alpha & \text{if } j = K + 1 \end{cases}$$

Let $P\{m_k\} = 1/K$. What is the largest value that α can have such that Z_{K+1} is not null?

5.6-5 Consider the ternary decision problem where the decision space is the same as the message space and

$$P\{m_1\} = \tfrac{1}{2} \qquad P\{m_2\} = \tfrac{1}{3} \qquad P\{m_3\} = \tfrac{1}{6}$$

A cost function is assigned where

$$C_{kj} = (k - j)^2$$

The observation space is a set of four discrete points z_1, z_2, z_3, and z_4. Define the transition probability: $P\{z_i \text{ observed} | m_k\} = P_{i,k}$. These are shown in the matrix

$$\mathbf{P} = \begin{bmatrix} 0.6 & 0.1 & 0.2 \\ 0.1 & 0.6 & 0.1 \\ 0.2 & 0.1 & 0.6 \\ 0.1 & 0.2 & 0.1 \end{bmatrix}$$

Derive the minimum cost rule.

5.6-6 The signal set for a ternary ($K = 3$) decision problem consists of the three waveforms shown in Fig. 5.6-1. The observation is

$$z(t) = s(t) + n(t) \qquad 0 \leq t \leq T = 4$$

where $n(t)$ is zero-mean white gaussian noise with power spectral density V. Assume that the three messages are equiprobable.

(a) For minimum probability of error, show that the decision can be based on variables

$$y_k = \int_0^T s_k(t)z(t)\, dt \qquad k = 1, 2, 3$$

(b) Draw a block diagram of a matched-filter receiver that computes y_k and then makes a decision.

(c) Use the Gram-Schmidt orthogonalization procedure to show that only a two-dimensional statistic is needed to make an optimal decision and draw a block diagram of a matched-filter receiver that uses this statistic.

(d) Find a one-filter receiver that minimizes probability of error.

Hint: Sketch the signal space picture of your answer to c.

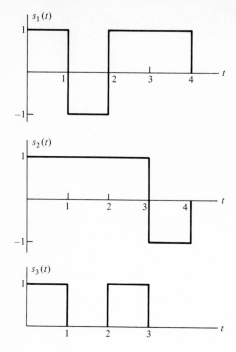

Figure 5.6-1 Waveforms for problem 5.6-6.

5.6-7 Suppose that we have a problem with three messages and six decisions of the form

$$d_1 = \text{message } m_1 \text{ sent}$$

$$d_2 = \text{message } m_2 \text{ sent}$$

$$d_3 = \text{message } m_3 \text{ sent}$$

$$d_4 = \text{either message } m_2 \text{ or } m_3 \text{ sent}$$

$$d_5 = \text{either message } m_1 \text{ or } m_3 \text{ sent}$$

$$d_6 = \text{either message } m_1 \text{ or } m_2 \text{ sent}$$

Let the messages be equally likely. If we choose a cost matrix of the form

$$\mathbf{C} = \begin{bmatrix} 0 & 1 & 1 \\ 1 & 0 & 1 \\ 1 & 1 & 0 \\ \alpha & 0 & 0 \\ 0 & \alpha & 0 \\ 0 & 0 & \alpha \end{bmatrix}$$

Find the decision regions in the Λ_2, Λ_3 plane for $\alpha = 1, 3$, and 5. What happens as α becomes large.

5.6-8 Consider the quadriary decision problem with

$$m_k: p(z|m_k) = \frac{1}{\sqrt{2\pi}} e^{-(z - k\mu)^2/2}$$

Find the probability-of-error decision rule for $\mu = 1$ and $\mu = 2$. Determine the exact probability of error for each case and the bounds given by Eqs. (5.3-10) and (5.3-13). Assume that the messages are equally likely.

5.6-9 Consider the quadriary decision problem with

$$m_1: p(z|m_1) = \frac{1}{\sqrt{2\pi}} e^{-z^2/2}$$

$$m_2: p(z|m_2) = \frac{1}{2\sqrt{2\pi}} e^{-z^2/8}$$

$$m_3: p(z|m_3) = \frac{1}{\sqrt{2\pi}} e^{-(z-1)^2/2}$$

$$m_4: p(z|m_4) = \frac{1}{2\sqrt{2\pi}} e^{-(z-1)^2/8}$$

Find the decision rule using the probability-of-error criterion and assuming equally likely messages.

5.6-10 Suppose you have to design a communication system that can send one of eight messages every T seconds. All that you have available to construct your system is an oscillator whose output phase and amplitude you can vary. Thus, your signals are of the form

$$s_k(t) = A_k \cos(\omega t - \phi_k)$$

where A_k must be less than or equal to $\sqrt{8/T}$. Using a signal-space approach and assuming additive white gaussian noise of unit power spectral density, bound or approximate the probability of error when you use the following signal sets:

(a) $A_k = \sqrt{\dfrac{8}{T}}$ $\phi_k = \dfrac{\pi k}{4}$

(b) $A_1 = A_5 = \sqrt{\dfrac{8}{T}}$ $A_2 = A_6 = \sqrt{\dfrac{2}{T}}$ $A_3 = A_7 = -\sqrt{\dfrac{2}{T}}$

$A_4 = A_8 = -\sqrt{\dfrac{8}{T}}$

$$\phi_k = \begin{cases} 0 & k = 1, 2, 3, 4 \\ \dfrac{\pi}{2} & k = 5, 6, 7, 8 \end{cases}$$

(c) The best other signal set you can devise

CHAPTER
SIX

SEQUENTIAL DECISION THEORY

In all the decision problems discussed so far, it has always been assumed that the number of observations was fixed. For example, in the vector observation case, the receiver was to make a decision based on the l random variables that comprised the vector. Sometimes, however, it is possible for the receiver to take additional observations before making a final decision. For example, in a radar problem the transmitter sends pulses and the receiver observes the return until it is satisfied that it has enough information to make a decision. A doctor examining a patient can frequently think of additional tests to do on a patient before making a final diagnosis. In some communication problems, the receiver who is uncertain about a particular message can ask to have it retransmitted. In all these cases, more observations can be taken, but there is always a "cost" associated with the additional observations. The objective, therefore, is to take the additional observations only if they are needed.

The process just described can be modeled as one where in each time unit the receiver either decides one of the final decisions or it decides to take another observation. For the binary case, this means that the decision space has three points d_1 and d_2 as in the fixed-observation case and d_3 which means "take another observation." The class of problems where the receiver can continue to take observations is referred to as *sequential decision* problems.

To establish groundwork for analyzing sequential problems, we shall first consider the fixed-observation problem where the receiver has the option of making a "don't know" or "erasure" decision. This will correspond to the decision to take another sample in the sequential case. The effect of both assigning a Bayes cost to the observation and attempting to keep error probabilities below given thresholds will be analyzed. These results will be applied to the sequential problem and the resulting average number of observations will be computed.

One of the reasons for using a sequential decision method is that it requires, on the average, fewer samples to achieve the same probability-of-error performance as compared with a fixed-sample test. This means that a higher average data rate can be achieved by the use of sequential decision theory.

There are two major drawbacks of sequential decision theory. First, the interval between decisions is no longer fixed so that one must generally make use of buffers to transform data to a fixed rate. Second, the sequential decision method requires an error-free feedback or reverse channel so that the receiver can tell the transmitter when a decision has been reached. This requirement does not pose a serious limitation in some applications such as satellite communications where one can place a high-power transmitter at the ground station for the feedback transmission.

6.1 BINARY ERASURE CRITERIA

In this section we shall examine the binary decision problem where the observer tries to decide which of two messages was sent but is permitted to announce that he cannot make a decision. Such a model is obviously useful in the sequential decision problem, and it has other applications as well. For example, in communications, an error-correcting code can be used either to reconstruct erased symbols or to correct erroneous ones. Usually, it can fill in twice as many blanks as the number of errors it can correct. Thus, when deciding each letter of a code word, an erasure may be more desirable than a *hard decision* which might be in error.

Regardless of the application, the observer will be required to keep the number of "don't know" or "erasure" decisions to a minimum, and we shall look at two different formulations to ensure that this is done. The first has already been encountered in Chap. 5 and involves the assessment of a Bayes cost for the erasure decision. It requires the existence of known probabilities of the two messages $P\{m_1\}$ and $P\{m_2\}$.

For simplicity, we shall assume that the cost of being correct is 0 and that the cost of being wrong is 1. If the cost of an erasure when the message is m_k is α_k then the cost matrix $\mathbf{C}$ is

$$\mathbf{C} = \begin{bmatrix} 0 & 1 \\ 1 & 0 \\ \alpha_1 & \alpha_2 \end{bmatrix} \tag{6.1-1}$$

The expected Bayes cost will then be

$$B = P\{d_2|m_1\}P\{m_1\} + P\{d_1|m_2\}P\{m_2\} + \alpha_1 P\{d_3|m_1\}P\{m_1\}$$
$$+ \alpha_2 P\{d_3|m_2\} P\{m_2\}$$

If the conditional probabilities are written as integrals, and if it is assumed that α_1 and α_2 are each less than $\frac{1}{2}$, it is easy to show that the decision regions should be

$$\mathbf{Z}_1 = \left\{ \mathbf{z}: \Lambda(\mathbf{z}) < \frac{\alpha_1}{1-\alpha_2} \frac{P\{m_1\}}{P\{m_2\}} \right\}$$

$$\mathbf{Z}_2 = \left\{ \mathbf{z}: \Lambda(\mathbf{z}) > \frac{1-\alpha_1}{\alpha_2} \frac{P\{m_1\}}{P\{m_2\}} \right\} \qquad (6.1\text{-}2)$$

$$\mathbf{Z}_3 = \left\{ \mathbf{z}: \frac{\alpha_1}{1-\alpha_2} \frac{P\{m_1\}}{P\{m_2\}} \le \Lambda(\mathbf{z}) \le \frac{1-\alpha_1}{\alpha_2} \frac{P\{m_1\}}{P\{m_2\}} \right\}$$

The ratio $P\{m_2\}/P\{m_1\}$ can be viewed as the likelihood ratio before an observation is taken. If it is denoted Λ_0, then the decision rules can be written in the simplified form

$$\mathbf{Z}_1 = \{\mathbf{z}: \Lambda_0 \, \Lambda(\mathbf{z}) < T_1\}$$

$$\mathbf{Z}_2 = \{\mathbf{z}: \Lambda_0 \, \Lambda(\mathbf{z}) > T_2\} \qquad (6.1\text{-}3)$$

$$\mathbf{Z}_3 = \{\mathbf{z}: T_1 \le \Lambda_0 \, \Lambda(\mathbf{z}) \le T_2\}$$

where the two thresholds are

$$T_2 = \frac{1-\alpha_1}{\alpha_2}$$

$$\qquad (6.1\text{-}4)$$

$$T_1 = \frac{.\alpha_1}{1-\alpha_2}$$

Clearly, T_1 is smaller than 1 and T_2 is larger than 1. Thus, assigning a Bayes cost to an erasure decision leads to a likelihood-ratio test involving two thresholds.

An alternative formulation of the erasure problem based on the philosophy of the Neyman-Pearson test gives a similar result. The Neyman-Pearson decision design criterion introduced in Chap. 3 permitted the design of a decision rule that guaranteed that one of the two probabilities of error, say, $P\{d_1|m_2\}$, in a binary decision problem would not exceed a given threshold:

$$P\{d_1|m_2\} \le \alpha_0$$

The other probability of error $P\{d_2|m_1\}$, however, took on whatever value the minimization process gave it. Although this approach does have application, it may not always be satisfactory. Sometimes it may be necessary to ensure that both error probabilities are below given thresholds:

$$P\{d_1|m_2\} < \alpha_1$$

$$P\{d_2|m_1\} < \alpha_2 \qquad (6.1\text{-}5)$$

As might be expected, this is not always possible if the decision space is restricted to the two elements d_1 and d_2. That is, there may be no partitioning of $\mathbf{Z}$ into $\mathbf{Z}_1$ and $\mathbf{Z}_2$ that satisfies Eq. (6.1-5). However, there are cases where it is possible. One example of this latter situation is presented in the following example.

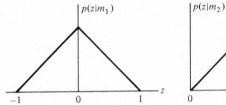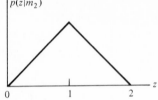

Figure 6.1-1 Probability densities for Example 6.1-1.

Example 6.1-1 For the density functions given in Fig. 6.1-1, find a binary decision rule that satisfies

$$P\{d_1|m_2\} \leq 0.05$$

$$P\{d_2|m_1\} \leq 0.3$$

A binary Neyman-Pearson approach to assure the first inequality yields a threshold test on z of

$$z \underset{d_1}{\overset{d_2}{\gtrless}} 0.316$$

For the second inequality, the test is

$$z \underset{d_1}{\overset{d_2}{\gtrless}} 0.225$$

If the threshold in the first inequality is reduced, then $P\{d_1|m_2\}$ will be smaller than 0.05. Similarly, if the second threshold is larger than 0.225, then $P\{d_2|m_1\}$ will be less than 0.3. Thus, any threshold test of the form

$$z \underset{d_1}{\overset{d_2}{\gtrless}} T$$

where T is between 0.225 and 0.316 will satisfy the constraints. The overlap between the two constraints is indicated in Fig. 6.1-2.

In general, for a given value of α_1, there is a range of values of α_2 such that the pair is *consistent* with the two-element decision space $\{d_1, d_2\}$; that is, the

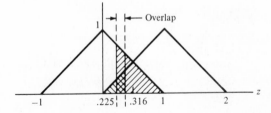

Figure 6.1-2 Solution for Example 6.1-1.

two constraints can be met with only two possible decisions. We shall establish a condition on α_1 and α_2 that will determine if they are a consistent pair. From the derivation of the Neyman-Pearson test, it is clear that the inequality constraint on $P\{d_1|m_2\}$ can be met with a threshold test of the form

$$\Lambda(z) \underset{d_1}{\overset{d_2}{\gtrless}} T(\alpha_1) \qquad (6.1\text{-}6)$$

where the threshold $T(\alpha_1)$ is defined implicitly by the equation

$$\int_0^{T(\alpha_1)} p(\Lambda|m_2) \, d\Lambda = \alpha_1 \qquad (6.1\text{-}7)$$

If this test yields a $P\{d_2|m_1\}$ that is smaller than α_2, then α_1 and α_2 are consistent. Since $p(\Lambda|m_2)$ is always positive, $T(\alpha_1)$ is a monotonically nondecreasing function of α_1. In other words, as α_1 gets larger, $T(\alpha_1)$ gets larger. If the decision rule in Eq. (6.1-6) is used, then $P\{d_2|m_1\}$ will be

$$P\{d_2|m_1\} = \int_{T(\alpha_1)}^{\infty} p(\Lambda|m_1) \, d\Lambda = A(\alpha_1) \qquad (6.1\text{-}8)$$

Since $T(\alpha_1)$ gets large as α_1 gets large, $A(\alpha_1)$ will get small as α_1 gets large. Therefore, if α_2 is larger than $A(\alpha_1)$, the threshold test in Eq. (6.1-6) will satisfy both constraints and α_1 and α_2 are consistent. However, if α_2 is smaller than $A(\alpha_1)$, there is no way to meet the requirement unless the decision space is enlarged. We shall call such a pair *inconsistent*.

The following example presents an inconsistent set of α_1 and α_2.

Example 6.1-2 For the density functions of Fig. 6.1-1, find a binary decision rule that satisfies

$$P\{d_1|m_2\} \leq 0.05$$

$$P\{d_2|m_1\} \leq 0.05$$

The threshold test for the first inequality is the same as in the previous example

$$z \underset{d_1}{\overset{d_2}{\gtrless}} 0.315$$

but for the second inequality, it becomes

$$z \underset{d_1}{\overset{d_2}{\gtrless}} 0.684$$

If the first threshold is *increased*, $P\{d_1|m_2\}$ will exceed 0.05, and if the second is *decreased*, $P\{d_2|m_1\}$ will exceed 0.05. Thus, there is no way to rec-

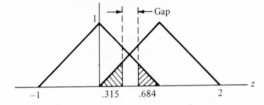

Figure 6.1-3 Solution for Example 6.1-2.

oncile these tests and still satisfy the constraints. The gap between the thresholds indicated in Fig. 6.1-3 cannot be assigned to either decision region.

The preceding example suggests a way of accommodating incompatible tests. If a third decision variable d_3 is introduced and treated as an erasure symbol, then the gap between $\mathbf{Z}_1$ and $\mathbf{Z}_2$ can be filled with decision region $\mathbf{Z}_3$. As noted previously, erasures are not as desirable as hard decisions and should be used only if needed. This leads to the following decision criterion.

Fixed-error-rate criterion For a binary-message ternary decision problem, the two *error* probabilities are constrained to satisfy

$$P\{d_1|m_2\} \leq \alpha_1$$

$$P\{d_2|m_1\} \leq \alpha_2$$

and the *correct decision* probabilities $P\{d_1|m_1\}$ and $P\{d_2|m_2\}$ are to be maximized.

We shall now show that a fixed-error-rate test gives a decision rule of the same form as the Bayes test. That is, it is a two-threshold test on the likelihood ratio. If α_1 and α_2 are large enough, in particular, if α_2 is bigger than $A(\alpha_1)$, then the erasure symbol will not be used and the problem reduces to a simple Neyman-Pearson test. However, if α_2 is smaller than $A(\alpha_1)$, the erasure must be used. We want to show that the resulting test will still depend only on the likelihood ratio

$$\Lambda(\mathbf{z}) = \frac{p(\mathbf{z}|m_2)}{p(\mathbf{z}|m_1)} \tag{6.1-9}$$

but will now require two thresholds to delimit the decision regions.

The problem of maximizing two dependent functions simultaneously is somewhat ill-formed. Thus, instead we shall maximize the sum $P\{d_1|m_1\} + \beta P\{d_2|m_2\}$ and show that if α_1 and α_2 are inconsistent, the decision rule does not depend on β. To maximize the sum subject to the constraints, we use Lagrange multipliers on the constraints and maximize the quantity

$$F = P\{d_1|m_1\} + \beta P\{d_2|m_2\} - \lambda_1[P\{d_1|m_2\} - \alpha_1]$$

$$- \lambda_2[P\{d_2|m_1\} - \alpha_2] \tag{6.1-10}$$

The multipliers λ_1 and λ_2 are to be selected to meet the constraints. Writing the probabilities as integrals and combining terms, F becomes

$$F = \int_{Z_1} [p(\mathbf{z}|m_1) - \lambda_1 p(\mathbf{z}|m_2)] \ d\mathbf{z} + \int_{Z_2} [\beta p(\mathbf{z}|m_2) \\ - \lambda_2 p(\mathbf{z}|m_1)] \ d\mathbf{z} + \lambda_1 \alpha_1 + \lambda_2 \alpha_2$$

If possible, the way to maximize F is to assign to $\mathbf{Z}_1$ *all* those $\mathbf{z}$ for which the integrand of the first integral is positive and to assign to $\mathbf{Z}_2$ *all* those z for which the second integrand is positive. It may not be possible to do this and still satisfy the constraints. However, if it is, the decision regions $\mathbf{Z}_1$ and $\mathbf{Z}_2$ become

$$\mathbf{Z}_1 = \{\mathbf{z}: p(\mathbf{z}|m_1) > \lambda_1 p(\mathbf{z}|m_2)\}$$

$$\mathbf{Z}_2 = \{\mathbf{z}: \beta p(\mathbf{z}|m_2) > \lambda_2 p(\mathbf{z}|m_1)\}$$

or, stated as functions of the likelihood ratio,

$$\mathbf{Z}_1 = \{\mathbf{z}: \Lambda(\mathbf{z}) < T_1\}$$

$$\mathbf{Z}_2 = \{\mathbf{z}: \Lambda(\mathbf{z}) > T_2\} \qquad (6.1\text{-}11)$$

$$\mathbf{Z}_3 = \{\mathbf{z}: T_1 \leq \Lambda(\mathbf{z}) \leq T_2\}$$

where T_1 is $1/\lambda_1$ and T_2 is λ_2/β.

This will be a possible decision rule if and only if T_1 is smaller than T_2. But λ_1 and λ_2 must be selected to meet the constraints on the error probabilities. Therefore the thresholds and hence the λ's are defined by

$$\int_0^{T_1} p(\Lambda|m_2) \ d\Lambda = \alpha_1$$

$$\int_{T_2}^{\infty} p(\Lambda|m_1) \ d\Lambda = \alpha_2 \qquad (6.1\text{-}12)$$

But since α_1 and α_2 are inconsistent, T_1 must be smaller than T_2. Note that the equations which define the thresholds do not depend on β, and we have shown that the fixed-error-rate criterion decision rule must be of the form of Eqs. (6.1-11). Therefore the structure of the fixed-error-rate test is the same as that of the minimum Bayes cost test.

6.2 SEQUENTIAL BAYES TESTS

As was pointed out in Sec. 6.1, one important application of erasure tests is the sequential problem where the observer can elect to take additional observations. Since generally there is a cost associated with the observation process, it is desirable to minimize the number of observations. For those cases where it is possible to measure the observation cost on the same scale as the error cost and where the unconditional message probabilities are known, the sequential problem can be stated as the minimum Bayes cost problem. In this section, we shall show that for an interesting subclass of these problems, this results in a sequential threshold test with fixed thresholds that terminates with probability one.

At each stage of the decision process, the decision regions should be selected so as to minimize the expected cost. But at each stage the decision problem is just the Bayes erasure problem of Sec. 6.1 and the optimal decision rules are threshold tests on the likelihood ratio. Since we are dealing with a Bayes test where the unconditional message probabilities are known, we shall define

$$\Lambda_0 = \frac{P\{m_2\}}{1 - P\{m_2\}} = \frac{P\{m_2\}}{P\{m_1\}} \tag{6.2-1}$$

and write the decision regions after i observations as

$$\mathbf{Z}_1 = \{\Lambda_0\Lambda(\mathbf{z}) < T_1(i)\} \tag{6.2-2a}$$

$$\mathbf{Z}_2 = \{\Lambda_0\Lambda(\mathbf{z}) > T_2(i)\} \tag{6.2-2b}$$

$$\mathbf{Z}_3 = \{T_1(i) \le \Lambda_0\Lambda(\mathbf{z}) \le T_2(i)\}$$

In general, the thresholds are functions of i and quite difficult to compute. However, if successive observations are independent and identically distributed and if the cost of observation does not vary with i, then it turns out that the optimal thresholds are constant.

To show that the thresholds are constant, consider first the decision of whether or not to take the first observation. If the cost matrix is

$$\mathbf{C} = \begin{bmatrix} 0 & C_{12} \\ C_{21} & 0 \\ \beta & \beta \end{bmatrix}$$

then each observation costs β and it may be cheaper to take no observations at all. If no observations are taken, the observer must decide solely on the basis of the a priori probabilities $P\{m_1\}$ and $P\{m_2\}$. For notational simplicity, we shall let P_0 denote $P\{m_2\}$, the probability of m_2 before any observations. Then the expected cost of making decision d_1 without taking any observations will be $P_0 C_{12}$, and the cost of d_2 will be $(1 - P_0)C_{21}$. If either of these is lower than the expected cost associated with taking an observation, no observations should be taken. The cost associated with the observation is the sum of the actual observation cost β and the additional expected Bayes cost after the observation has been made. This latter cost, which we shall write $B(P_0)$, is a function of the a priori probability P_0. As in Chap. 3, since it is the cost of the optimal decision rule, it will be a convex $\cap$ function of P_0. The costs of each of the three possible decisions are plotted in Fig. 6.2-1. If P_0 is smaller than T_1', it will be cheaper to take no observations and just announce d_1. If P_0 is larger than T_2', decision d_2 is cheapest. If P_0 is between T_1' and T_2', the optimum decision is d_3 and an observation should be taken.

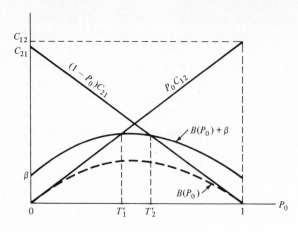

Figure 6.2-1 Costs associated with first observation decision.

The thresholds T_1' and T_2' are defined implicitly by

$$(1 - T_2')C_{21} = B(T_2') + \beta \tag{6.2-3a}$$

$$T_1'C_{12} = B(T_1') + \beta \tag{6.2-3b}$$

In general, Eqs. (6.2-3) are not easy to solve. However, we are concerned here only with the form of the test, and so we shall be content to know that solutions exist. Then, using the definition of Λ_0 given in (6.2-1), the decision regions can be stated as *likelihood-ratio* tests on Λ_0:

$$Z_1 = \left\{ \Lambda_0 < \frac{T_1'}{1 - T_1'} = T_1 \right\} \tag{6.2-4a}$$

$$Z_2 = \left\{ \Lambda_0 > \frac{T_2'}{1 - T_2'} = T_2 \right\} \tag{6.2-4b}$$

$$Z_3 = \{ T_1 \leq \Lambda_0 \leq T_2 \} \tag{6.2-4c}$$

This follows since Λ_0 is a monotonically increasing function of P_0.

The observer who does elect to take an observation will base the next decision on the likelihood ratio Λ_1 where

$$\Lambda_1 = \frac{p(z_1 | m_2)}{p(z_1 | m_1)} \Lambda_0$$

$$= \frac{P\{m_2 | z_1\}}{P\{m_1 | z_1\}}$$

Using P_1 to denote $P\{m_2 | z_1\}$, that is, the probability of m_2 after one observation, this ratio can be written as

$$\Lambda_1 = \frac{P_1}{1 - P_1} \tag{6.2-5}$$

Note the obvious similarity to Eq. (6.2-1). As in the previous decision, the observer has three options, and each has an associated cost. If the observer decides d_1, the cost will be β for the observation and C_{12} if the message was actually m_2. But now the probability that the message was m_2 is P_1 and the expected cost of d_1 is $\beta + P_1 C_{12}$. Similarly, the expected cost of d_2 is $\beta + (1 - P_1)C_{21}$. If the observer opts for an additional observation, 2β will have been "paid" in observation costs and a "final" decision must still be made.

Since we are assuming that all observations are independent and identically distributed, the decision process will have the same statistics as it had before the first observation. The only difference is that the a priori probability of m_2 is P_1 instead of P_0. Thus the additional expected cost of reaching a final decision after the second observation will be $B(P_1)$, and the total expected cost of d_3 is $2\beta + B(P_1)$. Figure 6.2-2 shows a plot of the three cost functions. Clearly the shapes of the curves are identical to those in Fig. 6.2-1 except they are all biased up by the addition of β. The thresholds T_1' and T_2' are the same as those given in Eq. (6.2-3), and the decision regions will be

$$Z_1 = \{z_1\colon \Lambda_1(z_1) < T_1\} \tag{6.2-6a}$$

$$Z_2 = \{z_1\colon \Lambda_1(z_1) < T_2\} \tag{6.2-6b}$$

$$Z_3 = \{z_1\colon T_1 \le \Lambda_1(z_1) \le T_2\} \tag{6.2-6c}$$

These same arguments can be repeated at each stage of the decision process. Therefore the same thresholds will be used for each i, and we have shown that average Bayes cost for independent identically distributed observations is minimized by a fixed-threshold sequential test.

In order for a sequential test to be useful, it must eventually terminate. Al-

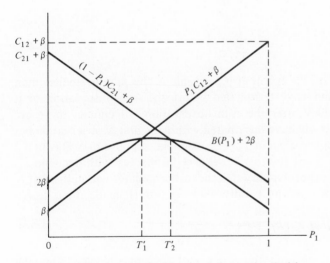

Figure 6.2-2 Costs associated with second observation decision.

though it would be surprising if it did not, it is worthwhile to prove that it will since the proof sheds considerable light on the sequential process. In particular, the following theorem will be proved.

Theorem 6.2-1 A fixed threshold sequential test with independent, identically distributed observations terminates with probability one. In other words, if the test requires I observations before reaching a final decision, then

$$\lim_{N \to \infty} P\{I \le N\} = 1$$

The proof will be presented only for the case when the message is m_1. The other half of the proof is essentially the same and is left as an exercise. The decision regions for fixed-threshold test can be defined in terms of the natural logarithm of the likelihood ratio. Therefore, $\mathbf{Z}_1$ and $\mathbf{Z}_2$ are

$$\mathbf{Z}_1 = \{\mathbf{z}: \ln \Lambda(\mathbf{z}) < \ln T_1\} \qquad (6.2\text{-}7a)$$

$$\mathbf{Z}_2 = \{\mathbf{z}: \ln \Lambda(\mathbf{z}) > \ln T_2\} \qquad (6.2\text{-}7b)$$

But for N observations the likelihood ratio $\Lambda(\mathbf{z})$ is just

$$\Lambda(\mathbf{z}) = \frac{p(\mathbf{z}|m_2)}{p(\mathbf{z}|m_1)}$$

$$= \prod_{i=1}^{N} \frac{p(z_i|m_2)}{p(z_i|m_1)}$$

and $\ln \Lambda(\mathbf{z})$ is the sum of independent random variables

$$\ln \Lambda(\mathbf{z}) = \sum_{i=1}^{N} \ln \frac{p(z_i|m_2)}{p(z_i|m_1)}$$

$$= \sum_{i=1}^{N} f(z_i) \qquad (6.2\text{-}8)$$

The proof is based on the fact that if for some N this sum is smaller than $\ln T_1$, the test will either have terminated before the Nth observation or it will terminate immediately after the Nth observation. Of course, there are some $\mathbf{z}$ for which the test will have terminated within the first N observation but for which the sum is not less than $\ln T_1$. For example, suppose $\ln \Lambda(\mathbf{z})$ is $\ln T_2$; this is larger than $\ln T_1$, but the test obviously terminates with decision d_2. However, it is true that the probability that the test terminates within the first N observations is larger than the probability that the sum is smaller than $\ln T_1$:

$$P\{I \le N\} \ge P\{\sum_{i=1}^{N} f(z_i) < \ln T_1\} \qquad (6.2\text{-}9)$$

Now, since the z_i are independent, the variance of the sum is N var $\{f\}$ and the mean is $N\bar{f}$. Thus, if $\bar{f}$ is negative, it will be possible to show that the sum will eventually be smaller an ln T_1 with probability one.

To show that $\bar{f}$ is negative, we shall make use of the inequality

$$\ln x \leq x - 1 \qquad (6.2\text{-}10)$$

where the equality holds only if $x = 1$. This inequality is illustrated in Fig. 6.2-3.

The expected value of $f(z)$ when the message is m_1 is given by

$$\bar{f} = \int_{-\infty}^{\infty} \ln \frac{p(z|m_2)}{p(z|m_1)} \, p(z|m_1) \, dz$$

Using Eq. (6.2-10), this becomes

$$\bar{f} \leq \int_{-\infty}^{\infty} \left[\frac{p(z|m_2)}{p(z|m_1)} - 1 \right] p(z|m_1) \, dz$$

$$\leq \int_{-\infty}^{\infty} p(z|m_2) \, dz - \int_{-\infty}^{\infty} p(z|m_1) \, dz = 0 \qquad (6.2\text{-}11)$$

The equality only holds if the argument of the logarithm is 1. If there is *any* measurable difference between $p(z|m_2)$ and $p(z|m_1)$, $\bar{f}$ will be strictly negative.

The final steps of the proof requires the Chebyshev inequality, which states that for any random variable x,

$$P\{|x - \bar{x}| > \epsilon\} < \frac{\text{var} \{x\}}{\epsilon^2} \qquad (6.2\text{-}12)$$

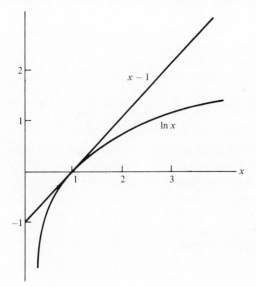

Figure 6.2-3 Bound on ln x.

To put the bound in a form that can use this inequality, Eq. (6.2-9) is rewritten as

$$P\{I \leq N\} \geq 1 - P\{\sum_{i=1}^{N} f(z_i) > \ln T_1\}$$

$$\geq 1 - P\{|\sum_{i=1}^{N} f(z_i) - N\bar{f}| > \ln T_1 - N\bar{f}\}$$

Then, applying Eq. (6.2-12), the probability that the test terminates within N observations can be bounded by

$$P\{I \leq N\} \geq 1 - \frac{N \text{ var } \{f\}}{(\ln T_1 - N\bar{f})^2}$$

Finally, for N large enough, the $N\bar{f}$ will predominate the denominator so that

$$P\{I \leq N\} \geq 1 - \frac{\text{var } \{f\}}{N\bar{f}^2} \tag{6.2-13}$$

Therefore, for large enough N, the probability that the test terminates gets arbitrarily close to 1.

6.3 THE WALD SEQUENTIAL TEST

There are many situations for which a priori probabilities and/or error costs are unknown. In these cases it is possible to formulate a sequential test based on the fixed-error-rate criterion described in Sec. 6.1. This approach was first described by Abraham Wald (1947), and the resulting test has become known as the *Wald sequential test*. In this section it will be shown that the optimal form of such a test matches that of the Bayes cost test and is a fixed-threshold likelihood-ratio test. The best thresholds for the test are quite difficult to calculate, but approximate expressions will be found.

The fixed-error-rate criterion, when applied to sequential tests, has two objectives: first to ensure that the error probabilities satisfy

$$P\{d_1|m_2\} \leq \alpha_1 \tag{6.3-1}$$

$$P\{d_2|m_1\} \leq \alpha_2$$

and second to minimize the number of observations required. Clearly the way to achieve these objectives is to continue to take observations only until the inequalities in Eq. (6.3-1) are satisfied. Section 6.1 implies that this will be achieved by using a likelihood-ratio test at each stage of the process with the thresholds matched to Eq. (6.3-1). Furthermore, since the equivalent Bayes test in Sec. 6.2 resulted in a *fixed*-threshold test, it is reasonable to assume that here the thresholds will not vary either. In fact, for independent, identically distributed observations, both these statements are true and their proof is surprisingly simple.

In Sec. 6.2, we proved that average Bayes cost is minimized by a fixed-threshold sequential test. This statement is true regardless of the values of a priori probabilities, error costs, or observation costs. In other words, if I represents the last observation to be taken, then the expression

$$B = P_0 C_{12} P\{d_1|m_2\} + (1 - P_0)C_{21}P\{d_2|m_1\}$$
$$+ (1 - P_0)\beta E\{I|m_1\} + P_0\beta E\{I|m_2\} \qquad (6.3\text{-}2)$$

is minimized for any set of $\{P_0, C_{12}, C_{21}, \beta\}$ by a fixed-threshold test.

For the fixed-error-rate case, we wish to minimize $E\{I|m_1\}$ and $E\{I|m_2\}$ subject to constraints on $P\{d_1|m_2\}$ and $P\{d_2|m_1\}$. As in Sec. 6.1, one way to minimize two related quantities is to minimize a linear combination of them and show that the result does not depend on the value of the coefficients. Since the minimization is to be carried out subject to constraints, the total quantity to be minimized is

$$F = AE\{I|m_1\} + BE\{I|m_2\} + \lambda_1[P\{d_1|m_2\} - \alpha_1]$$
$$+ \lambda_2[P\{d_2|m_1\} - \alpha_2] \qquad (6.3\text{-}3)$$

Once the quantity is minimized, the Lagrange multipliers λ_1 and λ_2 are selected to satisfy the constraints. Since all the coefficients in Eq. (6.3-3) will be positive (otherwise F would be minimized by maximizing the number of observations or an error probability), there will always be a set of $\{P_0, C_{12}, C_{21}, \beta\}$ such that, except for a constant, F will be the same as B in Eq. (6.3-2). Thus since B is minimized by a fixed-threshold test, F will be too.

Once the test is found to have fixed thresholds, the next step is to determine the values of the thresholds. Unfortunately exact expressions are very difficult to obtain. However, it is possible to find simple expressions that are good approximations to the optimal thresholds. The approximation follows from the fact that if the test terminates with decision d_1, then the likelihood ratio must be less than or equal to T_1. In other words, for all $\mathbf{z} \in \mathbf{Z}_1$,

$$p(\mathbf{z}|m_2) \le T_1 p(\mathbf{z}|m_1) \qquad (6.3\text{-}4)$$

Since Eq. (6.3-4) holds for all $\mathbf{z} \in \mathbf{Z}_1$, it can be integrated over $\mathbf{Z}_1$ to obtain

$$P\{d_1|m_2\} \le T_1[1 - P\{d_2|m_1\}] \qquad (6.3\text{-}5)$$

where $P\{d_1|m_1\}$ has been replaced by $1 - P\{d_2|m_1\}$. Similarly, for all $\mathbf{z} \in \mathbf{Z}_2$, $\Lambda(\mathbf{z})$ is greater than T_2 and

$$p(\mathbf{z}|m_2) \ge T_2 p(\mathbf{z}|m_1) \qquad (6.3\text{-}6)$$

Integrating this over all $\mathbf{Z}_2$ and replacing the integrals with error-probability expressions, it becomes

$$1 - P\{d_1|m_2\} \ge T_2 P\{d_2|m_1\} \qquad (6.3\text{-}7)$$

By themselves, Eq. (6.3-5) and Eq. (6.3-7) cannot be used to upper bound the error probabilities. However, note that if the test terminates with the likelihood ratio exactly on the threshold, both Eqs. (6.3-4) and (6.3-5) will be equalities. This, in turn, implies that if the likelihood ratio ends on a threshold, the inequalities in Eqs. (6.3-5) and (6.3-7) are equalities and the resulting error probabilities are

$$P\{d_1|m_2\} = T_1 \frac{T_2 - 1}{T_2 - T_1} \tag{6.3-8a}$$

$$P\{d_2|m_1\} = \frac{1 - T_1}{T_2 - T_1} \tag{6.3-8b}$$

Therefore, selecting T_1 and T_2 so that the right-hand sides of Eq. (6.3-8) are α_1 and α_2 would satisfy the design constraint given in Eq. (6.3-1). The appropriate thresholds would be

$$T_1 = \frac{\alpha_1}{1 - \alpha_2} \tag{6.3-9a}$$

$$T_2 = \frac{1 - \alpha_1}{\alpha_2} \tag{6.3-9b}$$

Of course, the restriction that the test terminate on a boundary is quite severe. However, if the test requires a large number of trials, the final value of $\Lambda(\mathbf{z})$ usually will not differ greatly from the thresholds. Thus, the thresholds in Eq. (6.3-9) will at least give probabilities of error that are approximated by α_1 and α_2.

Consider the following example of the Wald test.

Example 6.3-1 A binary symmetric channel, shown in Fig. 6.3-1, is used in a sequential decision problem. The channel is defined by the transition probabilities

$$P\{z = 1|m_1\} = P\{z = 2|m_2\} = 1 - p$$
$$P\{z = 2|m_1\} = P\{z = 1|m_2\} = p$$

For $p = \frac{1}{4}$, the test which guarantees

$$P\{d_1|m_2\} \leq \alpha_1$$
$$P\{d_2|m_1\} \leq \alpha_2$$

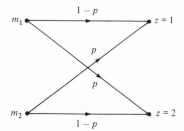

Figure 6.3-1 Binary symmetric channel.

is to be found and the resulting actual error probabilities are to be computed for the two cases

$$\alpha_1 = \alpha_2 = 0.1 \tag{1}$$

$$\alpha_1 = \tfrac{7}{71} \qquad \alpha_2 = \tfrac{8}{71} \tag{2}$$

According to Eq. (6.3-1), the thresholds for (1) should be

$$T_1 = \tfrac{1}{9}$$

$$T_2 = 9$$

The likelihood ratio actually will be a ratio of probabilities. For some observation $\mathbf{z}$, let $h(\mathbf{z})$ be the number of z_i that equal 1; then the ratio will be

$$\Lambda(\mathbf{z}) = \frac{P\{\mathbf{z}|m_2\}}{P\{\mathbf{z}|m_1\}}$$

$$= \frac{p^{h(\mathbf{z})} \, (1-p)^{l-h(\mathbf{z})}}{p^{l-h(\mathbf{z})} \, (1-p)^{h(\mathbf{z})}}$$

$$= \left(\frac{1-p}{p}\right)^{l-2h(\mathbf{z})}$$

Since $p = \tfrac{1}{4}$, the ratio becomes

$$\Lambda(\mathbf{z}) = 3^{l-2h(\mathbf{z})}$$

Then, taking base 3 logarithms, the decision regions are

$$\mathbf{Z}_1 = \{\mathbf{z}: l - 2h(\mathbf{z}) \leq -2\}$$

$$\mathbf{Z}_2 = \{\mathbf{z}: l - 2h(\mathbf{z}) \geq 2\}$$

In other words, as soon as there are two fewer 1s than 2s, the observer decides d_1; and if two more 1s than 2s are observed, the decision is d_2.

Since the test is always satisfied with equality, the error probabilities are exactly 0.1. For the second case, the thresholds will be

$$T_1 = \tfrac{1}{9}$$

$$T_2 = 8$$

However, since the likelihood ratio has values only of the form 3^n for positive or negative integer values of n, this test will yield exactly the same results as the test with thresholds $\tfrac{1}{9}$ and 9. Therefore, both the actual error probabilities will be 0.1. Thus, $P\{d_1|m_2\}$ will be larger than α_1, and $P\{d_2|m_1\}$ will be smaller than α_2. In other words, the approximate thresholds do not ensure that the fixed-error-rate criterion will be met—only that it will be approximated.

For the continuous case, usually it is not easy to find the actual error probabilities, as the following example illustrates.

Example 6.3-2 For the gaussian observations

$$z_i = s + n_i$$

with independent, zero-mean noise variables with variance v, let the signal s be zero for message m_1 and a for message m_2. What sequential test guarantees

$$P\{d_1|m_2\} \leq \alpha_1$$
$$P\{d_2|m_1\} \leq \alpha_2$$

As before, the approximate thresholds will be used. They are

$$T_1 = \frac{\alpha_1}{1 - \alpha_2}$$

$$T_2 = \frac{1 - \alpha_1}{\alpha_2}$$

The test which defines Z_1 is to determine if $\Lambda(\mathbf{z})$ is smaller than T_1. Since the observations are gaussian, this reduces to

$$\exp\left[\frac{1}{2}v\left(\sum_{i=1}^{I} z_i^2 - \sum_{i=1}^{I} (z_i - a)^2\right)\right] \underset{d_2 \text{ or } d_3}{\overset{d_1}{\lessgtr}} T_1$$

Combining terms, taking natural logarithms, and simplifying yields

$$\sum_{i=1}^{I} z_i \underset{d_2 \text{ or } d_3}{\overset{d_1}{\lessgtr}} \frac{Ia}{2} + \frac{v}{a}\ln T_1$$

Similarly, the test which defines Z_2 can be written as

$$\sum_{i=1}^{I} z_i \underset{d_1 \text{ or } d_3}{\overset{d_2}{\gtrless}} \frac{Ia}{2} + \frac{v}{a}\ln T_2$$

These two tests are illustrated in Fig. 6.3-2. Note that the performance requirements affect only the initial value of the boundary, not the slope of the line. It should be emphasized that the varying threshold shown in the figure is a test on the sufficient statistic $\Sigma_{i=1}^{I} z_i$, not on the likelihood ratio.

It is interesting to note that if the message is m_1, this sufficient statistic is a zero-mean variance Iv gaussian random variable. Clearly, for large I, the probability that it is less than the lower threshold becomes quite large. When the message is m_2, the statistic has mean Ia. Since the upper threshold increases as $Ia/2$, the probability that the statistic becomes large enough to terminate the test is large.

For a given value of a, the noise variance v alters only the initial values of the boundaries. The larger v, the further apart the two boundaries and the longer the test will take. Therefore, for larger v, the terminal value of

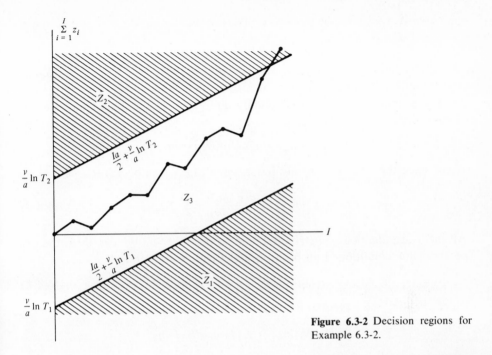

Figure 6.3-2 Decision regions for Example 6.3-2.

$\Lambda(\mathbf{z})$ will be closer to the boundary and the actual error probabilities will more nearly approximate those in Eq. (6.3-8).

6.4 AVERAGE SAMPLE NUMBER

It has been shown that for either a Bayes or fixed-error-rate criterion, the optimal sequential test in the sense of minimizing the expected number of observations is a fixed-threshold likelihood-ratio test. The next obvious question is just how good this test is. In other words, how many observations will it require. In this section a simple approximation to the expected number of observations will be found for the case where the observations are independent.

The first step in deriving this approximation is to show that the expected number of observations I, when conditioned on one of the messages, is

$$E\{I|m_k\} = \frac{E\{\ln \Lambda_I|m_k\}}{E\{f|m_k\}} \qquad (6.4\text{-}1)$$

where, it will be recalled, f is a function of a single observation z and is defined as

$$f(z) = \ln \frac{p(z|m_2)}{p(z|m_1)}$$

and where Λ_I is the final value of $\Lambda(\mathbf{z})$. The conditional expectation notation is a shorthand way of writing

$$E\{f|m_k\} = \int_{-\infty}^{\infty} fp(f|m_k)\, df \qquad (6.4\text{-}2)$$

The proof of Eq. (6.4-1) is actually quite simple. The expected value of $\ln \Lambda_I(\mathbf{z})$ is first written as

$$E\{\ln \Lambda_I|m_k\} = E\{E\{\ln \Lambda_I(\mathbf{z})|m_k, I\}\}$$

Then, since the observations are independent, $\ln \Lambda_I$ can be written as

$$\ln \Lambda_I = \sum_{i=1}^{I} \ln \frac{p(z_i|m_2)}{p(z_i|m_1)} = \sum_{i=1}^{I} f(z_i) \qquad (6.4\text{-}3)$$

All the z_i are identically distributed, and so the $f(z_i)$ will be too; thus, the expected value conditioned on both m_k and I can be written as

$$E\{\ln \Lambda_I|m_k, I\} = IE\{f|m_k\} \qquad (6.4\text{-}4)$$

Finally, taking the expected value of Eq. (6.4-4) with respect to I yields

$$E\{\ln \Lambda_I|m_k\} = E\{I|m_k\}\, E\{f|m_k\}$$

which verifies Eq. (6.4-4).

Therefore, to find the expected number of observations, one must compute both $E\{f|m_k\}$ and $E\{\ln \Lambda_I|m_k\}$. The first quantity is not dependent on the nature of the test since it is completely determined by $p(z|m_1)$ and $p(z|m_2)$. The only general statement that can be made about it is that for $k = 1$ it is negative and for $k = 2$ it is positive. The proof of this requires only the inequality

$$\ln x \leq x - 1 \qquad (6.4\text{-}5)$$

and is left as an exercise.

The second quantity $E\{\ln \Lambda_I|m_k\}$ is dependent on the nature of the test. It can be shown that for the fixed-threshold tests described here, it too will be negative for $k = 1$ and positive for $k = 2$. Therefore, the ratio in Eq. (6.4-1) is always positive, as it should be.

An approximation of $E\{\ln \Lambda_I|m_k\}$ can be found in much the same way as the approximation of error probability in the last section. First it is noted that if the test always ends on a boundary, the expected value of $\ln \Lambda_I$ is just

$$E\{\ln \Lambda_I|m_k\} = P\{d_1|m_k\} \ln T_1 + P\{d_2|m_k\} \ln T_2$$

For simplicity, only the $k = 2$ case will be treated in detail. The $k = 1$ case follows in an analogous manner. From Sec. 6.3 it is known that if the test terminates at a boundary, the error probability for m_2 is exactly

$$P\{d_1|m_2\} = \alpha_1 \qquad (6.4\text{-}6)$$

Therefore, the expected value will be

$$E\{\ln \Lambda_I|m_2\} = \alpha_1 \ln T_1 + (1 - \alpha_1) \ln T_2 \qquad (6.4\text{-}7)$$

If the test requires a large number of samples, usually it will terminate quite close to the boundary and Eq. (6.4-7) will be a good approximation to the actual value of $E\{\ln \Lambda_I | m_2\}$. Similarly, the expectation of $\ln \Lambda_I$ conditioned on m_1 can be approximated by

$$E\{\ln \Lambda_I | m_1\} = (1 - \alpha_2) \ln T_1 + \alpha_2 \ln T_2$$

Therefore, the expected number of observations required for a sequential test with thresholds T_1 and T_2 is approximately

$$E\{I | m_k\} = \begin{cases} \dfrac{(1 - \alpha_2) \ln T_1 + \alpha_2 \ln T_2}{E\{f | m_1\}} & \text{for } k = 1 \\[2em] \dfrac{\alpha_1 \ln T_1 + (1 - \alpha_1) \ln T_2}{E\{f | m_2\}} & \text{for } k = 2 \end{cases} \tag{6.4-8}$$

The use of this result is illustrated in the following two examples.

Example 6.4-1 Using the same problem statement as in Example 6.3-1, find the approximate average number of samples required for the two cases.

For (1), the test always terminates on a boundary. Therefore, the expression in Eq. (6.4-8) will be exact. The expected value of f when m_1 is sent is

$$E\{f | m_1\} = \frac{3}{4} \ln \frac{\frac{1}{4}}{\frac{3}{4}} + \frac{1}{4} \ln \frac{\frac{3}{4}}{\frac{1}{4}} = -\frac{1}{2} \ln 3$$

Therefore, the expected number of observations is

$$E\{I | m_1\} = \frac{0.9 \ln \frac{1}{9} + 0.1 \ln 9}{-\frac{1}{2} \ln 3}$$

$$= 3.2$$

By the symmetry, the expected number of observations given m_2 will also be 3.2.

For (2), Eq. (6.4-8) yields approximate expressions of

$$E\{I | m_1\} = 3.123$$

$$E\{I | m_2\} = 3.018$$

However, since this test always ends when the first test does, the actual expected number of observations will be 3.2.

The closeness of the approximation in Eq. (6.4-8) is illustrated in the following example.

Example 6.4-2 For the gaussian case of Example 6.3-2, the observations were

$$z_i = s + n_i$$

where the n_i were independent zero-mean gaussian noise variables with variance v. The signal s was zero for m_1 and a for m_2. The expected value of $f(z)$ is

$$E\{f(z)|m_k\} = E\left\{\ln\frac{p(z|m_2)}{p(z|m_1)}\bigg|m_k\right\}$$

$$= E\left\{\frac{1}{v}\left(za - \frac{a^2}{2}\right)\bigg|m_k\right\}$$

so that
$$E\{f(z)|m_k\} = \begin{cases} \dfrac{-a^2}{2v} & \text{for } k = 1 \\[2ex] \dfrac{a^2}{2v} & \text{for } k = 2 \end{cases}$$

Then, the expected number of observations that will be required is approximated by Eq. (6.4-8) as

$$E\{I|m_k\} = \begin{cases} \dfrac{-2v}{a^2}\left[(1-\alpha_2)\ln\dfrac{\alpha_1}{1-\alpha_2} + \alpha_2\ln\dfrac{1-\alpha_1}{\alpha_2}\right] & \text{for } k = 1 \\[3ex] \dfrac{2v}{a^2}\left[\alpha_1\ln\dfrac{\alpha_1}{1-\alpha_2} + (1-\alpha_1)\ln\dfrac{1-\alpha_1}{\alpha_2}\right] & \text{for } k = 2 \end{cases}$$

Therefore large noise variances and/or small signals require more samples. For $\alpha_1 = \alpha_2 = 0.1$ and $a = 1$, $E\{I|m_1\}$ is given by

$$E\{I|m_1\} = 3.52v$$

For comparison purposes, let us find the number of samples required by a fixed-sample size test to achieve the same error probabilities. By using the results of Chap. 4, we can show that the distance measure for this problem is

$$\delta^2 = \frac{I}{v}$$

Therefore we must select the sample size I and threshold λ to satisfy

$$P\{d_1|m_2\} = Q\left(\frac{\delta}{2} - \frac{\ln\lambda}{\delta}\right) = 0.1$$

$$P\{d_2|m_1\} = Q\left(\frac{\delta}{2} + \frac{\ln\lambda}{\delta}\right) = 0.1$$

Since $Q^{-1}(0.1) = 1.28$, we have

$$\frac{\sqrt{I/v}}{2} - \frac{\ln\lambda}{\sqrt{I/v}} = 1.28$$

$$\frac{\sqrt{I/v}}{2} + \frac{\ln\lambda}{\sqrt{I/v}} = 1.28$$

or $\quad \sqrt{I/v} = 2.56$

Solving for I yields

$$I = 6.55 v$$

Hence we see that the fixed-sample-size test requires almost twice as many samples, on the average, as the sequential test.

6.5 SUMMARY

In this chapter we have analyzed those decision problems where the receiver can elect to take another observation before reaching a final decision. We began by seeing that for a binary erasure problem, the optimal decision rule was a two-threshold test on the likelihood ratio. This was true for both the minimum Bayes cost and the fixed-error-rate criteria.

Building on the results for the erasure criteria, we have shown that the optimal decision rule for both the sequential Bayes test and the Wald test were fixed-threshold tests on the likelihood ratio provided that successive observations were independent, identically distributed, and in the case of the Bayes test, equally costly.

Although no exact expressions were found for the optimal thresholds for either test, it was shown that when the Wald test is designed to ensure that

$$P\{d_1|m_2\} \leq \alpha_1$$
$$P\{d_2|m_1\} \leq \alpha_2$$

the optimal thresholds are approximated by

$$T_1 = \frac{\alpha_1}{1 - \alpha_2}$$

$$T_2 = \frac{1 - \alpha_1}{\alpha_2}$$

In a similar way, it was shown that the average number of observations required for a sequential test with thresholds T_1 and T_2 can be approximated by

$$E\{I|m_k\} = \begin{cases} \dfrac{(1 - \alpha_2) \ln T_1 + \alpha_2 \ln T_2}{E\{f|m_1\}} & \text{for } k = 1 \\[4mm] \dfrac{\alpha_1 \ln T_1 + (1 - \alpha_1) \ln T_2}{E\{f|m_2\}} & \text{for } k = 2 \end{cases}$$

where the function f is

$$f(z) = \ln \frac{p(z|m_2)}{p(z|m_1)}$$

6.6 PROBLEMS

6.6-1 Find the sequential decision rule for

$$m_1: p(z_i|m_1) = \begin{cases} 2z_i & 0 \le z_i \le 1 \\ 0 & \text{otherwise} \end{cases}$$

$$m_2: p(z_i|m_2) = \begin{cases} z_i/2 & 0 \le z_i \le 2 \\ 0 & \text{otherwise} \end{cases}$$

Each observation is independent and identically distributed. Assume $P\{d_1|m_2\} = P\{d_2|m_1\} = 0.1$. Calculate the average sample number; do *not* use the standard formula.

6.6-2 Consider the sequential decision problem with

$$m_1: p(z_i|m_1) = \begin{cases} 2e^{-2z_i} & z_i \ge 0 \\ 0 & \text{otherwise} \end{cases}$$

$$m_2: p(z_i|m_2) = \begin{cases} e^{-z_i} & z_i \ge 0 \\ 0 & \text{otherwise} \end{cases}$$

Here the samples are independent and identically distributed. Let $P\{d_1|m_2\} = P\{d_2|m_1\} = 0.1$ and find the sequential (Wald) decision rule. What is the average sample number if m_1 is true?

6.6-3 Find the sequential decision test if

$$m_1: p(z_i|m_1) = \begin{cases} 2(1-z_i) & 0 \le z_i \le 1 \\ 0 & \text{otherwise} \end{cases}$$

$$m_2: p(z_i|m_2) = \begin{cases} 2z_i & 0 \le z_i \le 1 \\ 0 & \text{otherwise} \end{cases}$$

Let $P\{d_1|m_2\} = P\{d_2|m_1\} = 0.1$. Determine the average sample number if m_2 is true. The observations are independent and identically distributed.

6.6-4 Consider a binary decision problem with

$$m_1: z_i = v_i$$

$$m_2: z_i = av_i$$

where $a > 1$ is a known constant and v_i is a zero-mean gaussian noise process with $E\{v_i v_j\} = \sigma^2 \delta_{ij}$. Find the sequential decision rule if $P\{d_1|m_2\} = P\{d_2|m_1\} = 0.1$. Find the average sample number assuming m_1 is true.

6.6-5 For a sequential decision problem, define $f(z)$ as

$$f(z) = \ln \frac{p(z|m_2)}{p(z|m_1)}$$

Prove that unless $p(z|m_2)$ and $p(z|m_1)$ are identical, the expected value of $f(z)$ conditioned on m_2 is strictly positive and the expected value conditioned on m_1 is strictly negative.

6.6-6 For the erasure channel shown in Fig. 6.6-1 the crossover possiblilities are

$$P\{z = 1|m_1\} = P\{z = 2|m_2\} = 0.4$$

$$P\{z = 2|m_1\} = P\{z = 1|m_2\} = 0.1$$

$$P\{z = 3|m_1\} = P\{z = 3|m_2\} = 0.5$$

(*a*) Find the optimum sequential test that guarantees

$$P\{d_1|m_2\} \le 0.05$$

$$P\{d_2|m_1\} \le 0.10$$

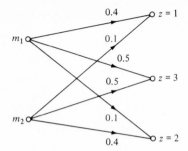

$z = 1$

m_1

0.4

0.1

0.5

0.5

$z = 3$

0.1

m_2

0.4

$z = 2$ **Figure 6.6-1** Problem 6.6-6.

(b) Find the actual error probabilities for the preceding test.

(c) Find the average number of observations required for each message.

6.6-7 For a binary sequential decision problem, the observations are

$$z_i = s_k + n_i \qquad i = 1, 2, \ldots$$

where $s_1 = 0$ and $s_2 = 1$. The n_i are statistically independent zero-mean, unit-variance gaussian random variables. Design tests to ensure that

$$P\{d_1 | m_2\} \leq 0.01$$

$$P\{d_2 | m_1\} \leq 0.01$$

using

(a) a fixed number of observations.

(b) a fixed-threshold sequential test.

6.6-8 For a binary decision problem, the observations are sequences of 1s and 2s and

$$P\{z_i = 1 | m_1\} = 1$$

$$P\{z_i = 1 | m_2\} = \tfrac{1}{2} \qquad i = 1, 2, \ldots, I$$

$$P\{z_i = 2 | m_2\} = \tfrac{1}{2}$$

Bayes costs of $C_{11} = C_{22} = 0$ and $C_{12} = C_{21} = 1$ are assigned, and $P\{m_1\} = P\{m_2\} = \tfrac{1}{2}$.

(a) Find the decision rule to minimize the Bayes risk if $I = 1$. What is the minimum risk?

(b) Find the decision rule as a function of $I = 1, 2, \ldots$ and the associated minimum Bayes risk.

(c) Suppose it costs $\tfrac{1}{12}$ to take each sample (i.e., for each sample taken $\tfrac{1}{12}$ is added to the cost). How many samples should be taken to minimize the overall cost (normal Bayes risk plus cost of sampling) for a fixed number of samples?

(d) Now assume we wish to form a sequential test to minimize the overall cost in which we make one of three decisions after each sample: d_1, d_2, or d_3 (take another sample). Discuss how this test would be formulated and the resultant expected number of samples.

6.6-9 In a binary decision problem, suppose

$$p(z_i | m_1) = \begin{cases} 1 & 0 \leq z_i \leq 1 \\ 0 & \text{otherwise} \end{cases} \qquad i = 1, 2, \ldots$$

$$p(z_i | m_2) = \begin{cases} 1 & \tfrac{1}{2} \leq z \leq \tfrac{3}{2} \\ 0 & \text{otherwise} \end{cases} \qquad i = 1, 2, \ldots$$

$$P\{m_1\} = P\{m_2\}$$

(a) How many observations are required to guarantee

$$P_e \leq 0.001$$

(b) Using Wald's sequential ratio test, what is the expected number of observations needed for

$$P\{d_1|m_2\} \le 0.001 \quad \text{and} \quad P\{d_2|m_1\} < 0.001$$

(c) Prove that a fixed-threshold test will always terminate if the message is m_2.

6.6-10 Consider a binary decision problem with

$$m_1: p(z_i|m_1) = \frac{1}{\sqrt{2\pi}} \, e^{-z_i^2/2}$$

$$i = 1, 2, \ldots, I$$

$$m_2: p(z_i|m_2) = \frac{1}{\sqrt{2\pi}} \, e^{-(z_i-1)^2/2}$$

(a) What is the smallest value of I such that $P\{d_1|m_2\}$ and $P\{d_2|m_1\}$ are both less than or equal to 0.1?

(b) If we used a sequential test, what would be the average value of I to achieve the same performance?

COMPOSITE AND NONPARAMETRIC
DECISION THEORY

In the preceding chapters, we have examined a number of different types of decision problems. In each of these cases, however, it has been assumed that the conditional probability density of the observation $p(\mathbf{z}|m_k)$ was completely known for all k. In this chapter we shall examine a number of methods for handling decision problems when this assumption is not satisfied.

In Sec. 7.1, we shall treat decision problems in which the form of the conditional density $p(\mathbf{z}|m_k)$ is known but there are certain unknown parameters. For example, $p(\mathbf{z}|m_k)$ may be gaussian, but the mean or variance may be unspecified. Such problems are referred to as *composite decision problems*.

Sections 7.2 and 7.3 treat another class of problems known as *nonparametric decision problems*. In nonparametric decision problems, the conditional probability density $p(\mathbf{z}|m_k)$ is assumed to be unknown except for general properties such as symmetry. In Sec. 7.2, a nonparametric decision rule known as the *sign test* is developed, which depends only on the sign of the observations. The *Wilcoxon test* presented in Sec. 7.3 is another nonparametric test which makes use of the relative ordering or rank of the observations.

7.1 COMPOSITE DECISIONS

As noted in the preceding introductory comments, in composite decision problems we assume that the form of the conditional probability density $p(\mathbf{z}|m_k)$ is known but that there are unknown parametric values. Hence we shall write this conditional density as $p(\mathbf{z}|m_k, \boldsymbol{\theta}_k)$ where $\boldsymbol{\theta}_k$ is a vector of unknown parameter values which are selected from a set $\boldsymbol{\Omega}_k$. For simplicity in our developments, the following treatment will be restricted to binary decision problems; the extension of the concepts to multiple decisions is direct.

As an example, consider $p(z|m_k, \boldsymbol{\theta})$ given by

$$p(z|m_k, \boldsymbol{\theta}) = \frac{1}{\sqrt{2\pi\theta_2}} \exp \frac{-(z-\theta_1)^2}{2\theta_2}$$

Here θ_1 is the mean and θ_2 is the variance. A possible choice for Ω might be the positive half plane or some subset of it. For example, we might know that θ_1 is positive or that it lies between 5 and 10.

In this chapter we shall examine three approaches for treating composite decision problems:

1. The decision rule is independent of the unknown parameters θ_1 and θ_2.
2. The parameter vector θ_k is a random variable with a known probability density function on Ω_k.
3. The parameter vector θ_k is an unknown deterministic constant.

The first approach is not really a method for treating composite decision problems but is rather a recognition that some composite problems may be handled by our standard procedures.

Consider, for example, a decision problem with

$$p(z|m_1, \sigma^2) = \frac{1}{\sqrt{2\pi}\,\sigma} \exp \frac{-z^2}{2\sigma^2} \qquad (7.1\text{-}1)$$

$$p(z|m_2, \sigma^2) = \frac{1}{\sqrt{2\pi}\,\sigma} \exp \frac{-(z-1)^2}{2\sigma^2} \qquad (7.1\text{-}2)$$

Here we assume that the variance is unknown but the same for $k = 1$ and $k = 2$. The likelihood-ratio test for this problem becomes

$$\frac{p(z|m_2, \sigma^2)}{p(z|m_1, \sigma^2)} = \exp \frac{-[(z-1)^2 - z^2]}{2\sigma^2} \overset{d_2}{\underset{d_1}{\gtrless}} T$$

or
$$z \overset{d_2}{\underset{d_1}{\gtrless}} \sigma^2 \ln T + \tfrac{1}{2}$$

Now if $T = 1$, then the test is independent of σ^2 and the fact that σ^2 is unknown will not affect the test. However, the value of σ^2 will have an effect on the error probabilities $P\{d_1|m_2\}$ and $P\{d_2|m_1\}$ and on the Bayes cost. Note that because $P\{d_1|m_2\}$ does depend on σ^2, a Neyman-Pearson test for the preceding problem will *not* be independent of σ^2. Also if $T \neq 1$, then the test is *not* independent of σ^2. Hence we note that whether a given test will be independent of an unknown parameter depends, not only on the parameter, but also on the type of test.

As another example, suppose that we have a decision problem defined by

$$p(z|m_1) = \frac{1}{\sqrt{2\pi}} e^{-z^2/2} \qquad (7.1\text{-}3)$$

$$p(z|m_2, \mu) = \frac{1}{\sqrt{2\pi}} e^{-(z-\mu)^2/2} \qquad (7.1\text{-}4)$$

Here μ is assumed to be unknown. The likelihood-ratio test for this problem is given by

$$\mu z \underset{d_1}{\overset{d_2}{\gtrless}} \frac{\mu^2}{2} + \ln T$$

There is no Bayes test which is independent of the unknown parameter μ. Let us try a Neyman-Pearson test. Suppose that $\mu > 0$; then the test becomes

$$z \underset{d_1}{\overset{d_2}{\gtrless}} \frac{\mu}{2} + \frac{1}{\mu} \ln T = T'$$

The probability of false alarm is given by

$$\int_{T'}^{\infty} \frac{1}{\sqrt{2\pi}} e^{-z^2/2} \, dz = Q(T') = \alpha_0$$

Since T' can be determined without knowledge of μ, the Neyman-Pearson test is independent of μ if it is known that $\mu > 0$. Note, however, that a Neyman-Pearson test cannot be determined for the problem if μ is not restricted to be either positive or negative.

When the Neyman-Pearson test is independent of a parameter θ, we say that the test is *uniformly most powerful* (UMP) with respect to that parameter. For the problem of Eqs. (7.1-3) and (7.1-4), the Neyman-Pearson test is UMP for μ if $\mu > 0$ or if $\mu < 0$ but is not UMP if μ can be either positive or negative. If one cannot find a suitable test which is independent of the unknown parameters, then it is necessary to make use of one of the other two approaches.

Let us consider first the case where the unknown parameter vector θ_k is a random variable with a known probability density $p(\theta_k)$. Since

$$p(\mathbf{z}|m_k) = \int_{\Omega_k} p(\mathbf{z}|m_k, \theta_k) p(\theta_k) \, d\theta_k \tag{7.1-5}$$

the likelihood ratio might be generalized to

$$\Lambda_g(\mathbf{z}) = \frac{\int_{\Omega_2} p(\mathbf{z}|m_2, \theta_2) p(\theta_2) \, d\theta_2}{\int_{\Omega_1} p(\mathbf{z}|m_1, \theta_1) p(\theta_1) \, d\theta_1} \tag{7.1-6}$$

It is easy to show that this result is, in fact, the correct answer. The Bayes criterion will be used for the derivation; any other criterion in Chap. 3 could also be used.

The Bayes risk is given by

$$
\begin{aligned}
B = E\{C_{jk}\} &= C_{11}P\{d_1, m_1\} + C_{12}P\{d_1, m_2\} + C_{21}P\{d_2, m_1\} + C_{22}P\{d_2, m_2\} \\
&= C_{11}P\{d_1|m_1\}P\{m_1\} + C_{21}P\{d_2|m_1\}P\{m_1\} \\
&\quad + C_{12}P\{d_1|m_2\}P\{m_2\} + C_{22}P\{d_2|m_2\}P\{m_2\}
\end{aligned}
\tag{7.1-7}
$$

Now making use of the fact that

$$P\{d_1|m_1\} = 1 - P\{d_2|m_1\}$$
$$P\{d_1|m_2\} = 1 - P\{d_2|m_2\}$$

we can write Eq. (7.1-7) as

$$B = C_{11} + (C_{21} - C_{11})P\{m_1\}P\{d_2|m_1\} + C_{12}$$
$$- (C_{12} - C_{22})P\{m_2\}P\{d_2|m_2\} \tag{7.1-8}$$

The required probabilities of error can be written in terms of $\mathbf{Z}_2$ as

$$P\{d_2|m_1\} = \int_{\mathbf{Z}_2} p(\mathbf{z}|m_1)\,d\mathbf{z} = \int_{\mathbf{Z}_2}\int_{\Omega_1} p(\mathbf{z}|m_1, \boldsymbol{\theta}_1)p(\boldsymbol{\theta}_1)\,d\boldsymbol{\theta}_1\,d\mathbf{z} \tag{7.1-9}$$

$$P\{d_2|m_2\} = \int_{\mathbf{Z}_2} p(\mathbf{z}|m_2)\,d\mathbf{z} = \int_{\mathbf{Z}_2}\int_{\Omega_2} p(\mathbf{z}|m_2, \boldsymbol{\theta}_2)p(\boldsymbol{\theta}_2)\,d\boldsymbol{\theta}_2\,d\mathbf{z} \tag{7.1-10}$$

Therefore the Bayes risk becomes

$$B = C_{11} + C_{12} + \int_{\mathbf{Z}_2}\left[(C_{21} - C_{11})P\{m_1\}\int_{\Omega_1} p(\mathbf{z}|m_1, \boldsymbol{\theta}_1)p(\boldsymbol{\theta}_1)\,d\boldsymbol{\theta}_1\right.$$
$$\left. - (C_{12} - C_{22})P\{m_2\}\int_{\Omega_2} p(\mathbf{z}|m_2, \boldsymbol{\theta}_2)p(\boldsymbol{\theta}_2)\,d\boldsymbol{\theta}_2\right]\,d\mathbf{z} \tag{7.1-11}$$

We should put into $\mathbf{Z}_2$ the values of $\mathbf{z}$ for which the integrand is negative, that is, those values of $\mathbf{z}$ for which

$$(C_{12} - C_{22})P\{m_2\}\int_{\Omega_2} p(\mathbf{z}|m_2, \boldsymbol{\theta}_2)p(\boldsymbol{\theta}_2)\,d\boldsymbol{\theta}_2 >$$

$$(C_{21} - C_{11})P\{m_1\}\int_{\Omega_1} p(\mathbf{z}|m_1, \boldsymbol{\theta}_1)p(\boldsymbol{\theta}_1)\,d\boldsymbol{\theta}_1$$

Assuming, as before, that $(C_{12} - C_{22}) > 0$, we can put the decision rule into the following form:

$$\frac{\int_{\Omega_2} p(\mathbf{z}|m_2, \boldsymbol{\theta}_2)p(\boldsymbol{\theta}_2)\,d\boldsymbol{\theta}_2}{\int_{\Omega_1} p(\mathbf{z}|m_1, \boldsymbol{\theta}_1)p(\boldsymbol{\theta}_1)\,d\boldsymbol{\theta}_1} \underset{d_1}{\overset{d_2}{\gtrless}} \frac{P\{m_1\}}{P\{m_2\}}\frac{(C_{21} - C_{11})}{(C_{12} - C_{22})} \tag{7.1-12}$$

as implied by Eq. (7.1-6). If there are no unknown parameters in the conditional density of $\mathbf{z}$ given m_1 or m_2, then the denominator or numerator of Eq. (7.1-12) reduces to its usual form.

Example 7.1-1 Suppose that the conditional densities of z are given by

$$p(z|m_1) = \frac{1}{\sqrt{2\pi}}\,e^{-z^2/2}$$

$$p(z|m_2, \mu) = \frac{1}{\sqrt{2\pi}}\,e^{-(z-\mu)^2/2}$$

Here μ is a random variable with the following probability density:

$$p(\mu) = \frac{1}{\sqrt{2\pi}\,\sigma} \, e^{-\mu^2/2\sigma^2}$$

The generalized likelihood ratio becomes

$$\Lambda_g(z) = \frac{\int_{-\infty}^{\infty} (1/\sqrt{2\pi}) \, e^{-(z-\mu)^2/2} \, (1/\sqrt{2\pi}\,\sigma) \, e^{-\mu^2/2\sigma^2} \, d\mu}{1/\sqrt{2\pi} \, e^{-z^2/2}}$$

$$= \frac{(1/\sqrt{2\pi}\,\sigma) \int_{-\infty}^{\infty} \exp\{-[\sigma^2 z^2 - 2\sigma^2 z\mu + (\sigma^2+1)\mu^2]/2\sigma^2\} \, d\mu}{e^{-z^2/2}}$$

To simplify, note that the exponent inside the integral is a quadratic expression in μ. Therefore, a little manipulation can make it look like a gaussian density, and it will be easy to integrate. Since the coefficient of μ^2 is $(\sigma^2 + 1)$ and the coefficient of μ is $-2\sigma^2 z$, the term that is missing to make it a perfect square is $\sigma^2 z^2/(\sigma^2 + 1)$. Adding and subtracting this term in the exponent and factoring some constant terms out of the integral, the generalized likelihood ratio is

$$\Lambda_g(z) = \frac{\exp\left[-z^2/(\sigma^2+1)\right]}{\exp\left(-z^2/2\right)} \int_{-\infty}^{\infty} \frac{1}{\sqrt{2\pi}\,\sigma}$$

$$\times \exp\left\{\frac{-[(\sigma^2+1)\mu^2 - 2\sigma^2 z\mu + \sigma^2 z^2/(\sigma^2+1)]}{2\sigma^2}\right\} d\mu$$

If the variable of integration is changed to $\sqrt{\sigma^2 + 1}\,\mu$, a factor of $1/\sqrt{\sigma^2 + 1}$ is brought out and the integral is 1. Therefore, the likelihood-ratio test is

$$\frac{(1/\sqrt{\sigma^2+1}) \exp\left[-z^2/(\sigma^2+1)\right]}{e^{-z^2/2}} \underset{d_1}{\overset{d_2}{\gtrless}} T$$

or

$$z^2 \underset{d_1}{\overset{d_2}{\gtrless}} 2\frac{\sigma^2+1}{\sigma^2} \ln\left(\sqrt{\sigma^2+1}\,T\right)$$

Example 7.1-2 Consider a composite decision problem with

$$p(z|m_2) = \frac{1}{\sqrt{2\pi}} \, e^{-z^2/2}$$

$$p(z|m_1, \theta_1) = \frac{1}{\sqrt{2\pi}} \, e^{-(z-\theta_1)^2/2}$$

where

$$p(\theta_1) = \begin{cases} 1 & \text{if } 1 \le \theta_1 \le 2 \\ 0 & \text{otherwise} \end{cases}$$

For this problem, the generalized likelihood ratio is

$$\Lambda_g(z) = \frac{(1/\sqrt{2\pi}) \, e^{-z^2/2}}{\int_1^2 (1/\sqrt{2\pi}) \, e^{-(z-\theta_1)^2/2} \, d\theta_1}$$

If we make the change of variables $\lambda = -z + \theta_1$, then the denominator can be written as

$$\int_1^2 \frac{1}{\sqrt{2\pi}} e^{-(z-\theta_1)^2/2} \, d\theta_1 = \int_{1-z}^{2-z} \frac{1}{\sqrt{2\pi}} e^{-\lambda^2/2} \, d\lambda = Q(1-z) - Q(2-z)$$

The generalized likelihood-ratio test is therefore

$$\lambda(z) = \frac{(1/\sqrt{2\pi})\, e^{-z^2/2}}{Q(1-z) - Q(2-z)} \mathop{\gtrless}_{d_1}^{d_2} T$$

For any given value of z, we can easily determine the correct decision by the use of the Table B.1 in App. B.

The preceding approach to composite decision problems has two major faults. First, the method generally leads to complicated integral expressions for the likelihood ratio which are hard to evaluate. Second, there are many problems for which we have no knowledge of a probability density function for the unknown parameters. Our third approach allows us to handle these problems and generally leads to a simpler mechanization.

When the parameter vector $\boldsymbol{\theta}_k$ is an unknown constant with no known probability density function, we shall select $\boldsymbol{\theta}_k$ so as to maximize $p(z|m_k, \boldsymbol{\theta}_k)$. Then our likelihood-ratio test takes the following form:

$$\Lambda(\mathbf{z}) = \frac{\displaystyle\max_{\boldsymbol{\theta}_2 \in \Omega_2} p(\mathbf{z}|m_2, \boldsymbol{\theta}_2)}{\displaystyle\max_{\boldsymbol{\theta}_1 \in \Omega_1} p(\mathbf{z}|m_1, \boldsymbol{\theta}_1)} \mathop{\gtrless}_{d_1}^{d_2} T \tag{7.1-13}$$

In Chap. 8 we shall show that this is equivalent to replacing the missing parameters with their maximum-likelihood estimates.

Example 7.1-3 To illustrate this approach, let us consider again the problem of Example 7.1-2 where

$$p(z|m_2) = \frac{1}{\sqrt{2\pi}} e^{-z^2/2}$$

$$p(z|m_1, \theta_1) = \frac{1}{\sqrt{2\pi}} e^{-(z-\theta_1)^2/2}$$

Here, however, we assume that θ_1 is an unknown constant. The value of θ_1 which maximizes $p(z|m_1, \theta_1)$ is z so that

$$\max_{\theta_1 \in \Omega_1} p(z|m_1, \theta_1) = \frac{1}{\sqrt{2\pi}} e^{-(z-z)^2/2} = \frac{1}{\sqrt{2\pi}}$$

The likelihood-ratio test is therefore

$$\frac{(1/\sqrt{2\pi})\,e^{-z^2/2}}{1/\sqrt{2\pi}} = e^{-z^2/2} \overset{d_2}{\underset{d_1}{\gtrless}} T$$

or

$$z^2 \overset{d_2}{\underset{d_1}{\gtrless}} -2\ln T$$

$$|z| \overset{d_2}{\underset{d_1}{\gtrless}} \sqrt{-2\ln T}$$

Here we see that the test reduces to a simple form with minimal effort.

Suppose that we take a set of I independent identically distributed observations of the preceding form. Then we must select θ_1 in order to maximize

$$p(z_1, z_2, \ldots, z_I | m_1, \theta_1) = \left(\frac{1}{\sqrt{2\pi}}\right)^I \exp -\frac{1}{2}\sum_{i=1}^{I}(z_i - \theta_1)^2$$

The value of θ_1 that maximizes this will also maximize its logarithm. If we take the derivative of the logarithm with respect to θ_1 and set the result to zero, after a small amount of algebra, we obtain

$$\sum_{i=1}^{I}(z_i - \theta_1) = 0$$

or

$$\theta_1 = \frac{1}{I}\sum_{i=1}^{I} z_i$$

Substituting this value back into $p(z|m_1, \theta_1)$ yields

$$\max_{\theta_1 \in \Omega_1} p(z|m_1, \theta_1) = \left(\frac{1}{\sqrt{2\pi}}\right)^I \exp\left[-\frac{1}{2}\sum_{i=1}^{I}\left(z_i - \frac{1}{I}\sum_{j=1}^{I} z_j\right)^2\right]$$

We should recognize θ_1 as the sample mean. Our approach says to replace the unknown mean by the sample mean. The likelihood-ratio test becomes

$$\frac{\exp\left(-\frac{1}{2}\sum_{i=1}^{I} z_i^2\right)}{\exp\left[-\frac{1}{2}\sum_{i=1}^{I}\left(z_i - \frac{1}{I}\sum_{j=1}^{I} z_j\right)^2\right]} = \exp\left[-\frac{1}{2I}\left(\sum_{i=1}^{I} z_i\right)^2\right] \overset{d_2}{\underset{d_1}{\gtrless}} T$$

Taking the logarithms on both sides and multiplying by -2 yields

$$\frac{1}{I}\left(\sum_{i=1}^{I} z_i\right)^2 \overset{d_2}{\underset{d_1}{\gtrless}} -2\ln T$$

or

$$\frac{1}{\sqrt{I}}\left|\sum_{i=1}^{I} z_i\right| \underset{d_1}{\overset{d_2}{\gtrless}} \sqrt{-2 \ln T}$$

In some composite problems, it may be necessary to combine all three approaches. Some unknown parameters may not affect the test, other unknown parameters may have known probability densities and the integral form should be used for these. Other parameters may be unknown constants and should be treated by the third approach.

7.2 SIGN TEST

In this and the following section, we shall treat two of the simple nonparametric decision rules. Although much has been written about the theory of nonparametric statistics, our discussion will be quite brief. The interested reader should consult the literature † for additional discussion of the problem. In nonparametric problems, the conditional density $p(\mathbf{z}|m_k)$ is unknown except for general properties such as a symmetry or positive mean.

Nonparametric decision rules are an important tool for many practical problems for several reasons. First, the density function for the observation noise often is unknown or known only approximately. Nonparametric decision rules provide a method for handling these problems.

Second, since nonparametric decision rules are based on the Neyman-Pearson criterion, they will yield a constant false-alarm probability for any $p(\mathbf{z}|m_1)$ which satisfies the basic assumptions of the problem. For example, if one restricts $p(\mathbf{z}|m_1)$ only to be zero mean, then the resulting nonparametric test will have $P\{d_2|m_1\} = \alpha_0$ for all $p(\mathbf{z}|m_1)$ which have zero mean. This is generally not true for parametric decision rules. Suppose that we have designed a decision rule based on a zero-mean gaussian density function for $p(z|m_1)$. Then if $p(z|m_1)$ is a zero-mean laplacian density, $P\{d_2|m_1\}$ may not be less than or equal to α_0. However, the nonparametric decision rule will maintain a constant $P\{d_2|m_1\}$ for any $p(z|m_1)$ with zero mean.

Finally, nonparametric decision rules are easy to implement. For example, we know that for the standard additive gaussian noise problem the decision takes the form

$$\sum_{i=1}^{I} z_i \underset{d_1}{\overset{d_2}{\gtrless}} T \qquad (7.2\text{-}1)$$

†J. D. Gibson and J. L. Melsa, "Introduction to Nonparametric Detection with Applications," Academic Press, Inc., New York, 1975, and J. D. Gibbons, "Nonparametric Statistical Inference," McGraw-Hill Book Company, New York, 1971.

This decision rule requires that we sum the observations. The simplest non-parametric decision rule, the sign test, takes the following form:

$$\sum_{i=1}^{I} u(z_i) \underset{d_1}{\overset{d_2}{\gtrless}} T' \tag{7.2-2}$$

where $u(z_i)$ is the unit step function.† Thus, the nonparametric decision rule requires only that we count the number of positive observations.

The sign test that we develop in this section requires a minimum amount of information about the probability distribution of the observations. If m_1 is true, then we assume that $p(z_i|m_1)$ has a zero median‡; while if m_2 is true, $p(z_i|m_2)$ has a positive median. Hence we can state the problem in the following form:

$$\begin{aligned} m_1: P\{z_i > 0|m_1\} &= \tfrac{1}{2} \\ m_2: P\{z_i > 0|m_2\} &= p > \tfrac{1}{2} \end{aligned} \qquad i = 1, 2, \dots, I \tag{7.2-3}$$

We assume that the z_i's are independent but not necessarily identically distributed.

Since we have information only regarding the sign of the observation, it is reasonable to assume that decision rule will only depend on the sign of the z_i's. Let x_i be defined as

$$x_i = u(z_i) = \begin{cases} 1 & \text{if } z_i > 0 \\ 0 & \text{if } z_i \le 0 \end{cases} \tag{7.2-4}$$

Then the problem can be stated in terms of x_i as

$$\begin{aligned} P\{x_i|m_1\} &= \begin{cases} \tfrac{1}{2} & x_i = 0 \\ \tfrac{1}{2} & x_i = 1 \end{cases} \\[2mm] P\{x_i|m_2\} &= \begin{cases} 1-p & x_i = 0 \\ p & x_i = 1 \end{cases} \end{aligned} \tag{7.2-5}$$

In terms of x_i, the likelihood ratio can be written as

$$\Lambda(\mathbf{x}) = \frac{p^{\sum_{i=1}^{I} x_i} (1-p)^{I - \sum_{i=1}^{I} x_i}}{(\tfrac{1}{2})^I} \tag{7.2-6}$$

If we let $I^+ = \sum_{i=1}^{I} x_i$, the number of positive observations, then $\Lambda(\mathbf{x})$ becomes

$$\Lambda(\mathbf{x}) = \frac{p^{I^+} (1-p)^{I - I^+}}{(\tfrac{1}{2})^I} = [2(1-p)]^I \left(\frac{p}{1-p}\right)^{I^+} \tag{7.2-7}$$

---

†The unit step function is defined by
$$u(x) = \begin{cases} 1 & \text{if } x > 0 \\ 0 & \text{if } x \le 0 \end{cases}$$
‡The random variable x has a median α if $P\{x \ge \alpha\} = \tfrac{1}{2}$.

and the likelihood-ratio test becomes†

$$[2(1-p)]^I \left(\frac{p}{1-p}\right)^{I^+} \underset{d_1}{\overset{d_2}{\gtrless}} T \qquad (7.2\text{-}8)$$

If we take logarithms to the base $p/(1-p)$ on both sides, we obtain

$$I^+ \underset{d_1}{\overset{d_2}{\gtrless}} T - I \log_{\frac{p}{1-p}} [2(1-p)] = T^* \qquad (7.2\text{-}9)$$

Hence the test consists of comparing the number of positive observations with the threshold T^* and is usually referred to as the *sign test*.

The threshold T^* is determined by setting the false-alarm probability $P\{d_2|m_1\}$ to be less than or equal to α_0. Since I^+ is the sum of I Bernoulli random variables, it will have a binomial distribution (see App. A). If m_1 is true, the binomial distribution will have parameters I and $\frac{1}{2}$ so that

$$P\{I^+ = n|m_1\} = \binom{I}{n}\left(\frac{1}{2}\right)^n \left(1 - \frac{1}{2}\right)^{I-n} = \binom{I}{n}\left(\frac{1}{2}\right)^I \qquad (7.2\text{-}10)$$

The false-alarm probability is therefore

$$P\{d_2|m_1\} = P\{I^+ > T^*|m_1\} = \sum_{n=T^*+1}^{I} \binom{I}{n}\left(\frac{1}{2}\right)^I$$

With a given value for I, we can find the smallest value of T^* such that $P\{d_2|m_1\} \leq \alpha_0$ or

$$\sum_{n=T^*+1}^{I} \binom{I}{n}\left(\frac{1}{2}\right)^I \leq \alpha_0 \qquad (7.2\text{-}11)$$

The inequality in Eq. (7.2-11) is necessary because I^+ is discrete random variable and only certain values of α_0 may be exactly achieved.

The probability of detection can be easily found once T^* is fixed. If m_2 is true, then I^+ has a binomial distribution with parameters I and p, and so

$$P\{I^+ = n|m_2\} = \binom{I}{n} p^n (1-p)^{I-n} \qquad (7.2\text{-}12)$$

Therefore the detection probability is

$$P\{d_2|m_2\} = \sum_{n=T^*+1}^{I} \binom{I}{n} p^n (1-p)^{I-n} \qquad (7.2\text{-}13)$$

Example 7.2-1 Let us consider the use of a sign test with $I = 10$ and $\alpha_0 = 0.25$. The threshold T^* for this test is obtained from Eq. (7.2-11) by

---

† Since we are dealing with discrete probability densities, exact equality of the test statistic and the threshold has a finite probability. Therefore, the assignment of the equality condition can no longer be made arbitrarily; we shall assign it to d_1.

finding the value of T^* for which

$$\sum_{n=T^*+1}^{10} \binom{10}{n} \left(\frac{1}{2}\right)^{10} \leq 0.25$$

or

$$\sum_{n=T^*+1}^{10} \binom{10}{n} \leq 2^{10}(0.25) = 256$$

The desired binomial coefficients are

$$\binom{10}{10} = 1 \quad \binom{10}{9} = 10 \quad \binom{10}{8} = 45 \quad \binom{10}{7} = 120 \quad \binom{10}{6} = 210$$

Hence if we let $T^* = 6$, we have

$$\sum_{n=7}^{10} \binom{10}{n} = 1 + 10 + 45 + 120 = 176 \leq 256$$

On the other hand, if $T^* = 5$, then

$$\sum_{n=6}^{10} \binom{10}{n} = 1 + 10 + 45 + 120 + 210 = 386 > 256$$

which does not work. Therefore, the sign test for this problem is given by

$$I^+ = \sum_{i=1}^{10} u(z_i) \underset{d_1}{\overset{d_2}{\gtrless}} 6$$

For $T^* = 6$, the actual value of $P\{d_2|m_1\}$ is

$$P\{d_2|m_1\} = \sum_{n=7}^{10} \binom{10}{n} 2^{-10} = \frac{176}{1024} = 0.17$$

Suppose that we obtain the following set of observations:

$$Z = \{-1, 2, 2, 4, 1, 4, -1, -4, 3, -2,\}$$

For this set of observations, $I^+ = 6$ and we decide d_1.

7.3 WILCOXON TEST

One of the major features of the sign test developed in Sec. 7.2 is the minimal amount of information concerning the probability distribution of the observation that is required. If, however, more information is available, it may be possible to devise a test which makes use of this additional information. In particular, in this section we shall consider the case where the observation probability densities are symmetric so that

$$p(z_i|m_1) = p(-z_i|m_1)$$
$$p(\mu + z_i|m_2) = p(\mu - z_i|m_2), \mu > 0$$
$$i = 1, 2, \ldots, I$$

Hence, if m_1 is true, the probability density $p(z_i|m_1)$ is symmetric about zero; while if m_2 is true, the density is symmetric about a positive value μ. The observations are assumed to be identically distributed and independent.

If m_1 is true, the number and magnitude of positive and negative observations will be approximately equal. However, when m_2 is true, not only will there be more positive observations, but also the positive observations will generally have larger absolute values. This amplitude information would be ignored by the sign test, but the Wilcoxon test makes efficient use of the additional information.

The Wilcoxon test is based on a branch of statistics known as *rank* or *order statistics*. The complete set of observations $Z = \{z_1, z_2, \ldots, z_l\}$ are ranked in order of increasing absolute value so that

$$|z_{k_1}| < |z_{k_2}| < \ldots < |z_{k_I}| \tag{7.3-1}$$

The rank R_i of the observation z_i is then 1 plus the number of observations whose absolute values are less than the absolute value of z_i.

Decision rules which make use of this rank information have the following form:

$$l(\mathbf{z}) = \sum_{i=1}^{I} f(R_i)u(z_i) \underset{d_1}{\overset{d_2}{\gtrless}} T \tag{7.3-2}$$

where $f(R_i)$ is some function of R_i and $u(z_i)$ is the unit step function. Different choices of $f(R_i)$ will lead to different decision rules. If $f(R_i)$ is just R_i, then the decision rule becomes

$$l(\mathbf{z}) = \sum_{i=1}^{I} R_i u(z_i) \underset{d_1}{\overset{d_2}{\gtrless}} T \tag{7.3-3}$$

which is known as the *Wilcoxon test*. We note that $l(\mathbf{z})$ is just the sum of the ranks of the positive observations.

For simplicity in the following developments, it is desirable to renumber the observations so that they occur in rank order, that is, $|z_i| < |z_j|$ if $i < j$. Then the Wilcoxon test becomes simply

$$l(\mathbf{z}) = \sum_{i=1}^{I} i u(z_i) \underset{d_1}{\overset{d_2}{\gtrless}} T \tag{7.3-4}$$

The problem now is how to select the threshold T in order to meet the Neyman-Pearson criterion that $P\{d_2|m_1\} = P\{l(\mathbf{z}) > T|m_1\} \leq \alpha_o$. The sufficient statistic $l(\mathbf{z})$ has the minimum value of zero if all observations are negative and a maximum of $\Sigma_{i=1}^{I} i = I(I + 1)/2$ if all observations are positive. If m_1 is true, then each of the $u(z_i)$'s will be 0 or 1 with equal likelihood due to the symmetry of the density function. Hence, there are 2^I equally likely ways to generate all the possible values of $l(\mathbf{z})$ if m_1 is true. Therefore, if we want

$P\{d_2|m_1\} \leq \alpha_0$, there must be no more than $2^I\alpha_0$ ways to generate values of $l(\mathbf{z})$ greater than T. In other words, T must be selected such that the number of ways in which $l(\mathbf{z})$ can equal $T + 1$, $T + 2, \ldots, I(I + 1)/2$ is less than or equal to $2^I\alpha_0$.

Example 7.3-1 Let us select a threshold T for a problem with $I = 5$ and $\alpha_0 = 0.2$. The maximum value which $l(\mathbf{z})$ can take is $5(6)/2 = 15$. The following table shows the number of ways that each possible value of $l(\mathbf{z})$ can be generated.

Value of $l(\mathbf{z})$	Ranks associated with positive observations	Number of ways generated
15	1, 2, 3, 4, 5	1
14	2, 3, 4, 5	1
13	1, 3, 4, 5	1
12	1, 2, 4, 5; 3, 4, 5	2
11	1, 2, 3, 5; 2, 4, 5	2
10	1, 2, 3, 4; 1, 4, 5; 2, 3, 5	3
9	2, 3, 4; 4, 5; 1, 3, 5	3
8	3, 5; 1, 3, 4; 1, 2, 5	3
7	2, 5; 3, 4; 1, 2, 4	3
6	1, 5; 2, 4; 1, 2, 3	3
5	5; 1, 4; 2, 3	3
4	4; 1, 3	2
3	3; 1, 2	2
2	2	1
1	1	1
0	. . .	1

As predicted, there are $2^I = 2^5 = 32$ possible ways to generate all the possible values of $l(\mathbf{z})$.

Since we want $P\{d_2|m_1\} \leq 0.2$, we must select T such that there are no more than $2^I\alpha_0 = (32)(0.2) = 6.4$ ways of generating values of $l(\mathbf{z})$ greater than T. If we let $T = 11$, then the total number of ways of generating $l(\mathbf{z}) = 12$, 13, 14, or 15 is 5. However, if $T = 10$, then the total number of ways of generating $l(\mathbf{z}) = 11$, 12, 13, 14, or 15 is 7, which is too large. Hence, we must set $T = 11$ and have an actual value of $P\{d_2|m_1\} = \frac{5}{32} = 0.156$.

Suppose, now, that we obtain the following set observations for this problem:

$$Z = \{-1, 6, 3.5, 2, -4\}$$

If we rank order the observations, we have

$$z_1 = -1 \quad z_2 = 2 \quad z_3 = 3.5 \quad z_4 = -4 \quad z_5 = 6$$

and the Wilcoxon test statistic becomes

$$l(\mathbf{z}) = 1u(-1) + 2u(2) + 3u(3.5) + 4u(-4) + 5u(6) = 2 + 3 + 5 = 10$$

Since this value of $l(\mathbf{z})$ is less than $T = 11$, we should decide d_1.

It should be noted that T depends only on α_0 and I. Tables have been compiled for values of I up to 15, and they can be used to readily find T for any given value of α_0 (see App. B, Table B.3). For large values of I, typically $I > 10$, it is easy to show that $l(\mathbf{z})$ is approximately gaussian with

$$E\{l(\mathbf{z})|m_1\} = \frac{I(I+1)}{4} \tag{7.3-5}$$

$$\text{var } \{l(\mathbf{z})|m_1\} = \frac{I(I+1)(2I+1)}{24} \tag{7.3-6}$$

The proof of Eqs. (7.3-5) and (7.3-6) is based on the fact that the $u(z_i)$'s are independent Bernoulli random variables with parameter $p = \frac{1}{2}$ if m_1 is true. Hence, the expected value of $l(\mathbf{z})$ when m_1 is true is

$$E\{l(\mathbf{z})|m_1\} = E\{\sum_{i=1}^{I} iu(z_i)|m_1\} = \sum_{i=1}^{I} iE\{u(z_i)|m_1\} \tag{7.3-7}$$

But $E\{u(z_i)|m_1\} = p = \frac{1}{2}$, and therefore

$$E\{l(\mathbf{z})|m_1\} = \frac{1}{2}\sum_{i=1}^{I} i = \frac{I(I+1)}{4}$$

as desired. The variance is

$$\text{var } \{l(\mathbf{z})|m_1\} = \sum_{i=1}^{I} i^2 \text{ var } \{u(z_i)|m_1\} \tag{7.3-8}$$

The variance of a Bernoulli random variable with parameter p is $p(1-p)$ or $\frac{1}{4}$ for $p = \frac{1}{2}$. Hence Eq. (7.3-8) becomes

$$\text{var } \{l(\mathbf{z})|m_1\} = \frac{1}{4}\sum_{i=1}^{I} i^2 = \frac{I(I+1)(2I+1)}{24}$$

By using this gaussian approximation, we can find T by solving the expression

$$Q\left[\frac{T - I(I+1)/4}{\sqrt{I(I+1)(2I+1)/24}}\right] = \alpha_0$$

or $$T = \sqrt{\frac{I(I+1)(2I+1)}{24}} \, Q^{-1}(\alpha_0) + \frac{I(I+1)}{4} \tag{7.3-9}$$

When using Eq. (7.3-9) to obtain T, one should always round up to the next larger integer.

Example 7.3-2 Let us use the gaussian approximation to find the threshold for Example 7.3-1, where $\alpha_0 = 0.2$ and $I = 5$. Even though I is too small for the approximation to be accurate, nonetheless it does work quite well. From the Table B.1 in App. B, we can find that $Q^{-1}(0.2) = 0.842$ so that

Eq. (7.3-9) becomes

$$T = [\sqrt{5(6)(11)/24}] \, 0.842 + \frac{5(6)}{4} = 10.62$$

Rounding up to the next larger integer would give $T = 11$, which is the same as we obtained before.

Nowhere in our derivations have we made use of the fact that $p(z_i|m_2)$ is symmetric about $\mu > 0$ or that the $p(z_i|m_k)$ are identically distributed. In fact, neither of these restrictions are necessary. However, we do need to place some restriction on $p(z_i|m_2)$ in order to make our assumption that if m_2 is true then the positive observations will generally have larger absolute values. This means simply that there must be some positive shift of the probability density, which can be stated in the following manner:

$$F(z_i|m_2) \leq F(z_i|m_1) \qquad \text{for all values of } z_i$$

$$F(z_i|m_2) < F(z_i|m_1) \qquad \text{for some values of } z_i$$

where $F(z_i|m_k)$ is the cumulative probability distribution function. Of course, the original requirement that $p(z_i|m_2)$ be symmetric about a positive mean was stronger than the preceding requirement. We shall continue to assume that the observations are independent.

At the beginning of the discussion of nonparametric tests in Sec. 7.2, it was noted that one of the major features of nonparametric tests is their ability to maintain a constant value for $P\{d_2|m_1\}$. The following example illustrates this point.

Example 7.3-3 Suppose that we have a decision problem with the following conditional densities:

$$p(z_i|m_1) \doteq \frac{1}{\sqrt{2\pi}} \, e^{-z_i^2/2}$$
$$i = 1, 2, \ldots, l = 5$$
$$p(z_i|m_2) = \frac{1}{\sqrt{2\pi}} \, e^{-(z_i - 1)^2/2}$$

The optimum Newman-Pearson decision rule for this problem takes the form

$$\sum_{i=1}^{5} z_i \underset{d_1}{\overset{d_2}{\gtrless}} T$$

The threshold T depends on the value of $P\{d_2|m_1\} = \alpha_o$ desired. For $\alpha_o = 0.2$, we find that $T = 1.88$. The Wilcoxon test that we found in Example 7.3-1 is valid for this problem and yields $P\{d_2|m_1\} = 0.156$.

Now, let us suppose that $p(z_i|m_1)$ changes to

$$p(z_i|m_1) = \frac{1}{2\sqrt{2\pi}} \, e^{-z_i^2/8} \qquad i = 1, 2, \ldots, 5$$

Then the false-alarm probability for the optimum test increases to

$$P\{d_2|m_1\} = \int_{1.88}^{\infty} \frac{1}{2\sqrt{5}\sqrt{2\pi}} e^{-x^2/40} \, dx$$

$$= \int_{0.42}^{\infty} \frac{1}{\sqrt{2\pi}} e^{-\lambda^2/2} \, d\lambda = Q(0.42)$$

$$= 0.34$$

Hence, $P\{d_2|m_1\}$ has exceeded the maximum design value of 0.2. The nonparametric test will still have $P\{d_2|m_1\} = 0.156$.

7.4 SUMMARY

This chapter completes our study of decision problems. We have examined two additional generalizations of the decision theory presented earlier. We have studied methods for handling composite decision problems in which the conditional densities $p(\mathbf{z}|m_k)$ are known except for certain missing parameters. The methods fall into three broad classes:

1. Problems that were independent of the unknown parameters
2. Problems that have unknown parameters which are random variables
3. Problems that have unknown parameters which are unknown deterministic constants

In addition, we have considered nonparametric decision problems in which the conditional probability densities $p(\mathbf{z}|m_k)$ are unknown except for some very general properties. Two simple nonparametric tests were developed: the sign test and the Wilcoxon test.

7.5 PROBLEMS

7.5-1 Let v be a zero-mean unit-variance gaussian random variable and consider the decision problem with

$$m_1: z = v$$

$$m_2: z = m + v$$

where m is some positive number. Determine the decision rule using the probability-of-error criterion.

7.5-2 Consider the single-observation, binary composite decision problem with

$$p(z|\beta, m_1) = \begin{cases} \beta^2 z & 0 \le z \le \dfrac{\sqrt{2}}{\beta} \\ 0 & \text{otherwise} \end{cases}$$

$$p(z|m_2) = \begin{cases} Ke^{-Kz} & z \ge 0 \\ 0 & \text{otherwise} \end{cases}$$

Here β is a random parameter which is uniformly distributed on $[0, 1]$ and K is an unknown positive constant. Form the generalized likelihood-ratio test.

7.5-3 Find the ideal-observer decision rule for the binary composite decision problem

$$m_1: z_i = v_i$$
$$m_2: z_i = 1 + w_i$$
$$i = 1, 2, \ldots, K$$

Here v_i and w_i are zero-mean gaussian random variables with

$$\text{cov}\{v_i, v_j\} = \sigma_v^2 \, \delta_K(i - j)$$
$$\text{cov}\{w_i, w_j\} = \sigma_w^2 \, \delta_K(i - j)$$

where σ_v^2 and σ_w^2 are unknown constants. Assume $P\{m_1\} = \frac{1}{2}$.

7.5-4 Consider the binary composite decision problem with

$$p(z_i | m_1) = \begin{cases} 1 - \dfrac{z_i}{2} & 0 \le z_i \le 2 \\ 0 & \text{otherwise} \end{cases}$$

$$p(z_i | m_2) = \begin{cases} \dfrac{1}{L} & a \le z_i \le a + L \\ 0 & \text{otherwise} \end{cases}$$

Here I-independent and identically distributed samples are taken. All the samples are in the closed interval $[0, 2]$, and a and L are unknown constants. Find the equally likely probability-of-error decision rule for this problem.

7.5-5 Consider the binary decision problem where

$$p(z | m_1) = 2(1 - z)[u(z) - u(z - 1)]$$
$$p(z | m_2) = 2(z - a)[u(z - a) - u(z - a - 1)]$$

and

$$a \ge 0 \qquad P\{m_1\} = \frac{1}{2}$$

(*a*) Use a maximum-likelihood estimate of a to find a decision rule that "minimizes" the probability of error.

(*b*) If

$$p(a) = \begin{cases} 1 & 0 \le a \le 1 \\ 0 & \text{otherwise} \end{cases}$$

find the minimum probability-of-error rule.

7.5-6 For a decision problem, it is known that

$$p(z_i | m_1) = p(-z_i | m_1)$$

and

$$P\{z_i > 0 | m_2\} > \frac{1}{2}$$

where the z_i are the components of the observation

$$\mathbf{z} = (z_1, z_2, z_3, z_4, z_5)$$

(*a*) Find a sign test that ensures

$$P\{d_2 | m_1\} \le 0.2$$

(*b*) Find a Wilcoxon test that ensures

$$P\{d_2 | m_1\} \le 0.2$$

(*c*) For the Wilcoxon test, find $P\{d_1 | m_2\}$ for the probability densities shown in Fig. 7.5-1.

(*d*) For the given density, if m_1 is sent, find a set of observations that the sign test maps into Z_1 and the Wilcoxon test maps into Z_2.

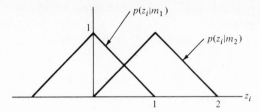

Figure 7.5-1 Probability densities for Probl. 7.5-6.

7.5-7 Given a set of 10 independent identically distributed observations of a random variable x with cumulative distribution function $F(x)$, we desire to determine if the message m_1

$$m_1: F(34) = 0.5$$

or the message m_2

$$m_2: F(34) < 0.5$$

is true by using the sign detector. Write an expression for the power function of the test and find the false-alarm probability $P\{d_2 | m_1\}$ if the threshold $T = 8$. Assume that $F(34) = 0.1$ when m_2 is true, and find the probability of detection $P\{d_2 | m_2\}$.

7.5-8 Given $I = 16$ independent observations from a gaussian distribution with mean $\mu = 29.04$ and variance $\sigma^2 = 1$, use the sign detector for the decision problem

$$m_1: F(28) = 0.5 \qquad \text{versus} \qquad m_2: F(28) < 0.5$$

The desired significance level α_o is 0.05. Specifically, find the threshold T for the given significance level and then use this value of T to find the true value of $P\{d_2 | m_1\}$. In order to determine the probability of detection $P\{d_2 | m_2\}$, we need to know $p = P\{x > 28\}$ when m_2 is true. Normally we would not have this information available; however, in this case we are given the distribution of x in the problem statement. Use the given distribution to determine p, and then use this value of p to obtain $P\{d_2 | m_2\}$. Compare the preceding results with the results obtained using the likelihood-ratio detector to test

$$m_1: \mu = 28 \qquad \text{versus} \qquad m_2: \mu = 29.04$$

that is, find T for $\alpha_0 = 0.05$ and calculate $P\{d_2 | m_2\}$.

7.5-9 Use the Wilcoxon test on the following decision problem:

$$m_1: F(0) = 0.5 \qquad \text{versus} \qquad m_2: F(0) < 0.5$$

where $F(x)$ is a continuous distribution function whose probability density is symmetric. You are given the following 18 independent identically distributed observations:

$$1.5, -0.5, 1.6, 0.4, 2.3, -0.8, 3.2, 0.9, 2.9, 0.3, 1.8, -0.1, 1.2, 2.5, 0.6, -0.7, 1.9, 1.3$$

Let $\alpha_o = 0.01$ and assume that the large sample approximation to the distribution of the test statistic is valid.

7.5-10 Given the following set of seven observations:

$$\{-5, -8, -1, 7, 2, 8, 10\}$$

Use (a) the sign test and (b) the Wilcoxon test with $P\{d_2 | m_1\} \leq 0.1$ to decide whether

$$m_1: P\{z_i \geq 0\} = \tfrac{1}{2}$$

or

$$m_2: P\{z_i \geq 0\} = p > \tfrac{1}{2}$$

is true. For each test, what is the exact $P\{d_2 | m_1\}$?

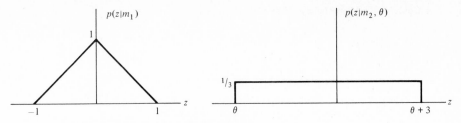

Figure 7.5-2 Probability densities for Probl. 7.5-13.

7.5-11 For a composite decision problem let

$$p(z|m_1) = \frac{1}{\sqrt{2\pi}\,v}\,e^{-z^2/2v^2}$$

$$p(z|m_2, \theta) = \frac{1}{\sqrt{2\pi}\,\theta}\,e^{-z^2/2\theta^2}$$

where θ is unknown but $\theta > v$. We require that $P\{d_2|m_1\} \le 10^{-2}$.

 (a) Find the lower bound on $P\{d_1|m_2\}$ if θ were known.

 (b) Does a uniformly most powerful test exist?

7.5-12 For a binary composite problem, the observation is

$$z = a\,\theta + n$$

where n is a zero-mean gaussian variable with variance v that is independent of the message. If the message is m_1, θ is zero; if it is m_2, θ is not zero. The probability density of a is

$$p(a) = \tfrac{1}{2}\,\delta(a - 1) + \tfrac{1}{2}\,\delta(a + 1)$$

 (a) Does a uniform most powerful test exist? If yes, do (b), if no, do (b').

 (b) Describe the UMP and give its power function. Derive necessary and sufficient conditions on $p(a)$ to ensure that a UMP exists.

 (b') Derive the generalized likelihood-ratio test and find its power function.

7.5-13 For a binary decision problem, the conditional densities of the observation are shown in Fig. 7.5-2. The quantity θ is an unknown parameter, and we have the following constraint:

$$P\{d_2|m_1\} \le 0.25$$

 (a) Find the generalized likelihood-ratio test and the resulting $P\{d_1|m_2\}$.

 (b) If it is known that θ is in the range $(0, \tfrac{1}{4})$, find the uniform most powerful test and the resulting $P\{d_1|m_2\}$.

 (c) For what values of a, b does a uniform most powerful test exist if it is known that θ is in the range (a, b).

7.5-14 Consider the binary composite decision problem with I independent and identically distributed observations with

$$p(z_i|m_1) = \theta e^{-z_i\theta}$$
$$p(z_i|m_2) = e^{-z_i} \qquad z_i > 0$$

Here θ is a positive unknown constant. Find the probability-of-error decision rule if $P\{m_1\} = 0.5$.

7.5-15 Consider the following multiple-observation problem:

$$p(z_i|m_1) = \frac{1}{\sqrt{2\pi}} e^{-z_i^2/2}$$

$$i = 1, 2, \dots, I$$

$$p(z_i|m_2) = \frac{1}{\sqrt{2\pi}} e^{-(z_i-1)^2/2}$$

The observations are independent and identically distributed and $I = 20$.

(a) Find a decision rule such that $P\{d_2|m_1\} = 0.1$ and $P\{d_1|m_2\}$ is as small as possible.

(b) Use the sign test to determine a decision rule with $P\{d_2|m_1\} \leq 0.1$. What is the resulting value of $P\{d_1|m_2\}$?

(c) Use the Wilcoxon test to determine a decision rule with $P\{d_2|m_1\} \leq 0.1$. (Use the gaussian approximation.) What is the resulting $P\{d_1|m_2\}$?

7.5-16 In Prob. 7.5-15, suppose that I can be selected to make both $P\{d_2|m_1\}$ and $P\{d_1|m_2\} \leq 0.1$. What would be the smallest value of I? If we used a sequential test, what would be the average value of I to achieve the same performance?

7.5-17 Consider the following multiple-observation problem:

$$p(z_i|m_1) = \frac{1}{\sqrt{2\pi}} e^{-z_i^2/2}$$

$$i = 1, 2, \dots, I$$

$$p(z_i|m_2) = \frac{1}{\sqrt{2\pi}} e^{-(z_i-\mu)^2/2}$$

The observations are independent and identically distributed, and $I = 9$.

(a) If $\mu = 1$, find the optimal decision rule such that $P\{d_2|m_1\} \leq 0.1$ and $P\{d_1|m_2\}$ is as small as possible. What is $P\{d_1|m_2\}$ for this test? If $\mu = 2$, is this test still optimal?

(b) Find a sign-test decision rule for this problem if $\mu > 0$ such that $P\{d_2|m_1\} \leq 0.1$. For $\mu = 1$, find the $P\{d_1|m_2\}$ for the sign test.

(c) Find a Wilcoxon test for this problem such that $P\{d_2|m_1\} \leq 0.1$ (assume $\mu > 0$ and use gaussian approximation).

7.5-18 Consider Prob. 7.5-17 again. Let $\mu = 1$ and I be variable.

(a) Using the optimal test, what is the smallest value of I such that both $P\{d_2|m_1\}$ and $P\{d_1|m_2\} = 0.1$?

(b) If the sign test is used, what is the minimum value of I to yield these same error probabilities?

(c) Find a Wald sequential test for this problem, and find the average value of I if $P\{m_1\} = 0.5$.

7.5-19 Consider the composite decision problem with

$$p(z_i|m_1) = \frac{1}{\sqrt{2\pi}} e^{-z_i^2/2}$$

$$i = 1, 2, \dots, I = 5$$

$$p(z_i|m_2, \sigma) = \frac{1}{\sqrt{2\pi}\sigma} e^{-z_i^2/2\sigma^2}$$

Here σ is an unknown positive constant.

(a) Find the Neyman-Pearson test with $P\{d_2|m_1\} \leq 0.2$.

(b) Find the probability-of-error test if $P\{m_1\} = 0.6$.

FUNDAMENTALS OF ESTIMATION

In this and the remaining chapters of this book, we shall be interested in *estimation problems*. Estimation problems are an extension of the multiple decision problem of Chap. 5 in which the number of messages is normally uncountably infinite. For example, instead of deciding whether a signal generator is on or off, we may want to estimate the magnitude of the signal.

The approach which we shall take in studying estimation will parallel closely the development of decision theory in the preceding chapters. In the decision problem, the message space M consists of a finite number of discrete points m_j; in the estimation problem, the message space consists of an uncountably infinite number of points such as segments of the real line or subsets of a euclidean n-space. The message to be transmitted to the receiver involves selecting a point m from M. The problem then is to determine (estimate) the value of m from the observation z in some optimal fashion. Of course, if we could directly observe the value m, there would be no difficulty. Normally we can observe m only through a noisy channel, and in this case, we must use an estimation technique to try to determine the value of m.

We shall call the value of m that we determine by this method the *estimate* $\hat{m}$ of m. The rule which we use to find $\hat{m}$ from z is the estimator. In other words, an *estimator* is the rule or procedure for processing a set of observations to generate an *estimate*. The estimator is the parallel of the decision rule, while the estimate is the parallel of the decision.

Let us consider a simple example to illustrate the formulation and concepts of an estimation problem. Suppose that the message consists of a number m selected from the real line. The signal s to be transmitted is a voltage which is equal to m. We make several independent observations z_i of s through a channel which adds gaussian noise n_i. A reasonable message model for this problem would be

$$z_i = s + n_i \qquad i = 1, 2, \ldots, I$$

From this information we can determine the conditional probability density

$p(z_i|m)$. We may or may not be given a density $p(m)$ which describes how m was selected.

Several methods for estimating m are possible. For example, we might use the sample mean given by $\Sigma_{i=1}^{I} z_i/I$. Another choice would be the sample median in which we order the samples and then select the one in the middle. We might also average the largest and smallest observations. Which one of these estimators, if any, is correct will depend on the criterion which we select. In this chapter, several different types of estimators and their relationships are discussed. In order to parallel the development of decision theory, we begin with *maximum-likelihood estimation* in Sec. 8.1. Section 8.2 is concerned with the Bayes approach to estimation and develops several important classes of estimators. The relationship of the various estimators is discussed in Sec. 8.3. Two additional methods for estimating m, known as *linear minimum-variance* and *least-squares estimation*, are presented in Sec. 8.4.

In this and the next two chapters, we shall use the symbol $\boldsymbol{\theta}$ to represent the unknown parameter vector to be estimated. We shall assume that $\boldsymbol{\theta}$ is constant; problems of this sort are referred to as *parameter* or *point estimation*. A brief introduction to *state estimation* is presented in Chap. 11. There the quantity to be estimated is the time-varying state of a dynamical system represented as $\mathbf{x}(t)$.

8.1 MAXIMUM-LIKELIHOOD METHOD

Although the maximum-likelihood method is one of the simplest methods of estimation, it is also extremely useful. We discussed maximum likelihood estimation briefly in Sec. 7.1 with regard to composite decision problems. The philosophy of the maximum-likelihood-estimation procedure is closely related to the maximum-likelihood decision criterion introduced in Sec. 3.1.

The probability density function of the observation $\mathbf{z}$ given the unknown parameter $\boldsymbol{\theta}$, that is, $p(\mathbf{z}|\boldsymbol{\theta})$, is assumed to be known. No probability density of $\boldsymbol{\theta}$ is required. The maximum-likelihood estimate is defined by the following criterion.

> **Maximum-likelihood estimation** For the observation $\mathbf{z}$, $\hat{\boldsymbol{\theta}}_{\mathrm{ML}}(\mathbf{z})$ is the maximum likelihood estimate of a parameter $\boldsymbol{\theta}$ if
> $$p(\mathbf{z}|\hat{\boldsymbol{\theta}}_{\mathrm{ML}}) \geq p(\mathbf{z}|\hat{\boldsymbol{\theta}}) \qquad (8.1\text{-}1)$$
> for any other estimate $\hat{\boldsymbol{\theta}} \neq \hat{\boldsymbol{\theta}}_{\mathrm{ML}}$. In other words, $\hat{\boldsymbol{\theta}}_{\mathrm{ML}}(\mathbf{z})$ maximizes the likelihood function $p(\mathbf{z}|\boldsymbol{\theta})$ for a given $\mathbf{z}$.

The maximum-likelihood estimator is extremely useful because of its simplicity and the minimal amount of required statistical information. Later we shall see that the maximum-likelihood estimator is a close approximation of several more complicated estimators especially as the number of observations becomes large.

Example 8.1-1 Consider the following observations of a scalar parameter θ:

$$z_i = \theta + n_i \qquad i = 1, 2, \ldots, I$$

where the n_i's are independent and identically distributed gaussian random variables with mean zero and variance σ^2. The density function $p(\mathbf{z}|\theta)$ is given by

$$p(\mathbf{z}|\theta) = \prod_{i=1}^{I} p(z_i|\theta)$$

$$= \left(\frac{1}{\sqrt{2\pi}\sigma} \right)^I \prod_{i=1}^{I} e^{-(z_i-\theta)^2/2\sigma^2}$$

$$= (\sqrt{2\pi}\sigma)^{-I} \exp\left[-\frac{1}{2\sigma^2} \sum_{i=1}^{I} (z_i - \theta)^2 \right]$$

We can maximize this function by setting the partial derivative of $p(\mathbf{z}|\theta)$ with respect to θ to zero. However, it is easier to work with the $\ln p(\mathbf{z}|\theta)$ in this case, and so we have

$$\left. \frac{\partial \ln p(\mathbf{z}|\theta)}{\partial \theta} \right|_{\theta = \hat{\theta}_{\text{ML}}} = 0 = \frac{1}{\sigma^2} \sum_{i=1}^{I} (z_i - \hat{\theta}_{\text{ML}})$$

$$= \frac{1}{\sigma^2} \left[\sum_{i=1}^{I} z_i - I\hat{\theta}_{\text{ML}} \right]$$

If we solve for $\hat{\theta}_{\text{ML}}$, we obtain

$$\hat{\theta}_{\text{ML}} = \frac{1}{I} \sum_{i=1}^{I} z_i$$

This result is called the *sample mean*. Note that our answer does not depend on the value of σ^2.

One of the important properties of the maximum-likelihood estimator is its invariance under invertible transformation. This result is stated in the following theorem.

Theorem 8.1-1 Invariance of maximum-likelihood estimator If $\mathbf{f}(\boldsymbol{\theta})$ is an invertible function defined for all $\boldsymbol{\theta}$, then the maximum likelihood estimator of $\mathbf{f}$ given by $\hat{\mathbf{f}}_{\text{ML}}$ is

$$\hat{\mathbf{f}}_{\text{ML}} = \mathbf{f}(\hat{\boldsymbol{\theta}}_{\text{ML}})$$

In other words, the maximum-likelihood estimate of $\mathbf{f}$ is just $\mathbf{f}(\hat{\boldsymbol{\theta}}_{\text{ML}})$.

PROOF Let the inverse of $\mathbf{f}$ be given by $\mathbf{f}^{-1}$ so that

$$\mathbf{f}^{-1}[\mathbf{f}(\boldsymbol{\theta})] = \boldsymbol{\theta}$$

for all $\boldsymbol{\theta}$. The conditional density function of $\mathbf{z}$ given $\mathbf{f}$ can be written as

$$p_{\mathbf{z}|\mathbf{f}}(\mathbf{z}|\mathbf{f}) = p_{\mathbf{z}|\boldsymbol{\theta}}[\mathbf{z}|\mathbf{f}^{-1}(\mathbf{f})] \qquad (8.1\text{-}2)$$

By definition of the maximum-likelihood estimate

$$p_{\mathbf{z}|\mathbf{f}}(\mathbf{z}|\hat{\mathbf{f}}_{\text{ML}}) \geq p_{\mathbf{z}|\mathbf{f}}(\mathbf{z}|\mathbf{f})$$

for all $\mathbf{f} \neq \hat{\mathbf{f}}_{\text{ML}}$.

Now, let $\mathbf{f}^* = \mathbf{f}(\hat{\boldsymbol{\theta}}_{\text{ML}})$; then from Eq. (8.1-2)

$$p_{\mathbf{z}|\mathbf{f}}(\mathbf{z}|\mathbf{f}^*) = p_{\mathbf{z}|\boldsymbol{\theta}}(\mathbf{z}|\hat{\boldsymbol{\theta}}_{\text{ML}})$$

By definition of $\hat{\boldsymbol{\theta}}_{\text{ML}}$ [Eq. (8.2-1)] we know that

$$p_{\mathbf{z}|\boldsymbol{\theta}}(\mathbf{z}|\hat{\boldsymbol{\theta}}_{\text{ML}}) \geq p_{\mathbf{z}|\boldsymbol{\theta}}(\mathbf{z}|\boldsymbol{\theta})$$

for all $\boldsymbol{\theta} \neq \hat{\boldsymbol{\theta}}_{ML}$; therefore

$$p_{\mathbf{z}|\mathbf{f}}(\mathbf{z}|\mathbf{f}^*) \geq p_{\mathbf{z}|\mathbf{f}}(\mathbf{z}|\mathbf{f})$$

for all $\mathbf{f} \neq \mathbf{f}^*$. Hence $\hat{\mathbf{f}}_{\text{ML}} = \mathbf{f}^* = \mathbf{f}(\hat{\boldsymbol{\theta}}_{\text{ML}})$.

8.2 BAYES COST METHOD

In Chap. 2, we discussed the Neyman-Pearson and probability-of-error methods for decision theory after the presentation of the maximum likelihood method. Neither of these two methods has a counterpart in estimation theory.

We noted in Chap. 5 that there was no general Neyman-Pearson approach for multiple decision problems. Since the estimation problem is a generalization of the multiple decision problem, one would not expect there to be a Neyman-Pearson approach to estimation problems.

The probability-of-error method does not exist for a closely related reason. The message now consists of the value of the parameter $\boldsymbol{\theta}$ which has, in general, a continuum of values. With probability 1, the value of $\hat{\boldsymbol{\theta}}$ and $\boldsymbol{\theta}$ will not be exactly the same. As a result, the probability of error in our usual definition would be 1; the use of the normal probability-of-error method is therefore meaningless. We shall see later, however, that there is a closely related method that is of value. Hence, we turn our attention to the Bayesian approach.

For decision problems, we defined a cost matrix $\mathbf{C}$ which assigned to each decision d_j and message m_k a unique cost. For estimation problems, we generalize this to become a function $C(\boldsymbol{\theta}, \hat{\boldsymbol{\theta}})$ which assigns to each combination of actual parameter value and estimate a unique cost. The expected value of the cost is given by

$$B(\hat{\boldsymbol{\theta}}) = E\{C[\boldsymbol{\theta}, \hat{\boldsymbol{\theta}}(\mathbf{z})]\} = \int_{-\infty}^{\infty} \int_{-\infty}^{\infty} C[\boldsymbol{\theta}, \hat{\boldsymbol{\theta}}(\mathbf{z})] p(\boldsymbol{\theta}, \mathbf{z}) \, d\boldsymbol{\theta} \, d\mathbf{z} \qquad (8.2\text{-}1)$$

Here we have written the expected value as a function of $\hat{\theta}$ to emphasize the dependence on the estimator rule. If we write $p(\theta, \mathbf{z})$ as $p(\mathbf{z}|\theta)p(\theta)$, then Eq. (8.2-1) can be written as

$$B(\hat{\theta}) = \int_{-\infty}^{\infty} \left[\int_{-\infty}^{\infty} C[\theta, \hat{\theta}(\mathbf{z})]p(\mathbf{z}|\theta)\, d\mathbf{z} \right] p(\theta)\, d\theta \qquad (8.2\text{-}2)$$

The inner integral is the conditional cost given θ, which we write as

$$B(\hat{\theta}\,|\theta) = E\{C(\theta, \hat{\theta}\,)|\theta\} = \int_{-\infty}^{\infty} C[\theta, \hat{\theta}(\mathbf{z})]p(\mathbf{z}|\theta)\, d\mathbf{z} \qquad (8.2\text{-}3)$$

This integral represents the expected value of the cost for a given value of θ. In terms of the conditional cost $B(\hat{\theta}|\theta)$, the Bayes cost can be written as

$$B(\hat{\theta}) = \int_{-\infty}^{\infty} B(\hat{\theta}\,|\theta)p(\theta)\, d\theta = E\{B(\hat{\theta}\,|\theta)\} \qquad (8.2\text{-}4)$$

The Bayes estimation criterion can be stated as follows:

Bayes estimation criterion For a given cost function $C(\theta, \hat{\theta})$, the estimation rule $\hat{\theta}_B$ is optimum if

$$B(\hat{\theta}_B) \leq B(\hat{\theta}) \qquad (8.2\text{-}5)$$

for any other $\hat{\theta} \neq \hat{\theta}_B$. In other words, the Bayes estimator minimizes the Bayes cost.

One can generate an infinitude of different estimators depending on the choice of $C(\theta, \hat{\theta})$. We shall consider three of the most useful choices for $C(\theta, \hat{\theta})$ and develop the associated estimator rules.

8.2-1 Mean Square Error

Before beginning the development for the mean square error (MSE) criterion, it is convenient to rewrite Eq. (8.2-1). If the density $p(\theta, \mathbf{z})$ is written as $p(\theta|\mathbf{z})p(\mathbf{z})$, then Eq. (8.2-1) becomes

$$B(\hat{\theta}\,) = \int_{-\infty}^{\infty} \left[\int_{-\infty}^{\infty} C[\theta, \hat{\theta}(\mathbf{z})]p(\theta|\mathbf{z})\, d\theta \right] p(\mathbf{z})\, d\mathbf{z} \qquad (8.2\text{-}6)$$

If we can minimize the inner integral of Eq. (8.2-6) for every possible value of $\mathbf{z}$, then $B(\hat{\theta})$ must also be minimized since $p(\mathbf{z})$ is nonnegative. Hence we shall select $\hat{\theta}$ to minimize

$$B(\hat{\theta}\,|\mathbf{z}) = \int_{-\infty}^{\infty} C[\theta, \hat{\theta}(\mathbf{z})]p(\theta|\mathbf{z})\, d\theta \qquad (8.2\text{-}7)$$

The mean square cost function is

$$C_{\mathrm{MS}}(\theta, \hat{\theta}) = \|\theta - \hat{\theta}\|^2 = \sum_{i=1}^{l} (\theta_i - \hat{\theta}_i)^2 \qquad (8.2\text{-}8)$$

The quantity $\tilde{\boldsymbol{\theta}} = \boldsymbol{\theta} - \hat{\boldsymbol{\theta}}$ is known as the *estimation error* and represents the difference between the true and estimated value of the parameter. If we substitute Eq. (8.2-8) into the expression for $B(\hat{\boldsymbol{\theta}})$, we have

$$B_{\mathrm{MS}}(\hat{\boldsymbol{\theta}}|\mathbf{z}) = \int_{-\infty}^{\infty} \int_{-\infty}^{\infty} \|\boldsymbol{\theta} - \hat{\boldsymbol{\theta}}\|^2 p(\boldsymbol{\theta}|\mathbf{z}) \, d\boldsymbol{\theta} \qquad (8.2\text{-}9)$$

We see that the Bayes cost is simply the mean or average of the squared error.

Let us return now to the minimization operation by substituting the mean square cost function into Eq. (8.2-7) to obtain

$$B_{\mathrm{MS}}(\hat{\boldsymbol{\theta}}|\mathbf{z}) = \int_{-\infty}^{\infty} \|\boldsymbol{\theta} - \hat{\boldsymbol{\theta}}\|^2 p(\boldsymbol{\theta}|\mathbf{z}) \, d\boldsymbol{\theta}$$

In order to minimize $B_{\mathrm{MS}}(\hat{\boldsymbol{\theta}}|\mathbf{z})$, we take the partial derivative of $B_{\mathrm{MS}}(\hat{\boldsymbol{\theta}}|\mathbf{z})$ with respect to $\hat{\boldsymbol{\theta}}$. This derivative should be zero for the optimum choice of $\hat{\boldsymbol{\theta}}$, which we will call $\hat{\boldsymbol{\theta}}_{\mathrm{MS}}$. Hence $\hat{\boldsymbol{\theta}}_{\mathrm{MS}}$ is given by

$$\frac{\partial B_{\mathrm{MS}}(\hat{\boldsymbol{\theta}}|\mathbf{z})}{\partial \boldsymbol{\theta}} \bigg|_{\hat{\theta}=\hat{\theta}_{\mathrm{MS}}} = 0 = -\int_{-\infty}^{\infty} 2(\boldsymbol{\theta} - \hat{\boldsymbol{\theta}}_{\mathrm{MS}}) p(\boldsymbol{\theta}|\mathbf{z}) \, d\boldsymbol{\theta}$$

Rearranging this result slightly yields

$$\int_{-\infty}^{\infty} \hat{\boldsymbol{\theta}}_{\mathrm{MS}} p(\boldsymbol{\theta}|\mathbf{z}) \, d\boldsymbol{\theta} = \int_{-\infty}^{\infty} \boldsymbol{\theta} p(\boldsymbol{\theta}|\mathbf{z}) \, d\boldsymbol{\theta}$$

Now since $\hat{\boldsymbol{\theta}}_{\mathrm{MS}}$ is not a function of $\boldsymbol{\theta}$, we can remove it from the left integral and obtain

$$\int_{-\infty}^{\infty} \hat{\boldsymbol{\theta}}_{\mathrm{MS}} p(\boldsymbol{\theta}|\mathbf{z}) \, d\boldsymbol{\theta} = \hat{\boldsymbol{\theta}}_{\mathrm{MS}} \int_{-\infty}^{\infty} p(\boldsymbol{\theta}|\mathbf{z}) \, d\boldsymbol{\theta} = \hat{\boldsymbol{\theta}}_{\mathrm{MS}} \qquad (8.2\text{-}10)$$

Therefore, we see that the optimum estimator for the mean-square cost criterion is given by

$$\hat{\boldsymbol{\theta}}_{\mathrm{MS}} = \int_{-\infty}^{\infty} \boldsymbol{\theta} p(\boldsymbol{\theta}|\mathbf{z}) \, d\boldsymbol{\theta} \qquad (8.2\text{-}11)$$

This estimator is simply the conditional mean of $\boldsymbol{\theta}$ given the observation $\mathbf{z}$. As a result, the estimator is also referred to as the *conditional mean estimator* $\hat{\boldsymbol{\theta}}_{\mathrm{CM}}$.

It is easy to show that the expected value of the estimation error is zero. The estimation error is given by

$$\tilde{\boldsymbol{\theta}} = \boldsymbol{\theta} - \hat{\boldsymbol{\theta}} = \boldsymbol{\theta} - \int_{-\infty}^{\infty} \boldsymbol{\theta} p(\boldsymbol{\theta}|\mathbf{z}) \, d\boldsymbol{\theta} \qquad (8.2\text{-}12)$$

The expected value of $\tilde{\boldsymbol{\theta}}$ can be written as

$$E\{\tilde{\boldsymbol{\theta}}\} = E\{E\{\tilde{\boldsymbol{\theta}}|\mathbf{z}\}\}$$
$$= E\{E\{\boldsymbol{\theta} - \hat{\boldsymbol{\theta}}|\mathbf{z}\}\}$$
$$= E\left\{\int_{-\infty}^{\infty} \boldsymbol{\theta} p(\boldsymbol{\theta}|\mathbf{z}) \, d\mathbf{z} - E\{\hat{\boldsymbol{\theta}}|\mathbf{z}\}\right\} \qquad (8.2\text{-}13)$$

However, if z is known, $\hat{\theta}$ is deterministic; therefore $E\{\hat{\theta}|z\} = \hat{\theta}$. The first term in the right side of Eq. (8.2-13) is also $\hat{\theta}$, so that we have

$$E\{\tilde{\theta}\} = E\{\hat{\theta} - \hat{\theta}\} = 0 \qquad (8.2\text{-}14)$$

Because $\tilde{\theta}$ is zero mean, $B(\hat{\theta})$ as given by Eq.(8.2-9) is also the variance of the estimation error. Because of this fact, $\hat{\theta}_{MS}$ is also called *minimum-error variance estimator*, or simply the *minimum-variance estimator* $\hat{\theta}_{MV}$.

The form of Eq. (8.2-11) is not computationally convenient since the density $p(\theta|z)$ generally is not easy to compute. If we express $p(\theta|z)$ by the use of Bayes rule as

$$p(\theta|z) = \frac{p(z|\theta)p(\theta)}{p(z)}$$

then Eq. (8.2-11) becomes

$$\hat{\theta}_{MS} = \frac{\int_{-\infty}^{\infty} \theta p(z|\theta)p(\theta) \, d\theta}{p(z)} \qquad (8.2\text{-}15)$$

Next $p(z)$ may be written as

$$p(z) = \int_{-\infty}^{\infty} p(z, \theta) \, d\theta = \int_{-\infty}^{\infty} p(z|\theta)p(\theta) \, d\theta$$

so that the final form for $\hat{\theta}_{MS}$ is

$$\hat{\theta}_{MS} = \frac{\int_{-\infty}^{\infty} \theta p(z|\theta)p(\theta) \, d\theta}{\int_{-\infty}^{\infty} p(z|\theta)p(\theta) \, d\theta} \qquad (8.2\text{-}16)$$

In this form, we need only $p(\theta)$ and $p(z|\theta)$, which are generally given or easy to find.

Example 8.2-1 Let us find the minimum mean square estimator for the scalar parameter θ based on the scalar observation

$$z = \ln \theta + n$$

where $$p(\theta) = \begin{cases} 1 & 0 \le \theta \le 1 \\ 0 & \text{otherwise} \end{cases}$$

$$p(n) = \begin{cases} e^{-n} & n \ge 0 \\ 0 & \text{otherwise} \end{cases}$$

The conditional density $p(z|\theta)$ is easily determined as

$$p(z|\theta) = p_n(z - \ln \theta) = \begin{cases} e^{-(z-\ln\theta)} & z > \ln \theta \\ 0 & \text{otherwise} \end{cases}$$

Now, let us calculate first the denominator of Eq. (8.2-16):

$$p(z) = \int_{-\infty}^{\infty} p(z|\theta)p(\theta) \, d\theta = \begin{cases} \int_0^1 e^{-(z-\ln\theta)} \, d\theta = \dfrac{e^{-z}}{2} & z \ge 0 \\[2ex] \int_0^{e^z} e^{-(z-\ln\theta)} \, d\theta = \dfrac{e^z}{2} & z \le 0 \end{cases}$$

The numerator is given by

$$\int_{-\infty}^{\infty} \theta p(z|\theta) p(\theta)\, d\theta = \begin{cases} \displaystyle\int_0^1 \theta e^{-(z-\ln\theta)}\, d\theta = \dfrac{e^{-z}}{3} & z \geq 0 \\[3mm] \displaystyle\int_0^{e^z} \theta e^{-(z-\ln\theta)}\, d\theta = \dfrac{e^{2z}}{3} & z < 0 \end{cases}$$

and therefore

$$\hat{\theta}_{MS} = \begin{cases} \dfrac{2}{3} & z \geq 0 \\[3mm] \dfrac{2e^z}{3} & z < 0 \end{cases}$$

Note that $\hat{\theta}_{MS}$ can never become larger than $\frac{2}{3}$ even though θ can take any value in the unit interval.

Example 8.2-2 Let us consider again the estimation problem of Example 8.1-1, but now we shall find the mean square estimator. In order to do this, we must assume an a priori density for θ. We shall assume that θ is also gaussian with mean μ_0 and variance V_0 so that

$$p(\hat{\theta}) = \frac{1}{\sqrt{2\pi V_0}} \exp\left\{ -\frac{(\theta - \mu_0)^2}{2V_0} \right\}$$

For notational convenience, it is desirable to write the observation sequence in vector form as

$$\mathbf{z} = \mathbf{H}\theta + \mathbf{n}$$

where
$$\mathbf{H} = \begin{bmatrix} 1 \\ 1 \\ \vdots \\ 1 \end{bmatrix}$$

Instead of carrying out the direct integrations involved in Eq. (8.2-16), in this case it is easier to make use of the fact that all the associated density functions are gaussian and can be completely determined by finding the appropriate mean and variance.

Using Bayes rule, we can write the conditional density $p(\theta|\mathbf{z})$ as

$$p(\theta|\mathbf{z}) = \frac{p(\mathbf{z}|\theta) p(\theta)}{p(\mathbf{z})}$$

Let us consider first the density $p(\mathbf{z})$. The mean of $\mathbf{z}$ is

$$E\{\mathbf{z}\} = E\{\mathbf{H}\theta + \mathbf{n}\} = \mathbf{H}\mu_0$$

while the variance is

$$\text{var } \{\mathbf{z}\} = E\{[\mathbf{z} - E\{\mathbf{z}\}][\mathbf{z} - E\{\mathbf{z}\}]^T\}$$
$$= E\{[\mathbf{H}(\theta - \mu_0) + \mathbf{n}][\mathbf{H}(\theta - \mu_0) + \mathbf{n}]^T\}$$
$$= \mathbf{H}V_0\mathbf{H}^T + \sigma^2\mathbf{I}$$

Here we have made use of the fact that the n_i sequence is white and have assumed that the n_i's and θ are uncorrelated. The density function $p(\mathbf{z})$ is therefore

$$p(\mathbf{z}) = K_1 \exp\{-\tfrac{1}{2}(\mathbf{z} - \mathbf{H}\mu_0)^T[\mathbf{H}V_0\mathbf{H}^T + \sigma^2\mathbf{I}]^{-1}(\mathbf{z} - \mathbf{H}\mu_0)\}$$

where K_1 is a normalizing constant.

Consider, next, the density $p(\mathbf{z}|\theta)$. The mean is

$$E\{\mathbf{z}|\theta\} = E\{\mathbf{H}\theta + \mathbf{n}|\theta\} = \mathbf{H}\theta$$

while the variance is

$$\text{var } \{\mathbf{z}|\theta\} = \mathbf{E}\{[\mathbf{z} - \mathbf{H}\theta][\mathbf{z} - \mathbf{H}\theta]^T\}$$
$$= \mathbf{E}\{\mathbf{n}\mathbf{n}^T\}$$
$$= \sigma^2\mathbf{I}$$

The conditional density $p(\mathbf{z}|\theta)$ is therefore

$$p(\mathbf{z}|\theta) = K_2 \exp\left\{-\tfrac{1}{2}[\mathbf{z} - \mathbf{H}\theta]^T\frac{1}{\sigma^2}[\mathbf{z} - \mathbf{H}\theta]\right\}$$

We combine these two results with the known $p(\theta)$ to obtain

$$p(\theta|\mathbf{z}) = K \exp\left\{-\frac{1}{2}(\mathbf{z} - \mathbf{H}\theta)^T\frac{1}{\sigma^2}(\mathbf{z} - \mathbf{H}\theta)\right.$$
$$\left. -\frac{1}{2V_0}(\theta - \mu_0)^2 - \frac{1}{2}(\mathbf{z} - \mathbf{H}\mu_0)^T[\mathbf{H}V_0\mathbf{H}^T + \sigma^2\mathbf{I}]^{-1}(\mathbf{z} - \mathbf{H}\mu_0)\right\}$$

Because this density function is gaussian, it can be written in the form

$$p(\theta|\mathbf{z}) = K \exp\left\{-\frac{1}{2V}(\theta - \hat{\theta}_{MS})^2\right\}$$
$$= K \exp\left\{-\frac{1}{2V}(\theta^2 - 2\theta\hat{\theta}_{MS} + \hat{\theta}_{MS}^2)\right\}$$

Simply by equating the terms which are first- and second-order in θ, we obtain

$$\frac{1}{V} = \frac{\mathbf{H}^T\mathbf{H}}{\sigma^2} + \frac{1}{V_0}$$

$$\frac{2}{V}\hat{\theta}_{MS} = 2\mathbf{H}^T\mathbf{z}\left(\frac{1}{\sigma^2}\right) + 2\frac{\mu_0}{V_0}$$

Solving for $\hat{\theta}_{MS}$, we find that

$$\hat{\theta}_{MS} = [\mathbf{H}^T\mathbf{H}V_0 + \sigma^2]^{-1}[V_0\mathbf{H}^T\mathbf{z} + \sigma^2\mu_0]$$

Note that $\mathbf{H}^T\mathbf{H} = I$ and $\mathbf{H}^T\mathbf{z} = \Sigma_{i=1}^I z_i$, so that

$$\hat{\theta}_{MS} = \frac{\displaystyle\sum_{i=1}^I z_i}{I + \sigma^2/V_0} + \frac{\sigma^2/V_0}{I + \sigma^2/V_0}\mu_0$$

For large I or large V_0, this becomes

$$\hat{\theta}_{MS} \sim \frac{1}{I}\sum_{i=1}^I z_i = \hat{\theta}_{ML}$$

This result says that if enough samples are received, the a priori information about θ becomes unimportant.

8.2-2 Uniform Cost Function

Let us turn now to another cost function which we will refer to as the *uniform cost function* given by

$$C_{UC}(\boldsymbol{\theta}, \hat{\boldsymbol{\theta}}) = \begin{cases} 0 & \text{if } |\theta_k - \hat{\theta}_k| < \epsilon \text{ for } k = 1, 2, \ldots, K \\ 1 & \text{otherwise} \end{cases} \qquad (8.2\text{-}17)$$

where ϵ is small. This cost function gives zero penalty if all components of the estimation error are small and a unit penalty if any component of the estimation error becomes larger than ϵ.

This cost function is the counterpart of the probability-of-error cost matrix in decision theory. Here, we say that an error occurs whenever one or more of the components of $\tilde{\boldsymbol{\theta}}$ exceed ϵ. If we substitute this cost function into Eq. (8.2-7), we obtain

$$B_{UC}(\hat{\boldsymbol{\theta}}|\mathbf{z}) = \int_{\substack{|\theta_k - \hat{\theta}_k| > \epsilon \\ x = 1, 2, \ldots, K}} p(\boldsymbol{\theta}|\mathbf{z})\, d\theta$$

$$= \int_{-\infty}^{\infty} p(\boldsymbol{\theta}|\mathbf{z})\, d\theta - \int_{\hat{\theta}-\epsilon}^{\hat{\theta}+\epsilon} p(\boldsymbol{\theta}|\mathbf{z})\, d\theta \qquad (8.2\text{-}18)$$

where
$$\boldsymbol{\epsilon} = \begin{bmatrix} \epsilon \\ \epsilon \\ \vdots \\ \epsilon \end{bmatrix}$$

The first integral on the right-hand side of Eq. (8.2-18) equals 1. If we apply the mean-value theorem for integrals to the second term, then for small ϵ,

$B_{UC}(\hat{\boldsymbol{\theta}}|\mathbf{z})$ becomes

$$B_{UC}(\hat{\boldsymbol{\theta}}|\mathbf{z}) = 1 - (2\epsilon)^K p(\hat{\boldsymbol{\theta}}|\mathbf{z}) \qquad (8.2\text{-}19)$$

To minimize $B_{UC}(\hat{\boldsymbol{\theta}}|\mathbf{z})$, we must make $p(\hat{\boldsymbol{\theta}}|\mathbf{z})$ as large as possible: hence the optimum estimator $\hat{\boldsymbol{\theta}}_{UC}$ is defined by

$$p(\hat{\boldsymbol{\theta}}_{UC}|\mathbf{z}) \geq p(\hat{\boldsymbol{\theta}}|\mathbf{z}) \qquad (8.2\text{-}20)$$

for all $\hat{\boldsymbol{\theta}} \neq \hat{\boldsymbol{\theta}}_{UC}$. In other words, $\hat{\boldsymbol{\theta}}_{UC}$ is the mode† of the conditional density function $p(\boldsymbol{\theta}|\mathbf{z})$. As a result, this estimator is also called the *conditional mode estimator*. Because $\hat{\boldsymbol{\theta}}_{UC}$ maximized the a posteriori density $p(\boldsymbol{\theta}|\mathbf{z})$, that is, the density of $\boldsymbol{\theta}$ after $\mathbf{z}$ is obtained, $\hat{\boldsymbol{\theta}}_{UC}$ is also called the *maximum a posteriori* (MAP) *estimator* $\hat{\boldsymbol{\theta}}_{MAP}$. We shall use this notation in the following development since it is most common. Since it is possible that $p(\boldsymbol{\theta}|\mathbf{z})$ may be multimodal, the MAP estimator may not be unique.

The fact that the uniform cost function leads to the MAP estimator should not be surprising. As noted at the beginning of this development, the uniform cost function is the counterpart of the probability-of-error cost in decision theory. We know that the probability-of-error decision rule is a MAP decision rule.

Using Bayes rule, we can write $p(\boldsymbol{\theta}|\mathbf{z})$ as

$$p(\boldsymbol{\theta}|\mathbf{z}) = \frac{p(\mathbf{z}|\boldsymbol{\theta})p(\boldsymbol{\theta})}{p(\mathbf{z})}$$

Since $p(\mathbf{z})$ does not depend on $\boldsymbol{\theta}$, an equivalent definition of the MAP estimator is

$$p(\hat{\boldsymbol{\theta}}_{MAP})p(\mathbf{z}|\hat{\boldsymbol{\theta}}_{MAP}) \geq p(\hat{\boldsymbol{\theta}})p(\mathbf{z}|\hat{\boldsymbol{\theta}}) \qquad (8.2\text{-}21)$$

for all $\hat{\boldsymbol{\theta}} \neq \hat{\boldsymbol{\theta}}_{MAP}$. Quite often $\hat{\boldsymbol{\theta}}_{MAP}$ occurs at a stationary point of $p(\boldsymbol{\theta}|\mathbf{z})$ given by

$$\left. \frac{\partial p(\boldsymbol{\theta}|\mathbf{z})}{\partial \boldsymbol{\theta}} \right|_{\boldsymbol{\theta}=\hat{\boldsymbol{\theta}}_{MAP}} = \mathbf{0} \qquad (8.2\text{-}22)$$

or equivalently

$$\left. \frac{\partial p(\mathbf{z}|\boldsymbol{\theta})p(\boldsymbol{\theta})}{\partial \boldsymbol{\theta}} \right|_{\boldsymbol{\theta}=\hat{\boldsymbol{\theta}}_{MAP}} = \mathbf{0} \qquad (8.2\text{-}23)$$

For gaussian problems, it is usually helpful to find the stationary points of $\ln p(\boldsymbol{\theta}|\mathbf{z})$ rather than $p(\boldsymbol{\theta}|\mathbf{z})$ so that $\hat{\boldsymbol{\theta}}_{MAP}$ is given by

$$\left. \frac{\partial \ln p(\boldsymbol{\theta}|\mathbf{z})}{\partial \boldsymbol{\theta}} \right|_{\boldsymbol{\theta}=\hat{\boldsymbol{\theta}}_{MAP}} = \frac{\partial \ln p(\mathbf{z}|\boldsymbol{\theta})}{\partial \boldsymbol{\theta}} + \left. \frac{\partial \ln p(\boldsymbol{\theta})}{\partial \boldsymbol{\theta}} \right|_{\boldsymbol{\theta}=\hat{\boldsymbol{\theta}}_{MAP}} = \mathbf{0} \qquad (8.2\text{-}24)$$

Example 8.2-3 Let us consider again the estimation problem of Example 8.2-1. The density function $p(z|\theta)$ was found there; the product $p(z|\theta)p(\theta)$

---

†The mode of a probability density function $p(\mathbf{x})$ is the value(s) of $\mathbf{x}$ for which $p(\mathbf{x})$ is maximum.

becomes

$$p(z|\theta)p(\theta) = \begin{cases} e^{-(z-\ln \theta)} & \text{if } 0 \leq \theta \leq 1 \text{ and } z > \ln \theta \\ 0 & \text{otherwise} \end{cases}$$

We can maximize this product by making the quantity $(z - \ln \theta)$ as positive as possible. Thus

$$\hat{\theta}_{\text{MAP}} = e^z \qquad \text{if } z \leq 0$$

and

$$\hat{\theta}_{\text{MAP}} = 1 \qquad \text{if } z \geq 0$$

Example 8.2-4 As a second example of MAP estimation, let us consider again the gaussian problem of Example 8.2-2. There we found that $p(\mathbf{z}|\theta)$ was given by

$$p(\mathbf{z}|\theta) = K_2 \exp \{-\tfrac{1}{2}[\mathbf{z} - \mathbf{H}\theta]^T \frac{1}{\sigma^2}[\mathbf{z} - \mathbf{H}\theta]\}$$

Therefore, the product $p(\mathbf{z}|\theta)p(\theta)$ becomes

$$p(\mathbf{z}|\theta)p(\theta) = K_3 \exp \left\{-\frac{1}{2}[\mathbf{z} - \mathbf{H}\theta]^T \frac{1}{\sigma^2}[\mathbf{z} - \mathbf{H}\theta] - \frac{1}{2V_0}[\theta - \mu_0]^2\right\}$$

To find $\hat{\theta}_{\text{MAP}}$, we shall use Eq. (8.2-24) to write following equation:

$$\left. \frac{\partial \ln p(\mathbf{z}|\theta)p(\theta)}{\partial \theta}\right|_{\theta = \hat{\theta}_{\text{MAP}}} = 0 = \frac{1}{\sigma^2}\mathbf{H}^T[\mathbf{z} - \mathbf{H}\hat{\theta}_{\text{MAP}}] - \frac{1}{V_0}[\hat{\theta}_{\text{MAP}} - \mu_0]$$

Solving for $\hat{\theta}_{\text{MAP}}$ yields

$$\hat{\theta}_{\text{MAP}} = [\mathbf{H}^T\mathbf{H}V_0 + \sigma^2]^{-1}[V_0\mathbf{H}^T\mathbf{z} + \sigma^2\mu_0]$$

We note that this result is identical to $\hat{\theta}_{\text{MS}}$. Of course, this result is not surprising since we know that the conditional mean $\hat{\theta}_{\text{MS}}$ and conditional mode $\hat{\theta}_{\text{MAP}}$ of a gaussian density are identical.

These two examples demonstrate that the MAP estimation procedure is generally computationally simpler than the conditional mean method.

In decision theory we saw that if the messages were all equiprobable, the ML and the MAP decision rules were identical. A similar result holds for the estimation problem. Although it is not possible for *all* values of $\boldsymbol{\theta}$ to be "equiprobable" (i.e., $\boldsymbol{\theta}$ uniformly distributed over the entire K-dimensional euclidean space), we can consider the case where $\boldsymbol{\theta}$ is uniformly distributed over enough of that space. By "enough," we mean that $\hat{\boldsymbol{\theta}}_{\text{ML}}$ is included in the region.

In other words, we require that

$$p(\boldsymbol{\theta}) = \begin{cases} C & \boldsymbol{\theta} \in \mathbf{R} \\ 0 & \text{otherwise} \end{cases}$$

where $\hat{\boldsymbol{\theta}}_{\text{ML}} \in \mathbf{R}$. [We assume that $\mathbf{R}$ is defined in such a way that the derivative of $p(\boldsymbol{\theta})$ is well defined.] If this is the case, then $\hat{\boldsymbol{\theta}}_{\mathrm{MAP}}$ is clearly in **R** and, for $\boldsymbol{\theta} \in \mathbf{R}$, Eq. (8.2-24) becomes

$$\left.\frac{\partial \ln p(\mathbf{z}|\boldsymbol{\theta})}{\partial \boldsymbol{\theta}}\right|_{\boldsymbol{\theta}=\hat{\boldsymbol{\theta}}_{\mathrm{MAP}}} = \mathbf{0} \qquad (8.2\text{-}25)$$

However, from Sec. 8.1, we know that

$$\left.\frac{\partial \ln p(\mathbf{z}|\boldsymbol{\theta})}{\partial \boldsymbol{\theta}}\right|_{\boldsymbol{\theta}=\hat{\boldsymbol{\theta}}_{\mathrm{ML}}} = \mathbf{0} \qquad (8.2\text{-}26)$$

A comparison of Eqs. (8.2-25) and (8.2-26) indicates that $\hat{\boldsymbol{\theta}}_{\mathrm{MAP}} = \hat{\boldsymbol{\theta}}_{\mathrm{ML}}$ for the previous conditions. In other words, if we have no a priori knowledge concerning $\boldsymbol{\theta}$ other than that it is in a given region, then the ML and MAP estimates are equal. In general, the ML estimate is different from and inferior to the MAP estimate if any other a priori knowledge about $\boldsymbol{\theta}$ is available. We shall elaborate on this point in Chap. 9.

8.2-3 Absolute-Value Cost Function

We conclude our discussion of Bayes estimation procedures by examining one more cost function and its associated estimator. The usefulness of this class of estimators is significantly less than the two preceding techniques for two reasons. First is limited to scalar parameters, and second, it is generally computationally more difficult to use.

The absolute-value cost function is defined by

$$C_{\mathrm{AB}}(\theta, \hat{\theta}) = |\theta - \hat{\theta}|$$

By substituting this cost function in Eq. (8.2-7) we obtain

$$B_{\mathrm{AB}}(\hat{\theta}|\mathbf{z}) = \int_{-\infty}^{\infty} |\theta - \hat{\theta}|p(\theta|\mathbf{z})\,d\theta$$

$$= -\int_{-\infty}^{\hat{\theta}} (\theta - \hat{\theta})p(\theta|\mathbf{z})\,d\theta + \int_{\hat{\theta}}^{\infty} (\theta - \hat{\theta})p(\theta|\mathbf{z})\,d\theta \qquad (8.2\text{-}27)$$

Now if we take the partial derivative with respect to $\hat{\theta}$, we obtain

$$\left.\frac{\partial B_{\mathrm{AB}}(\hat{\theta}|\mathbf{z})}{\partial \theta}\right|_{\hat{\theta}=\hat{\theta}_{\mathrm{AB}}} = 0 = \int_{-\infty}^{\hat{\theta}_{\mathrm{AB}}} p(\theta|\mathbf{z})\,d\theta - \int_{\hat{\theta}_{\mathrm{AB}}}^{\infty} p(\theta|\mathbf{z})\,d\theta$$

or
$$\int_{-\infty}^{\hat{\theta}_{\mathrm{AB}}} p(\theta|\mathbf{z})\,d\theta = \int_{\hat{\theta}_{\mathrm{AB}}}^{\infty} p(\theta|\mathbf{z})\,d\theta \qquad (8.2\text{-}28)$$

Hence, we see that $\hat{\theta}_{\mathrm{AB}}$ is the *median* of the conditional density $p(\theta|\mathbf{z})$. In other words, if $F(\theta|\mathbf{z})$ is the cumulative distribution of θ given $\mathbf{z}$, then $\hat{\theta}_{\mathrm{AB}}$ is defined as

$$F(\hat{\theta}_{\mathrm{AB}}|\mathbf{z}) = \tfrac{1}{2} \qquad (8.2\text{-}29)$$

To illustrate the determination of an absolute-value cost-function estimator, let us consider again the simple scalar problem of Example 8.2-1.

Example 8.2-5 Using the results obtained in Example 8.2-1, we can write $p(\theta|z)$ as

$$p(\theta|z) = \frac{p(z|\theta)p(\theta)}{p(z)} = \begin{cases} 2\theta & \text{if } 0 \leq \theta \leq 1; z \geq 0 \\ 2e^{-2z}\theta & \text{if } 0 \leq \theta \leq e^z; z \leq 0 \end{cases}$$

For $z \geq 0$, $\hat{\theta}_{AB}$ is defined by

$$\int_{-\infty}^{\hat{\theta}_{AB}} 2\theta \, d\theta = \hat{\theta}_{AB}^2 = \tfrac{1}{2}$$

or $\hat{\theta}_{AB} = 1/\sqrt{2}$. For $z \leq 0$, $\hat{\theta}_{AB}$ is defined by

$$e^{-2z} \int_0^{\hat{\theta}_{AB}} 2\theta \, d\theta = e^{-2z}\hat{\theta}_{AB}^2 = \tfrac{1}{2}$$

or $\hat{\theta}_{AB} = e^z/\sqrt{2}$.

It should be noted that $\hat{\theta}_{AB}$ may not be unique. If there is a range of values for θ such that $p(\theta|z)$ is exactly zero and one value of θ in this range satisfies Eq. (8.2-29), then all the values in the range satisfy the equation.

In this section, we have examined the Bayesian approach to the design of estimator rules. Three separate cost functions have been studied. In the Sec. 8.3, we examine the relationship of these and other estimators.

8.3 RELATIONSHIP OF ESTIMATORS

In Secs. 8.1 and 8.2, we developed a number of different estimators. During these developments, we noted certain relationships between estimators. For example, we noted conditions under which the maximum-likelihood and maximum a posteriori estimators were equivalent or approximately equivalent. The purpose of this section is to examine in more detail the relationship between various classes of estimators.

There are some simple relationships that we can develop easily. If the conditional density $p(\theta|\mathbf{z})$ is symmetric, then $\hat{\theta}_{MS} = \hat{\theta}_{AB}$ since the conditional mean and median† are equal. Note that we must restrict ourselves to a scalar parameter. If, in addition to being symmetric, the density $p(\theta|\mathbf{z})$ is unimodal, then $\hat{\theta}_{MS} = \hat{\theta}_{MAP}$. Since the gaussian density function is both symmetric and unimodal, all these estimators will be equal if $p(\theta|\mathbf{z})$ is gaussian.

Although there are conditions for which the three Bayes estimators are equal, obviously there are many cases where they will not be equal. One obvious situation in which the MAP and MS estimators will differ is if $p(\theta|\mathbf{z})$ is symmetric but bimodal. Another case where all three estimators are different is illustrated in Examples 8.2-1, 8.2-3, and 8.2-5. The following theorem indicates

---

†If the conditional median is not unique, then one of its possible values is θ_{MS}.

some conditions for which the MS estimator (the conditional mean) is the best estimator.

Theorem 8.3-1 If the cost function $C(\theta, \hat{\theta}) = C^*(\tilde{\theta})$ is symmetric about $\tilde{\theta} = 0$,

$$C^*(\tilde{\theta}) = C^*(-\tilde{\theta}) \tag{8.3-1}$$

and convex $\cup$ so that for any $0 \leq a \leq 1$

$$C^*[ax + (1-a)y] \leq aC^*(x) + (1-a)C^*(y) \tag{8.3-2}$$

And if $p(\theta|z)$ is symmetric† about $\hat{\theta}_{MS}$ such that for any ξ

$$p_{\theta|z}(\hat{\theta}_{MS} + \xi|z) = p_{\theta|z}(\hat{\theta}_{MS} - \xi|z) \tag{8.3-3}$$

then $\hat{\theta}_{MS}$ is the optimum estimator for the cost function C^*.

PROOF The conditional Bayes cost $B(\hat{\theta}|z)$ for any estimator $\hat{\theta}$ is given by Eq. (8.2-7) as

$$B(\hat{\theta}|z) = \int_{-\infty}^{\infty} C^*(\theta - \hat{\theta})p_{\theta|z}(\theta|z)\, d\theta \tag{8.3-4}$$

Now let $\xi = \theta - \hat{\theta}_{MS}$; then $B(\hat{\theta}|z)$ becomes

$$B(\hat{\theta}|z) = \int_{-\infty}^{\infty} C^*(\xi + \hat{\theta}_{MS} - \hat{\theta})p_{\theta|z}(\hat{\theta}_{MS} + \xi|z)\, d\xi \tag{8.3-5}$$

Next we make the change of variables $\xi = -\xi$ in Eq. (8.3-5) to obtain

$$B(\hat{\theta}|z) = \int_{-\infty}^{\infty} C^*(-\xi + \hat{\theta}_{MS} - \hat{\theta})p_{\theta|z}(\hat{\theta}_{MS} - \xi|z)\, d\xi$$

Because C^* is symmetric, this can also be written as

$$B(\hat{\theta}|z) = \int_{-\infty}^{\infty} C^*(\xi - \hat{\theta}_{MS} + \hat{\theta})p_{\theta|z}(\hat{\theta}_{MS} - \xi|z)\, d\xi$$

and if we use the symmetry of $p(\theta|z)$, we have

$$B(\hat{\theta}|z) = \int_{-\infty}^{\infty} C^*(\xi - \hat{\theta}_{MS} + \hat{\theta})p_{\theta|z}(\hat{\theta}_{MS} + \xi|z)\, d\xi \tag{8.3-6}$$

Since $B(\hat{\theta}|z)$ is equal to each of the integrals in Eqs. (8.3-5) and (8.3-6), $B(\hat{\theta}|z)$ must also be equal to one-half the sum of the two integrals, or

$$B(\hat{\theta}|z) = \int_{-\infty}^{\infty} \tfrac{1}{2}[C^*(\xi + \hat{\theta}_{MS} - \hat{\theta}) + C^*(\xi - \hat{\theta}_{MS} + \hat{\theta})]p_{\theta|z}(\hat{\theta}_{MS} + \xi|z)\, d\xi \tag{8.3-7}$$

---

†If $p(\theta|z)$ is symmetric about any value θ^*, then θ^* must equal $\hat{\theta}_{MS}$.

From the convexity property of C^*, we know that

$$\tfrac{1}{2}[C^*(\boldsymbol{\xi} + \hat{\boldsymbol{\theta}}_{MS} - \hat{\boldsymbol{\theta}}) + C^*(\boldsymbol{\xi} - \hat{\boldsymbol{\theta}}_{MS} + \boldsymbol{\theta})] \geq C^*(\boldsymbol{\xi})$$

Using this result in Eq. (8.3-7), we obtain

$$B(\hat{\boldsymbol{\theta}}|\mathbf{z}) \geq \int_{-\infty}^{\infty} C^*(\boldsymbol{\xi}) p_{\theta|z}(\hat{\boldsymbol{\theta}}_{MS} + \boldsymbol{\xi}|\mathbf{z})\, d\boldsymbol{\xi} \qquad (8.3\text{-}8)$$

If we make the substitution $\boldsymbol{\theta} = \hat{\boldsymbol{\theta}}_{MS} + \boldsymbol{\xi}$ in the right side of Eq. (8.3-8), we find that

$$\int_{-\infty}^{\infty} C^*(\boldsymbol{\xi}) p_{\theta|z}(\hat{\boldsymbol{\theta}}_{MS} + \boldsymbol{\xi}|\mathbf{z})\, d\boldsymbol{\xi} = \int_{-\infty}^{\infty} C^*(\boldsymbol{\theta} - \hat{\boldsymbol{\theta}}_{MS}) p(\boldsymbol{\theta}|\mathbf{z})\, d\boldsymbol{\theta}$$

$$= B(\hat{\boldsymbol{\theta}}_{MS}|\mathbf{z}) \qquad (8.3\text{-}9)$$

The combination of Eqs. (8.3-8) and (8.3-9) yields the following result:

$$B(\hat{\boldsymbol{\theta}}|\mathbf{z}) \geq B(\hat{\boldsymbol{\theta}}_{MS}|\mathbf{z}) \qquad (8.3\text{-}10)$$

This result says that the conditional Bayes cost associated with any estimator can never be less than the cost associated with MS estimator. Hence the minimum cost that can be achieved is $B(\hat{\boldsymbol{\theta}}_{MS}|\mathbf{z})$, and we can achieve it if $\hat{\boldsymbol{\theta}} = \hat{\boldsymbol{\theta}}_{MS}$. This establishes the fact that $\hat{\boldsymbol{\theta}}_{MS}$ is the optimum estimator.

Various trade-offs can be made in the conditions of Theorem 8.3-1. In particular, if we strengthen the requirements on C^*, we can loosen them on $p(\boldsymbol{\theta}|\mathbf{z})$ and vice versa. For example, if C^* not only satisfies Eqs. (8.3-1) and (8.3-2), but is quadratic of the form

$$C^*(\tilde{\boldsymbol{\theta}}) = \|\tilde{\boldsymbol{\theta}}\|^2$$

then from Sec. 8.2-1 we know that $\hat{\boldsymbol{\theta}}_{MS}$ is the optimum estimator for all $p(\boldsymbol{\theta}|\mathbf{z})$. Theorem 8.3-1 is also valid if $p(\boldsymbol{\theta}|\mathbf{z})$ rather than C^* is convex.

If we restrict $p(\boldsymbol{\theta}|\mathbf{z})$ to be gaussian, then the restrictions on C^* can be extremely mild. This result is summarized in the following theorem (Deutsch, 1965) for scalar parameters, which is stated without proof.

Theorem 8.3-2 If $p(\theta|\mathbf{z})$ is gaussian and $C^*(\tilde{\theta})$ is nonnegative and nondecreasing for $\tilde{\theta} > 0$ and nonincreasing for $\tilde{\theta} < 0$ so that

$$C^*(\tilde{\theta}) \leq C^*(\sigma\tilde{\theta})$$

for $\sigma > 1$, then $\hat{\theta}_{MS}$ is the optimum estimator.†

In this section, we have examined the relationship between various estimators and, in particular, some conditions for which the MS estimator is optimum. These results can sometimes be helpful in eliminating the need to compute a new optimum estimator if we can show that it must be equivalent to a known

---

†The generalization of this result to vector parameter is difficult and will not be presented here.

estimator. They can also be helpful by allowing us to combine the properties of various estimators. For example we shall derive some estimators for gaussian problems in Chap. 9. We shall use MAP procedures for the derivations to simplify computational work, but, we shall make use of the fact that the estimator is also a mean-square estimator.

8.4 LINEAR MINIMUM-VARIANCE AND LEAST-SQUARES METHODS

In Sec. 8.2 we studied the Bayes cost approach to estimation, which required a complete probabilistic description of both the parameter to be estimated and all noise terms. The maximum-likelihood method did not require a description for θ but did require a probabilistic description for all disturbances. In this section, we shall examine two methods of parameter estimation which require a minimum of stochastic description: The *linear minimum-variance method* is based on first and second statistical moments of the parameter and disturbances. The *least-squares method* abandons all need for stochastic information and treats the estimation problem as a deterministic optimization problem.

8.4-1 Linear Minimum-Variance Method

Until now, we have found general solutions for the best possible estimators in various situations. We have not been concerned with the structure of these estimators, only with their optimality. In this section we will do something a little different. We will find the best estimator of a certain type, even though it may not be the overall optimum. The type we have selected is both easy to evaluate and easy to implement. In Sec. 8.2-1, we derived the mean-square (or minimum-variance) estimation method. We found that the estimator was the mean of the conditional density $p(\theta|\mathbf{z})$. In general, the conditional mean will *not* be a linear function of the observation $\mathbf{z}$.

In this section, we shall restrict our attention to *linear estimators* of the form

$$\hat{\theta}_L = \mathbf{b} + \mathbf{Az} \qquad (8.4\text{-}1)$$

The observation $\mathbf{z}$ is assumed to be a linear function of θ of the form

$$\mathbf{z} = \mathbf{H}\theta + \mathbf{n} \qquad (8.4\text{-}2)$$

where $\mathbf{n}$ is noise. The first- and second-order moments of θ and $\mathbf{n}$ are given by

$$E\{\theta\} = \boldsymbol{\mu}_\theta \qquad \text{var}\{\theta\} = \mathbf{V}_\theta \qquad (8.4\text{-}3)$$

and $\qquad\qquad\qquad E\{\mathbf{n}\} = 0 \qquad \text{var}\{\mathbf{n}\} = \mathbf{V}_\mathbf{n} \qquad (8.4\text{-}4)$

The parameter θ and noise $\mathbf{n}$ are assumed to be uncorrelated. The objective is to select $\mathbf{b}$ and $\mathbf{A}$ in order to minimize the error variance. We shall call such estimators *linear minimum-variance estimators;* they are the best, in the sense of minimum-error-variance, *linear* estimators.

As noted previously, the minimum-error-variance estimator, in general, is *not* a linear estimator of the form of Eq. (8.4-1). As a result, the linear minimum-variance estimator is not optimum in the sense that some nonlinear estimator can be found which will yield a smaller error variance. In the Chap. 9, we shall show that if $p(\boldsymbol{\theta}|\mathbf{z})$ is gaussian, then the conditional mean (minimum-variance) estimator is, in fact, linear. The linear minimum-variance estimator is therefore optimum when compared with all other estimators for gaussian problems. However, in general, the linear minimum-variance estimator is optimum only when compared with other linear estimators.

The advantages of the linear-variance estimator are (1) the ease with which they may be derived, (2) the mathematical tractability of the linear form, and (3) the minimum amount of stochastic information which is required for their development. Because of these factors, the linear minimum-variance estimator is a popular form.

Let us return to the problem of selecting $\mathbf{A}$ and $\mathbf{b}$. In fact, the form of Eq. (8.4-1) is more general than needed to minimize the error variance. We shall make use of this additional generality to impose an additional restriction on the estimator. We shall require that the expected value of the estimator $\hat{\boldsymbol{\theta}}_L$ be equal to the expected value of the parameter $\boldsymbol{\theta}$. When an estimator satisfies this property, we say that it is unbiased (see Sec. 10.1). In terms of Eq. (8.4-1), this requirement becomes

$$E\{\hat{\boldsymbol{\theta}}_L\} = \mathbf{b} + \mathbf{A}E\{\mathbf{z}\} = E\{\boldsymbol{\theta}\} = \boldsymbol{\mu}_\theta$$

If we substitute from Eq. (8.4-2) for $\mathbf{z}$, then we have

$$\mathbf{b} + \mathbf{AH}\boldsymbol{\mu}_\theta = \boldsymbol{\mu}_\theta \tag{8.4-5}$$

or $\mathbf{b}$ is given by

$$\mathbf{b} = \boldsymbol{\mu}_\theta - \mathbf{AH}\boldsymbol{\mu}_\theta \tag{8.4-6}$$

Next let us substitute this result into Eq. (8.4-1) to obtain the unbiased linear estimator:

$$\hat{\boldsymbol{\theta}}_L = \boldsymbol{\mu}_\theta + \mathbf{A}(\mathbf{z} - \mathbf{H}\boldsymbol{\mu}_\theta) \tag{8.4-7}$$

Note that because the estimator is unbiased, the estimation error $\tilde{\boldsymbol{\theta}} = \boldsymbol{\theta} - \hat{\boldsymbol{\theta}}_L$ is zero mean. The next step is to select $\mathbf{A}$ in order to minimize the error variance.

Although we have indicated our intent to minimize the error variance, such an optimization problem is ill-defined because the error variance is a matrix. In order to have a well-defined optimization, we need a scalar goodness measure. Therefore, we shall try to minimize the sum of the variances of each component of $\boldsymbol{\theta}$. This is the sum of the main diagonal terms of the variance matrix and is defined as the *trace* of the matrix

$$\text{tr}\,\{\text{var}\,\{\tilde{\boldsymbol{\theta}}\}\} = \sum_{k=1}^{K} \text{var}\,\{\tilde{\theta}_k\}$$

Therefore, we wish to select **A** to minimize the trace of the error variance, or

$$\min_{\mathbf{A}} \text{ tr } \{\text{var } \{\tilde{\boldsymbol{\theta}}\}\} = \min_{\mathbf{A}} \text{ tr } \{E\{\tilde{\boldsymbol{\theta}}\tilde{\boldsymbol{\theta}}^T\}\} \qquad (8.4\text{-}8)$$

where $\tilde{\boldsymbol{\theta}} = \boldsymbol{\theta} - \hat{\boldsymbol{\theta}}_L$ as usual. By substituting Eq. (8.4-7) in Eq. (8.4-8), we obtain the following problem:

$$\min_{\mathbf{A}} \text{ tr } \{\text{var } \{\tilde{\boldsymbol{\theta}}\}\} = \min_{\mathbf{A}} \text{ tr } \{E\{[\boldsymbol{\theta} - \boldsymbol{\mu}_{\theta} - \mathbf{A}(\mathbf{z} - \mathbf{H}\boldsymbol{\mu}_{\theta})]$$

$$\times [\boldsymbol{\theta} - \boldsymbol{\mu}_{\theta} - \mathbf{A}(\mathbf{z} - \mathbf{H}\boldsymbol{\mu}_{\theta})]^T\}\} \quad (8.4\text{-}9)$$

We shall make use of a variational calculus approach to obtain the correct value for **A**. The matrix **A** is written as

$$\mathbf{A} = \mathbf{A}^* + \epsilon \mathbf{\Xi} \qquad (8.4\text{-}10)$$

where $\mathbf{A}^*$ is the optimum (as yet unknown) matrix and $\epsilon\mathbf{\Xi}$ is called the *variation*. Note that tr $\{\text{var } \{\tilde{\boldsymbol{\theta}}\}\}$ must have its minimum value where $\epsilon = 0$ independent of $\mathbf{\Xi}$. Hence we can find $\mathbf{A}^*$ by forcing the following equation to be true:

$$\frac{\partial \text{ tr } \{\text{var } \{\tilde{\boldsymbol{\theta}}\}\}}{\partial \epsilon}\bigg|_{\epsilon=0} = 0 \qquad (8.4\text{-}11)$$

independent of $\mathbf{\Xi}$. The logic of this requirement is seen by examining Fig. 8.4-1 where we see that the derivative of tr $\{\text{var } \{\tilde{\boldsymbol{\theta}}\}\}$ with respect to ϵ becomes zero independent of $\mathbf{\Xi}$. If we substitute Eq. (8.4-10) into Eq. (8.4-9) and carry out the steps indicated in Eq. (8.4-11), we obtain

$$2E\{[(\boldsymbol{\theta} - \boldsymbol{\mu}_{\theta}) - \mathbf{A}^*(\mathbf{z} - \mathbf{H}\boldsymbol{\mu}_{\theta})]\mathbf{z}^T\mathbf{\Xi}^T\} =$$

$$2[\text{cov } \{\boldsymbol{\theta}, \mathbf{z}\} - \mathbf{A}^* \text{ var } \{\mathbf{z}\}]\mathbf{\Xi}^T = \mathbf{0} \quad (8.4\text{-}12)$$

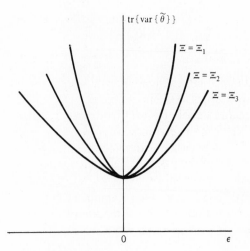

Figure 8.4-1 Cost plots for different variations.

In order for Eq. (8.4-12) to be satisfied for any Ξ, it is necessary that

$$\text{cov } \{\boldsymbol{\theta}, \mathbf{z}\} - \mathbf{A}^* \text{ var } \{\mathbf{z}\} = \mathbf{0}$$

or that $\mathbf{A}^*$ be given by

$$\mathbf{A}^* = \text{cov } \{\boldsymbol{\theta}, \mathbf{z}\} [\text{var } \{\mathbf{z}\}]^{-1} \tag{8.4-13}$$

If we use Eq. (8.4-2) for $\mathbf{z}$, then cov $\{\boldsymbol{\theta}, \mathbf{z}\}$ becomes

$$\text{cov } \{\boldsymbol{\theta}, \mathbf{z}\} = \text{cov } \{\boldsymbol{\theta}, \mathbf{H}\boldsymbol{\theta} + \mathbf{n}\} = \mathbf{V}_\theta \mathbf{H}^T \tag{8.4-14}$$

since $\boldsymbol{\theta}$ and $\mathbf{n}$ are uncorrelated. The var $\{\mathbf{z}\}$ is

$$\text{var } \{\mathbf{z}\} = \text{var } \{\mathbf{H}\boldsymbol{\theta} + \mathbf{n}\} = \mathbf{H}\mathbf{V}_\theta \mathbf{H}^T + \mathbf{V}_\mathbf{n} \tag{8.4-15}$$

Substituting these two results in Eq. (8.4-13) yields the following result for $\mathbf{A}^*$:

$$\mathbf{A}^* = \mathbf{V}_\theta \mathbf{H}^T [\mathbf{H}\mathbf{V}_\theta \mathbf{H}^T + \mathbf{V}_\mathbf{n}]^{-1}$$

and the linear minimum variance is

$$\hat{\boldsymbol{\theta}}_{\text{LMV}} = \boldsymbol{\mu}_\theta + \mathbf{V}_\theta \mathbf{H}^T [\mathbf{H}\mathbf{V}_\theta \mathbf{H}^T + \mathbf{V}_\mathbf{n}]^{-1}(\mathbf{z} - \mathbf{H}\boldsymbol{\mu}_\theta) \tag{8.4-16}$$

Note that this result depends only on the first- and second-order moments of $\boldsymbol{\theta}$ and $\mathbf{n}$.

Example 8.4-1 As an illustration of the use of the preceding result, let us consider a two-dimensional observation of a scalar parameter given by

$$\mathbf{z} = \begin{bmatrix} 1 \\ 1 \end{bmatrix} \theta + \begin{bmatrix} n_1 \\ n_2 \end{bmatrix}$$

where the statistical parameters are

$$\mu_\theta = 0 \qquad V_\theta = V$$

$$\boldsymbol{\mu}_\mathbf{n} = \mathbf{0} \qquad \mathbf{V}_\mathbf{n} = \sigma^2 \mathbf{I}$$

If we substitute into Eq. (8.4-16), we obtain

$$\hat{\theta}_{\text{LMV}} = V[1 \quad 1] \left\{ V \begin{bmatrix} 1 & 1 \\ 1 & 1 \end{bmatrix} + \sigma^2 \begin{bmatrix} 1 & 0 \\ 0 & 1 \end{bmatrix} \right\}^{-1} \mathbf{z}$$

$$= V[1 \quad 1] \begin{bmatrix} V + \sigma^2 & V \\ V & V + \sigma^2 \end{bmatrix}^{-1} \mathbf{z}$$

$$= V[1 \quad 1] \frac{1}{\sigma^2(2V + \sigma^2)} \begin{bmatrix} V + \sigma^2 & -V \\ -V & V + \sigma^2 \end{bmatrix} \mathbf{z}$$

$$= \frac{1}{2 + \sigma^2/V} (z_1 + z_2)$$

If we make use of the matrix inversion lemma (see Lemma 11.2-1), it is possible to rewrite Eq. (8.4-16) in a form that is often computationally more convenient. Using the matrix inversion lemma, we can write

$$[HV_\theta H^T + V_n]^{-1} = V_n^{-1} - V_n^{-1}H[H^TV_n^{-1}H + V_\theta^{-1}]^{-1}H^TV_n^{-1} \quad (8.4\text{-}17)$$

If we premultiply this by $V_\theta H^T$ to obtain A^* and then factor $H^TV_n^{-1}$ out, we obtain

$$A^* = \{V_\theta - V_\theta H^TV_n^{-1}H[H^TV_n^{-1}H + V_\theta^{-1}]^{-1}\}H^TV_n^{-1}$$

Next the quantity $[H^TV_n^{-1}H + V_\theta^{-1}]^{-1}$ is factored out so that A^* becomes

$$A^* = \{V_\theta[H^TV_n^{-1}H + V_\theta^{-1}] - V_\theta H^TV_n^{-1}H\}[H^TV_n^{-1}H + V_\theta^{-1}]^{-1}H^TV_n^{-1}$$

$$= [H^TV_n^{-1}H + V_\theta^{-1}]^{-1}H^TV_n^{-1} \quad (8.4\text{-}18)$$

Therefore $\hat{\theta}_{LMV}$ can be written as

$$\hat{\theta}_{LMV} = \mu_\theta + [H^TV_n^{-1}H + V_\theta^{-1}]^{-1}H^TV_n^{-1}(z - H\mu_\theta) \quad (8.4\text{-}19)$$

Combining the two terms involving μ_θ yields

$$\hat{\theta}_{LMV} = [H^TV_n^{-1}H + V_\theta^{-1}]^{-1}H^TV_n^{-1}z$$
$$+ \{I - [H^TV_n^{-1}H + V_\theta^{-1}]^{-1}H^TV_n^{-1}H\}\mu_\theta$$

If we factor $[H^TV_n^{-1}H + V_\theta^{-1}]^{-1}$ out of the second term, we have

$$\hat{\theta}_{LMV} = [H^TV_n^{-1}H + V_\theta^{-1}]^{-1}H^TV_n^{-1}z$$
$$+ [H^TV_n^{-1}H + V_\theta^{-1}]^{-1}[H^TV_n^{-1}H + V_\theta^{-1} - H^TV_n^{-1}H]\mu_\theta$$

or
$$\hat{\theta}_{LMV} = [H^TV_n^{-1}H + V_\theta^{-1}]^{-1}(H^TV_n^{-1}z + V_\theta^{-1}\mu_\theta) \quad (8.4\text{-}20)$$

which is the desired form.

The advantage of the form of Eq. (8.4-20) over Eq. (8.4-16) is the size of the matrix to be inverted. In Eq. (8.4-16), the matrix to be inverted has the dimensionality I of the observation vector z; in Eq. (8.4-20) the matrix to be inverted has the dimensionality K of the parameter θ. Since K is generally much smaller than I, Eq. (8.4-20) generally requires less computational effort. In Sec. 9.2 we shall show that for sequential estimation Eq. (8.4-16) is actually the more desirable form.

Example 8.4-2 Let us rework Example 8.4-1 making use of Eq. (8.4-20). The quantity $H^TV_n^{-1}H + V_\theta^{-1}$ is given by

$$H^TV_n^{-1}H + V_\theta^{-1} = [1 \quad 1]\frac{1}{\sigma^2}\begin{bmatrix} 1 \\ 1 \end{bmatrix} + V^{-1}$$

$$= \frac{2}{\sigma^2} + \frac{1}{V} = \frac{2 + \sigma^2/V}{\sigma^2}$$

Therefore $\hat{\theta}_{LMV}$ is

$$\hat{\theta}_{LMV} = \frac{\sigma^2}{2 + \sigma^2/V}[1 \quad 1]\begin{bmatrix} z_1 \\ z_1 \end{bmatrix}\frac{1}{\sigma^2}$$

$$= \frac{z_1 + z_2}{2 + \sigma^2/V}$$

as before. Note that there was no matrix inversion in this case because θ is a scalar.

Example 8.4-3 A number of physical phenomena are described by an autoregressive model of the form

$$z_i = \sum_{k=1}^{K} \theta_k z_{i-k} + n_i$$

$$= \mathbf{H}_i \boldsymbol{\theta} + n_i \qquad i = 1, 2, \ldots, I$$

where $\qquad \mathbf{H}_i = [z_{i-1} z_{i-2} \cdots z_{i-K}]$

The noise samples n_i are assumed to be uncorrelated and identically distributed so that

$$\mathbf{V_n} = \sigma^2 \mathbf{I}$$

A standard approach is to assume no previous knowledge of $\boldsymbol{\theta}$. No knowledge of $\boldsymbol{\theta}$ would imply an infinite variance matrix $\mathbf{V}_\theta$; it is more convenient to represent this as

$$\mathbf{V}_\theta^{-1} = \mathbf{0} \qquad \text{and} \qquad \boldsymbol{\mu}_\theta = \mathbf{0}$$

The observation model for this problem is given by

$$\mathbf{z} = \mathbf{H}\boldsymbol{\theta} + \mathbf{n}$$

where

$$\mathbf{H} = \begin{bmatrix} \mathbf{H}_1 \\ \hline \mathbf{H}_2 \\ \hline \vdots \\ \hline \mathbf{H}_I \end{bmatrix}$$

The linear minimum-variance estimate given by Eq. (8.4-20) is then

$$\hat{\boldsymbol{\theta}}_{\text{LMV}} = \left[\frac{1}{\sigma^2} \mathbf{H}^T \mathbf{H} \right]^{-1} \frac{1}{\sigma^2} \mathbf{H}^T \mathbf{z}$$

$$= (\mathbf{H}^T \mathbf{H})^{-1} \mathbf{H}^T \mathbf{z}$$

The elements of the matrix $\mathbf{H}^T \mathbf{H} = \mathbf{R}$ are given by

$$r_{ij} = \sum_{l=1}^{I} z_{l-i} z_{l-j}$$

while the elements of the vector $\mathbf{H}^T \mathbf{z} = \boldsymbol{\phi}$ are

$$\phi_i = \sum_{l=1}^{I} z_{l-i} z_l$$

In terms of $\mathbf{R}$ and $\boldsymbol{\phi}$,

$$\hat{\boldsymbol{\theta}}_{\text{LMV}} = \mathbf{R}^{-1} \boldsymbol{\phi}$$

There are some interesting properties of the linear minimum-variance estimator. Consider, for example, the covariance between $\hat{\boldsymbol{\theta}}_{\text{LMV}}$ and $\tilde{\boldsymbol{\theta}}_{\text{LMV}} = \boldsymbol{\theta} - \hat{\boldsymbol{\theta}}_{\text{LMV}}$. Using Eq. (8.4-20) for $\hat{\boldsymbol{\theta}}_{\text{LMV}}$, this becomes

$$\text{cov}\,\{\hat{\boldsymbol{\theta}}_{\text{LMV}}, \tilde{\boldsymbol{\theta}}_{\text{LMV}}\} = \text{cov}\,\{[\mathbf{H}^T\mathbf{V}_\mathbf{n}^{-1}\mathbf{H} + \mathbf{V}_\theta^{-1}]^{-1}(\mathbf{H}^T\mathbf{V}_\mathbf{n}^{-1}\mathbf{z} + \mathbf{V}_\theta^{-1}\boldsymbol{\mu}_\theta),$$
$$\boldsymbol{\theta} - [\mathbf{H}^T\mathbf{V}_\mathbf{n}^{-1}\mathbf{H} + \mathbf{V}_\theta^{-1}]^{-1}(\mathbf{H}^T\mathbf{V}_\mathbf{n}^{-1}\mathbf{z} + \mathbf{V}_\theta^{-1}\boldsymbol{\mu}_\theta)\}$$

If we use the fact that $\mathbf{z} = \mathbf{H}\boldsymbol{\theta} + \mathbf{n}$ and that $\boldsymbol{\theta}$ and $\mathbf{n}$ are uncorrelated, we obtain

$$\text{cov}\,\{\hat{\boldsymbol{\theta}}_{\text{LMV}}, \tilde{\boldsymbol{\theta}}_{\text{LMV}}\} = [\mathbf{H}^T\mathbf{V}_\mathbf{n}^{-1}\mathbf{H} + \mathbf{V}_\theta^{-1}]^{-1}\{\mathbf{H}^T\mathbf{V}_\mathbf{n}\mathbf{H}\mathbf{V}_\theta$$
$$- \{\mathbf{H}^T\mathbf{V}_\mathbf{n}^{-1}\mathbf{H}\mathbf{V}_\theta \mathbf{H}^T\mathbf{V}_\mathbf{n}^{-1}\mathbf{H} + \mathbf{H}^T\mathbf{V}_\mathbf{n}^{-1}\mathbf{V}_\mathbf{v}\mathbf{V}_\mathbf{v}^{-1}\mathbf{H}\}$$
$$\times [\mathbf{H}^T\mathbf{V}_\mathbf{n}^{-1}\mathbf{H} + \mathbf{V}_\theta^{-1}]^{-1}\}$$
$$= [\mathbf{H}^T\mathbf{V}_\mathbf{n}^{-1}\mathbf{H} + \mathbf{V}_\theta^{-1}]^{-1}\{\mathbf{H}^T\mathbf{V}_\mathbf{n}\mathbf{H}\mathbf{V}_\theta(\mathbf{I} - [\mathbf{H}^T\mathbf{V}_\mathbf{n}^{-1}\mathbf{H} + \mathbf{V}_\theta^{-1}]$$
$$\times [\mathbf{H}^T\mathbf{V}_\mathbf{n}^{-1}\mathbf{H} + \mathbf{V}_\theta^{-1}]^{-1})\} \qquad (8.4\text{-}21)$$

By canceling the common term, we have

$$\text{cov}\,\{\hat{\boldsymbol{\theta}}_{\text{LMV}}, \tilde{\boldsymbol{\theta}}_{\text{LMV}}\} = \mathbf{0} \qquad (8.4\text{-}22)$$

This result says that the estimate and estimation error are orthogonal. Equation (8.4-22) is a statement of a general result known as the *orthogonal projection lemma* which says that the linear minimum-variance estimate is the orthogonal projection of $\boldsymbol{\theta}$ onto the space spanned by observation z.† By beginning with Eq. (8.4-22), one can derive the linear minimum variance estimator of Eqs. (8.4-16) or (8.4-20).

Previously we set the expected value of $\boldsymbol{\theta}$ to zero by selection of **b**. Let us now calculate the variance of $\tilde{\boldsymbol{\theta}}$. Since $\tilde{\boldsymbol{\theta}}_{\text{LMV}} = \boldsymbol{\theta} - \hat{\boldsymbol{\theta}}_{\text{LMV}}$, we have

$$\text{var}\,\{\tilde{\boldsymbol{\theta}}_{\text{LMV}}\} = \text{cov}\,\{\boldsymbol{\theta} - \hat{\boldsymbol{\theta}}_{\text{LMV}}, \tilde{\boldsymbol{\theta}}_{\text{LMV}}\}$$
$$= \text{cov}\,\{\boldsymbol{\theta}, \tilde{\boldsymbol{\theta}}_{\text{LMV}}\} - \text{cov}\,\{\hat{\boldsymbol{\theta}}_{\text{LMV}}, \tilde{\boldsymbol{\theta}}_{\text{LMV}}\}$$

However, from Eq. (8.4-22), we know that the second term is zero so that

$$\text{var}\,\{\tilde{\boldsymbol{\theta}}_{\text{LMV}}\} = \text{cov}\,\{\boldsymbol{\theta}, \tilde{\boldsymbol{\theta}}_{\text{LMV}}\}$$

Now substituting for $\tilde{\boldsymbol{\theta}}_{\text{LMV}}$, we obtain

$$\text{var}\,\{\tilde{\boldsymbol{\theta}}_{\text{LMV}}\} = \text{cov}\,\{\boldsymbol{\theta}, \boldsymbol{\theta} - [\mathbf{H}^T\mathbf{V}_\mathbf{n}^{-1}\mathbf{H} + \mathbf{V}_\theta^{-1}]^{-1}(\mathbf{H}^T\mathbf{V}_\mathbf{n}^{-1}\mathbf{z} + \mathbf{V}_\theta^{-1}\boldsymbol{\mu}\boldsymbol{\theta})\}$$
$$= \mathbf{V}_\theta - \mathbf{V}_\theta\mathbf{H}^T\mathbf{V}_\mathbf{n}^{-1}\mathbf{H}[\mathbf{H}^T\mathbf{V}_\mathbf{n}^{-1}\mathbf{H} + \mathbf{V}_\theta^{-1}]^{-1}$$

Let us factor $\mathbf{V}_\theta$ to the left and $[\mathbf{H}^T\mathbf{V}_\mathbf{n}^{-1}\mathbf{H} + \mathbf{V}_\theta^{-1}]^{-1}$ to the right to obtain

$$\text{var}\,\{\tilde{\boldsymbol{\theta}}_{\text{LMV}}\} = \mathbf{V}_\theta\{\mathbf{H}^T\mathbf{V}_\mathbf{n}^{-1}\mathbf{H} + \mathbf{V}_\theta^{-1} - \mathbf{H}^T\mathbf{V}_\mathbf{n}^{-1}\mathbf{H}\}[\mathbf{H}^T\mathbf{V}_\mathbf{n}^{-1}\mathbf{H} + \mathbf{V}_\theta^{-1}]^{-1}$$

or $\quad \text{var}\,\{\tilde{\boldsymbol{\theta}}_{\text{LMV}}\} = [\mathbf{H}^T\mathbf{V}_\mathbf{n}^{-1}\mathbf{H} + \mathbf{V}_\theta^{-1}]^{-1} \qquad (8.4\text{-}23)$

An alternative method for deriving the linear minimum-variance estimator is to assume the $p(\boldsymbol{\theta}|\mathbf{z})$ is gaussian with the appropriate first- and second-order

---

†For further discussion of the orthogonal projection lemma, see Sage and Melsa (1971).

moments. One then derives the conditional mean estimator which is linear, and this is the best linear minimum-variance estimator. (We shall discuss this approach in Chap. 9.)

8.4-2 Least-Squares Method

The linear minimum-variance method discussed in Sec. 8.4-1, required only the first- and second-order moments of the random variables. In this section, we consider the *least-squares approach*, which uses no stochastic information but instead treats the parameter-estimation task as a deterministic optimization problem. This method is also known as a *least-squares curve fitting* and is closely related to linear regression methods.

We assume again a linear observation model of the form

$$\mathbf{z} = \mathbf{H}\boldsymbol{\theta} + \mathbf{n} \tag{8.4-24}$$

Here $\mathbf{n}$ is an unknown disturbance. As usual, $\mathbf{z}$ is l-dimensional while $\boldsymbol{\theta}$ is K-dimensional with K normally much smaller than l.

The problem is then to select an estimate $\hat{\boldsymbol{\theta}}$ of $\boldsymbol{\theta}$ such that the quadratic performance index

$$J(\hat{\boldsymbol{\theta}}) = \tfrac{1}{2}(\mathbf{z} - \mathbf{H}\hat{\boldsymbol{\theta}})^T \mathbf{W}(\mathbf{z} - \mathbf{H}\hat{\boldsymbol{\theta}}) \tag{8.4-25}$$

is minimized. The weighting matrix $\mathbf{W}$ is assumed to be positive definite and symmetric. This weighting matrix may be used to assign different costs to each of the errors $(\mathbf{z} - \mathbf{H}\hat{\boldsymbol{\theta}})_i$. The estimator which minimizes $J(\hat{\boldsymbol{\theta}})$ is known as the *least-squares estimator* $\hat{\boldsymbol{\theta}}_{\text{LS}}$. This method is sometimes referred to as *weighted least squares* because of the use of the weighting matrix $\mathbf{W}$.

A necessary condition for the least-squares estimator is

$$\left. \frac{\partial J(\hat{\boldsymbol{\theta}})}{\partial \hat{\boldsymbol{\theta}}} \right|_{\boldsymbol{\theta} = \hat{\boldsymbol{\theta}}_{\text{LS}}} = 0 \tag{8.4-26}$$

Note that $J(\hat{\boldsymbol{\theta}})$ is a quadratic form in the variable $\hat{\boldsymbol{\theta}}$, that is, it contains terms where the degree of $\hat{\boldsymbol{\theta}}$ is no higher than 2. The derivative of a quadratic form appears with some regularity in estimation problems, and it is useful to examine it in some depth. The following lemma contains the results which are required to evaluate an expression such as Eq. (8.4-26).

Lemma 8.4-1 For any square matrix $\mathbf{A}$ the following derivatives are true:

$$\frac{\partial}{\partial \mathbf{x}} \mathbf{x}^T \mathbf{A} \mathbf{z} = \mathbf{A} \mathbf{z}$$

$$\frac{\partial}{\partial \mathbf{x}} \mathbf{z}^T \mathbf{A} \mathbf{x} = \mathbf{A}^T \mathbf{z}$$

$$\frac{\partial}{\partial \mathbf{x}} \mathbf{x}^T \mathbf{A} \mathbf{x} = (\mathbf{A} + \mathbf{A}^T) \mathbf{x}$$

PROOF We shall prove only the first relation and leave the second two as exercises. Our proof will be simply to evaluate the indicated derivative. The expression $\mathbf{x}^T\mathbf{A}\mathbf{z}$ can be written as

$$\mathbf{x}^T\mathbf{A}\mathbf{z} = \sum_{i=1}^{K}\sum_{j=1}^{K} x_i A_{ij} z_j$$

Therefore, the derivative of this quantity with respect to x_k is

$$\frac{\partial}{\partial x_k}\mathbf{x}^T\mathbf{A}\mathbf{z} = \sum_{j=1}^{K} A_{kj} z_j$$

And when this is repeated for all values of k, the form given in the lemma is obtained. (The proof for the other two forms follows in an analogous manner.)

Now if we use Eq. (8.4-25) for $J(\hat{\boldsymbol{\theta}})$ and carry out the operations indicated by Eq. (8.4-26) we obtain

$$\mathbf{H}^T\mathbf{W}(\mathbf{z} - \mathbf{H}\hat{\boldsymbol{\theta}}_{LS}) = 0$$

so that the least-squares estimator is

$$\hat{\boldsymbol{\theta}}_{LS} = (\mathbf{H}^T\mathbf{W}\mathbf{H})^{-1}\mathbf{H}^T\mathbf{W}\mathbf{z} \qquad (8.4\text{-}27)$$

Note that the estimator depends only on $\mathbf{H}$ and the weighting matrix $\mathbf{W}$.

Example 8.4-4 To illustrate the use of the least-squares estimator, let us consider again Example 8.4-1, where the $\mathbf{H}$ matrix was

$$\mathbf{H} = \begin{bmatrix} 1 \\ 1 \end{bmatrix}$$

Let us use the following $\mathbf{W}$ matrix:

$$\mathbf{W} = \begin{bmatrix} 2 & 1 \\ 1 & 2 \end{bmatrix}$$

Then $\hat{\boldsymbol{\theta}}_{LS}$ is given by

$$\hat{\boldsymbol{\theta}}_{LS} = \left(\begin{bmatrix} 1 & 1 \end{bmatrix} \begin{bmatrix} 2 & 1 \\ 1 & 2 \end{bmatrix} \begin{bmatrix} 1 \\ 1 \end{bmatrix} \right)^{-1} \begin{bmatrix} 1 & 1 \end{bmatrix} \begin{bmatrix} 2 & 1 \\ 1 & 2 \end{bmatrix} \mathbf{z}$$

$$= \frac{z_1 + z_2}{2}$$

Example 8.4-5 Consider the case where the observation is related to a known parameter ξ by a $(K-1)$st-degree polynomial of the form

$$z_i = \theta_1 + \theta_2\xi_i + \theta_3\xi_i^2 + \cdots + \theta_K\xi_i^{K-1} + n_i$$

Now we take I observations for different values of ξ_i to obtain

$$\mathbf{z} = \mathbf{H}\boldsymbol{\theta} + \mathbf{n}$$

$$\mathbf{H} = \begin{bmatrix} 1 & \xi_1 & \xi_1^2 & \cdots & \xi_1^{K-1} \\ 1 & \xi_2 & \xi_2^2 & \cdots & \xi_2^{K-1} \\ \cdots\cdots\cdots\cdots\cdots\cdots\cdots \\ 1 & \xi_I & \xi_I^2 & \cdots & \xi_I^{K-1} \end{bmatrix}$$

Now by the use of Eq. (8.4-27), we can estimate the polynomial coefficients $\theta_1, \theta_2, \ldots, \theta_K$.

A special case of the preceding problem occurs when $K = 2$. This case is called *linear regression*, or just *regression*, analysis and is an attempt to find the best (in the least-squares sense) straight line to fit a given set of data. We consider here only the case when $\mathbf{W} = \mathbf{I}$, For this case, the matrix product $\mathbf{H}^T\mathbf{H}$ becomes

$$\mathbf{H}^T\mathbf{H} = \begin{bmatrix} 1 & 1 & \cdots & 1 \\ \xi_1 & \xi_2 & \cdots & \xi_I \end{bmatrix} \begin{bmatrix} 1 & \xi_1 \\ 1 & \xi_2 \\ \vdots & \vdots \\ 1 & \xi_I \end{bmatrix}$$

$$= \begin{bmatrix} I & \displaystyle\sum_{i=1}^{I} \xi_i \\ \displaystyle\sum_{i=1}^{I} \xi_i & \displaystyle\sum_{i=1}^{I} \xi_i^2 \end{bmatrix}$$

so that $\hat{\boldsymbol{\theta}}_{\mathrm{LS}}$ is given by

$$\hat{\boldsymbol{\theta}}_{\mathrm{LS}} = \frac{1}{\displaystyle I\sum_{i=1}^{I} \xi_i^2 - \left(\sum_{i=1}^{I} \xi_i\right)^2} \begin{bmatrix} \displaystyle\sum_{i=1}^{I} \xi_i^2 & -\displaystyle\sum_{i=1}^{I} \xi_i \\ -\displaystyle\sum_{i=1}^{I} \xi_i & I \end{bmatrix} \begin{bmatrix} 1 & 1 & \cdots & 1 \\ \xi_1 & \xi_2 & \cdots & \xi_I \end{bmatrix} \mathbf{z}$$

If we carry out the indicated matrix manipulations, we find that

$$\hat{\boldsymbol{\theta}}_1 = \frac{\displaystyle\sum_{i=1}^{I} \xi_i^2 \sum_{i=1}^{I} z_i - \sum_{i=1}^{I} \xi_i \sum_{i=1}^{I} \xi_i z_i}{\displaystyle I\sum_{i=1}^{I} \xi_i^2 - \left(\sum_{i=1}^{I} \xi_i\right)^2}$$

and
$$\hat{\theta}_2 = \frac{I \sum_{i=1}^{I} \xi_i z_i - \sum_{i=1}^{I} \xi_i \sum_{i=1}^{I} z_i}{I \sum_{i=1}^{I} \xi_i^2 - \left(\sum_{i=1}^{I} \xi_i\right)^2}$$

Now, given a set of parameter values ξ_i and observations z_i, we can easily calculate $\hat{\theta}$.

Example 8.4-5 is a special case of the general problem of curve fitting by generalized functions. In this case, we write the observation as

$$z_i = \sum_{k=1}^{K} \theta_k \phi_k(\xi_i) + n_i \qquad (8.4\text{-}28)$$

where the ϕ_k are known functions of the parameter ξ_i. As usual, the problem is to determine the value of the coefficients θ_k. By using functions which are orthogonal over the given data set, it is possible to cause the matrix $\mathbf{H}^T\mathbf{H}$ to be diagonal, thereby significantly reducing the computational requirements. Typical examples of such functions are Legendre polynomials.

As a final step in the study of least-squares estimators, let us consider some of the properties of these estimators. First, let us find the expected value of the estimation error. The estimation error is given by

$$\tilde{\theta}_{LS} = \theta - \hat{\theta}_{LS} = \theta - (\mathbf{H}^T\mathbf{W}\mathbf{H})^{-1}\mathbf{H}^T\mathbf{W}\mathbf{z}$$

If we use Eq. (8.4-24) for $\mathbf{z}$, then $\tilde{\theta}_{LS}$ is

$$\tilde{\theta}_{LS} = \theta - (\mathbf{H}^T\mathbf{W}\mathbf{H})^{-1}\mathbf{H}^T\mathbf{W}(\mathbf{H}\theta + \mathbf{n})$$

$$= \theta - (\mathbf{H}^T\mathbf{W}\mathbf{H})^{-1}(\mathbf{H}^T\mathbf{W}\mathbf{H})\theta - (\mathbf{H}^T\mathbf{W}\mathbf{H})^{-1}\mathbf{H}^T\mathbf{W}\mathbf{n}$$

or
$$\tilde{\theta}_{LS} = -(\mathbf{H}^T\mathbf{W}\mathbf{H})^{-1}\mathbf{H}^T\mathbf{W}\mathbf{n} \qquad (8.4\text{-}29)$$

Therefore the expected value of $\tilde{\theta}$ is

$$E\{\tilde{\theta}_{LS}\} = -(\mathbf{H}^T\mathbf{W}\mathbf{H})^{-1}\mathbf{H}^T\mathbf{W}E\{\mathbf{n}\} \qquad (8.4\text{-}30)$$

Hence we see that if $E\{\mathbf{n}\} = \mathbf{0}$, then $E\{\tilde{\theta}_{LS}\} = \mathbf{0}$. The variance of the least-squares estimation error is given by

$$\text{var }\{\tilde{\theta}_{LS}\} = \text{var }\{-(\mathbf{H}^T\mathbf{W}\mathbf{H})^{-1}\mathbf{H}^T\mathbf{W}\mathbf{n}\}$$

$$= (\mathbf{H}^T\mathbf{W}\mathbf{H})^{-1}\mathbf{H}^T\mathbf{W}\mathbf{V}_n\mathbf{W}\mathbf{H}(\mathbf{H}^T\mathbf{W}\mathbf{H})^{-1} \qquad (8.4\text{-}31)$$

For a linear minimum-variance estimator with no a priori information about θ so that $\mathbf{V}_\theta^{-1} = \mathbf{0}$, the estimator as given by Eq. (8.4-20) is

$$\hat{\theta}_{LMV} = (\mathbf{H}^T\mathbf{V}_n^{-1}\mathbf{H})^{-1}\mathbf{H}^T\mathbf{V}_n^{-1}\mathbf{z} \qquad (8.4\text{-}32)$$

and the associated error variance is

$$\text{var } \{\tilde{\boldsymbol{\theta}}_{\text{LMV}}\} = (\mathbf{H}^T \mathbf{V}_n^{-1} \mathbf{H})^{-1}$$

A comparison of Eqs. (8.4-27) and (8.4-32) indicates that if $\mathbf{W} = \mathbf{V}_n^{-1}$, then the least-squares estimator will be a linear minimum variance (with no a priori parameter information). And we see that the error variances for these two cases are also identical. Since the least-squares estimator is linear and the linear minimum-variance estimator has minimum variance, it is clear that

$$\text{var } \{\tilde{\boldsymbol{\theta}}_{\text{LMV}}\} \leq \text{var } \{\tilde{\boldsymbol{\theta}}_{\text{LS}}\} \qquad (8.4\text{-}33)$$

for all $\mathbf{W}$. The equality in Eq. (8.4-33) will hold for $\mathbf{W} = \mathbf{V}_n^{-1}$.

Example 8.4-6 Let us find the error variance for Examples 8.4-1 and 8.4-5. For the linear minimum-variance estimator, the estimation error variance is given by Eq. (8.4-23):

$$\text{var } \{\tilde{\boldsymbol{\theta}}_{\text{LMV}}\} = \left(\begin{bmatrix} 1 & 1 \end{bmatrix} \frac{1}{\sigma^2} \begin{bmatrix} 1 \\ 1 \end{bmatrix} + \frac{1}{V} \right)^{-1}$$

$$= \left(\frac{2}{\sigma^2} + \frac{1}{V} \right)^{-1}$$

$$= \frac{\sigma^2}{2 + \sigma^2/V}$$

For the least-squares estimator the estimation error variance is given by Eq. (8.4-31):

$$\text{var } \{\tilde{\boldsymbol{\theta}}_{\text{LS}}\} = \left(\begin{bmatrix} 1 & 1 \end{bmatrix} \begin{bmatrix} 2 & 1 \\ 1 & 2 \end{bmatrix} \begin{bmatrix} 1 \\ 1 \end{bmatrix} \right)^{-1} \begin{bmatrix} 1 & 1 \end{bmatrix} \begin{bmatrix} 2 & 1 \\ 1 & 2 \end{bmatrix} \sigma^2 \begin{bmatrix} 2 & 1 \\ 1 & 2 \end{bmatrix} \begin{bmatrix} 1 \\ 1 \end{bmatrix}$$

$$\times \left(\begin{bmatrix} 1 & 1 \end{bmatrix} \begin{bmatrix} 2 & 1 \\ 1 & 2 \end{bmatrix} \begin{bmatrix} 1 \\ 1 \end{bmatrix} \right)^{-1}$$

$$= \frac{\sigma^2}{2}$$

Hence we see that

$$\text{var } \{\tilde{\boldsymbol{\theta}}_{\text{LMV}}\} < \text{var } \{\tilde{\boldsymbol{\theta}}_{\text{LS}}\}$$

Note, however, that the two error variances will be equal if $V^{-1} = 0$ even though $\mathbf{W} \neq \mathbf{V}_n$. Of course, both estimators will also be equal when $\mathbf{W} = \mathbf{V}_n$.

8.5 SUMMARY

In this chapter, we have examined the basic concepts and methods of parameter estimation. A number of different types of estimators have been developed, and several relationships between the estimators have been studied.

We began our study of estimation with the simple maximum-likelihood estimator. Next, the Bayes cost method was used to derive the mean-square-error, maximum a posteriori, and absolute-cost estimators. Section 8.3 pointed out conditions under which these estimators are equivalent.

The estimators developed in Sec. 8.1 and 8.2 require a rather complete probabilistic description of the estimation problem. The linear minimum-variance and least-squares estimators of Sec. 8.4 need only minimal statistical structure and therefore provide a complement to the other methods.

In Chap. 9 we shall consider the gaussian estimation problem in detail.

8.6 PROBLEMS

8.6-1 Find the MAP, ML, and CM estimators of θ from the observation

$$z = \theta + n$$

where $p(\theta) = \frac{1}{2} \delta_D(\theta) + \frac{1}{2} \delta_D(\theta - 1)$

$p(n) = \frac{1}{2} e^{-|n|}$

8.6-2 Determine the CM and MAP estimators of the parameter θ given

$$z = \ln \theta + n$$

where $p(n) = \begin{cases} e^{-n} & n > 0 \\ 0 & \text{otherwise} \end{cases}$

$p(\theta) = \begin{cases} \frac{1}{2}\theta & 0 \leq \theta \leq 2 \\ 0 & \text{otherwise} \end{cases}$

Plot both $\hat{\theta}_{CM}(z)$ and $\hat{\theta}_{MAP}(z)$ for $-2 < z < 3$.

8.6-3 Find the ML and MAP estimator for the parameter θ given

$$z = 2\theta + n$$

where $p(n) = \begin{cases} 1 - |n| & |n| \leq 1 \\ 0 & \text{otherwise} \end{cases}$

$p(\theta) = \begin{cases} \frac{1}{2} & |\theta| \leq 1 \\ 0 & \text{otherwise} \end{cases}$

8.6-4 Show that the ML estimate of θ given

$$z = \ln \theta + n$$

is

$$\hat{\theta}_{ML} = e^z$$

if $p(n)$ is such that $p_n(0) > p_n(\alpha)$ for all $\alpha \neq 0$.

8.6-5 Find the MAP and ML estimators for the scalar parameter θ given the observation

$$z = \theta + n$$

if $p_\theta(\alpha) = \begin{cases} \frac{1}{10} & -5 \le \alpha \le 5 \\ 0 & \text{otherwise} \end{cases}$

$p_n(\beta) = \begin{cases} \frac{1}{2}\beta & 0 \le \beta \le 2 \\ 0 & \text{otherwise} \end{cases}$

8.6-6 Find the ML, CM, and MAP estimates of the parameter θ given the observation

$$z = \theta + n$$

where $p(n) = \dfrac{1}{\sqrt{2\pi}\,\sigma}\, e^{-(n-1)^2/2\sigma^2}$

$p(\theta) = \begin{cases} \frac{1}{2} & 0 \le \theta \le 2 \\ 0 & \text{otherwise} \end{cases}$

8.6-7 Find the ML estimates of the parameters a and b given the set of observations

$$z_i = a + bn_i \qquad i = 1, 2, \ldots, I$$

where the n_i are independent and identically distributed with

$$p(n_i) = \dfrac{1}{\sqrt{2\pi}}\, e^{-n_i{}^2/2}$$

8.6-8 Consider Prob. 8.6-7 again, but let $b = 1$. Derive a sequential ML estimator for the parameter a. Find the sequence of estimates if the observation sequence is $\{4, -3, 3, 1, -2\}$,

8.6-9 Find the CM estimate of θ given

$$z = a\theta + n$$

where $p(a) = \begin{cases} 1 & 0 \le a \le 1 \\ 0 & \text{otherwise} \end{cases}$

$p(n) = \dfrac{1}{\sqrt{2\pi}}\, e^{-n^2/2}$

$p(\theta) = \dfrac{1}{\sqrt{2\pi}}\, e^{-(\theta-1)^2/2}$

Hint: First find $E\{\theta|z, a\}$.

8.6-10 Find the ML, MAP, and CM estimators for the parameter θ given the observation z if

$$z = 2\theta + \theta^2 + n$$

$$p(n) = \begin{cases} e^{-n} & n > 0 \\ 0 & \text{otherwise} \end{cases}$$

$$p(\theta) = \tfrac{1}{4}\delta_D(\theta) + \tfrac{3}{4}\delta_D(\theta - 2)$$

8.6-11 Find the CM estimator of θ if

$$z = \lambda\theta + n$$

and
$$p(\lambda) = \tfrac{1}{2}\delta_D(\lambda) + \tfrac{1}{2}\delta_D(\lambda - 1)$$

$$p(n) = \frac{1}{\sqrt{2\pi}}\, e^{-n^2/2}$$

$$p(\theta) = \frac{1}{\sqrt{2\pi}}\, e^{-(\theta-1)^2/2}$$

8.6-12 Find the MAP estimator of θ if

$$z = \sqrt{\theta} + n$$

where $p(\theta) = \begin{cases} e^{-\theta} & \theta \le 0 \\ 0 & \text{otherwise} \end{cases}$

and $p(n) = \dfrac{1}{\sqrt{2\pi}}\, e^{-n^2/2}$

8.6-13 Find the CM and map estimators of θ given the observation

$$z = \lambda\theta + \mathbf{n}$$

where $p(\lambda) = \begin{cases} 1 & 0 \le \lambda \le 1 \\ 0 & \text{otherwise} \end{cases}$

$$p(\theta) = \tfrac{1}{2}\delta(\theta) + \tfrac{1}{2}\delta(\theta - 1)$$

$$p(n) = \begin{cases} e^{-n} & n \ge 0 \\ 0 & \text{otherwise} \end{cases}$$

8.6-14 Given the observation

$$z = \theta n$$

where n and θ are independent random variables with

$$p_n(\alpha) = p_n(-\alpha) \qquad \text{and} \qquad p_\theta(\beta) = p_\theta(-\beta)$$

(a) Show that $p(\theta|z)$ is symmetric about $\theta = 0$.
(b) Assuming part (a) is true, find the estimator $\hat\theta$ which minimizes

$$J = E\{e^{+|\theta-\hat\theta|^2}\,|z\}$$

8.6-15 We wish to estimate the variable θ from the observation

$$z = \theta + n$$

so as to minimize

$$C(\theta,\hat\theta) = e^{(\theta-\hat\theta)^2} + |\theta - \hat\theta|^3$$

when θ and n are independent and

$$p(\theta) = \begin{cases} 1 & 0 \le \theta \le 1 \\ 0 & \text{otherwise} \end{cases}$$

$$p(n) = \begin{cases} 2 & -\tfrac{1}{4} < n < \tfrac{1}{4} \\ 0 & \text{otherwise} \end{cases}$$

What rule should be used? (Fully justify your answer.)

8.6-16 In an estimation problem with observation z and unknown θ, show that if the cost function is a symmetric and nondecreasing function of $\theta - \hat{\theta}$ and if $p(\theta|z)$ is symmetric about its mean and is unimodal (nonincreasing as you move away from the mean) and if

$$\lim_{\theta \to \infty} C(\theta, \hat{\theta})p(\theta|z) = 0$$

then the optimal estimate is

$$\hat{\theta}(z) = E\{\theta|z\}$$

ESTIMATION WITH GAUSSIAN NOISE

In this chapter the general problem of estimating a gaussian vector in the presence of gaussian noise will be discussed. It is a problem of considerable interest both because it has many applications and because the complete solution is easy to find. Our treatment will begin (Sec. 9.1) with the situation where the observation is a noisy version of the result of a linear operation on the signal. We shall analyze this problem in some detail and then use it as the basis for the next two sections. In Sec. 9.2, we shall consider the problem of sequentially estimating the message in an efficient way. Finally, in Sec. 9.3, we shall describe nonlinear observation problems and show how they can be solved by a simple extension of the linear technique.

9.1 LINEAR OBSERVATIONS

In Chap. 8, one of the estimation problems considered was the case of a gaussian message corrupted by the addition of gaussian noise. In this section we shall generalize that problem one step further and consider the case where the observation is a noisy replica of a linear operation on the message. In the most general case, the message will be a K-dimensional gaussian vector and the observation will be an I-dimensional gaussian vector. As noted, the observation is a linear combination of the message $\boldsymbol{\theta}$ and the gaussian noise process $\mathbf{n}$ such that

$$\mathbf{z} = \mathbf{H}\boldsymbol{\theta} + \mathbf{n} \tag{9.1-1}$$

(Throughout this chapter it will be assumed that $\boldsymbol{\theta}$ and $\mathbf{n}$ are independent.)

The system described by Eq. (9.1-1) can represent a number of actual situations. For example, suppose that $\boldsymbol{\theta}$ was a scalar random variable being transmitted by an amplitude modulation system and that the observations were samples from the received signal. The objective would be to use this sequence of samples to estimate the value of the parameter $\boldsymbol{\theta}$. A more general case, which will be studied in detail in Chap. 11, is where θ represents the state vector of a linear system. The observation z might then be a noisy replica of the output of this system.

The objective of this section will be to form the minimum-variance estimate of θ based on the observation z. The first step is to write the conditional probability density of θ as a function of z; the estimate would then be the mean of this density. The density can easily be obtained from Bayes' rule, which states that

$$p(\theta|z) = \frac{p(z|\theta)p(\theta)}{p(z)} \qquad (9.1\text{-}2)$$

Since all the density functions on the right side of Eq. (9.1-2) are gaussian densities, they are completely determined by their mean vectors and their variance matrices. For simplicity, it will be assumed that the noise is zero mean. The mean of θ will be denoted by μ. The variance matrices of θ and n will be given by

$$\text{var } \{\theta\} = V_0 \qquad \text{var } \{n\} = V_n$$

Now, it is clear that since θ is a K-dimensional vector, its density function is just

$$p(\theta) = \frac{1}{(2\pi)^{K/2}(\det V_0)^{1/2}} \exp\left[-\frac{1}{2}(\theta - \mu)^T V_0^{-1}(\theta - \mu)\right] \qquad (9.1\text{-}3)$$

When θ is known, z is just the sum of a constant and a zero-mean gaussian vector. Therefore, its mean is just this constant, and its variance matrix is the variance matrix for the noise vector. Therefore, the conditional density of z is just

$$p(z|\theta) = \frac{1}{(2\pi)^{l/2}(\det V_n)^{1/2}} \exp\left\{-\frac{1}{2}(z - H\theta)^T V_n^{-1}(z - H\theta)\right\} \qquad (9.1\text{-}4)$$

Finally, to find the unconditional density of z, one need observe only that since it is the combination of two gaussian vectors, it is gaussian. Its mean is clearly $H\mu$, and since θ and n are independent, its variance is

$$\text{var } \{z\} = HV_0 H^T + V_n$$

Therefore, the unconditional probability density of z can be written as

$$p(z) = \frac{1}{(2\pi)^{l/2}[\det (HV_0 H^T + V_n)]^{1/2}}$$
$$\times \exp\left\{-\tfrac{1}{2}(z - H\mu)^T(HV_0 H^T + V_n)^{-1}(z - H\mu)\right\} \qquad (9.1\text{-}5)$$

Now, Eqs. (9.1-3) to (9.1-5) could be used in Eq. (9.1-2) to obtain an expression for the conditional density of θ. Clearly this will be a gaussian density, and when it is written in the proper form, the conditional mean of θ can be identified readily. Unfortunately, the procedure of writing it in the proper form is quite complex.

An alternative way of finding the conditional mean estimate is to recall that it is identical with the MAP estimate. Using the logic of Chap. 8, the MAP estimate is that value of $\boldsymbol{\theta}$ which maximizes the joint density function $p(\mathbf{z}, \boldsymbol{\theta})$. Using Eqs. (9.1-3) and (9.1-4),

$$p(\mathbf{z}, \boldsymbol{\theta}) = p(\mathbf{z})p(\mathbf{z}|\boldsymbol{\theta}) = \frac{1}{(2\pi)^{(K+1)/2}[\det \mathbf{V_n} \det \mathbf{V_0}]^{1/2}}$$

$$\times \exp\left\{-\frac{1}{2}[(\boldsymbol{\theta} - \boldsymbol{\mu})^T\mathbf{V_0}^{-1}(\boldsymbol{\theta} - \boldsymbol{\mu}) + (\mathbf{z} - \mathbf{H}\boldsymbol{\theta})^T\mathbf{V_n}^{-1}(\mathbf{z} - \mathbf{H}\boldsymbol{\theta})]\right\} \quad (9.1\text{-}6)$$

Taking logarithms and discarding terms that do not vary with $\boldsymbol{\theta}$, we find that the value of $\boldsymbol{\theta}$ which minimizes $p(\mathbf{z}, \boldsymbol{\theta})$ is the same value that maximizes the bracketed term in the exponent of Eq. (9.1-6). Therefore, the components of the MAP estimate of $\boldsymbol{\theta}$ should be selected to satisfy

$$\frac{\partial}{\partial \theta_k}[(\boldsymbol{\theta} - \boldsymbol{\mu})^T\mathbf{V_0}^{-1}(\boldsymbol{\theta} - \boldsymbol{\mu}) + (\mathbf{z} - \mathbf{H}\boldsymbol{\theta})^T\mathbf{V_n}^{-1}(\mathbf{z} - \mathbf{H}\boldsymbol{\theta})]\bigg|_{\theta_k = \hat{\theta}_k} = 0$$

$$k = 1, 2, \ldots, K \quad (9.1\text{-}7)$$

Or, using vector notation to write all K of these equations at once, we have

$$\frac{\partial}{\partial \boldsymbol{\theta}}[(\boldsymbol{\theta} - \boldsymbol{\mu})^T\mathbf{V_0}^{-1}(\boldsymbol{\theta} - \boldsymbol{\mu}) + (\mathbf{z} - \mathbf{H}\boldsymbol{\theta})^T\mathbf{V_n}^{-1}(\mathbf{z} - \mathbf{H}\boldsymbol{\theta})]\bigg|_{\theta = \hat{\theta}} = \mathbf{0} \quad (9.1\text{-}8)$$

Using Lemma 8.4-1, we can write the derivative indicated in Eq. (9.1-8) as

$$-\mathbf{H}^T\mathbf{V_n}^{-1}(\mathbf{z} - \mathbf{H}\hat{\boldsymbol{\theta}}) + \mathbf{V_0}^{-1}(\hat{\boldsymbol{\theta}} - \boldsymbol{\mu}) = \mathbf{0} \quad (9.1\text{-}9)$$

Collecting terms which involve $\hat{\boldsymbol{\theta}}$, this equation becomes

$$(\mathbf{H}^T\mathbf{V_n}^{-1}\mathbf{H} + \mathbf{V_0}^{-1})\hat{\boldsymbol{\theta}} = \mathbf{H}^T\mathbf{V_n}^{-1}\mathbf{z} + \mathbf{V_0}^{-1}\boldsymbol{\mu} \quad (9.1\text{-}10)$$

Finally, premultiplying both sides of Eq. (9.1-10) by the inverse of the quantity in parentheses yields the desired minimum-variance estimate of $\boldsymbol{\theta}$:

$$\hat{\boldsymbol{\theta}} = (\mathbf{H}^T\mathbf{V_n}^{-1}\mathbf{H} + \mathbf{V_0}^{-1})^{-1}(\mathbf{H}^T\mathbf{V_n}^{-1}\mathbf{z} + \mathbf{V_0}^{-1}\boldsymbol{\mu}) \quad (9.1\text{-}11)$$

This estimate is both the conditional mean and the MAP estimate, as well as the optimal estimate for a broad class of Bayes cost criteria. As a check, the expected value of this estimate should be the same as the expected value of $\boldsymbol{\theta}$. The only random term on the right-hand side of Eq. (9.1-11) is the vector $\mathbf{z}$. Its expected value is $\mathbf{H}\boldsymbol{\mu}$, so that we can write

$$E\{\hat{\boldsymbol{\theta}}\} = (\mathbf{H}^T\mathbf{V_n}^{-1}\mathbf{H} + \mathbf{V_0}^{-1})^{-1}(\mathbf{H}^T\mathbf{V_n}^{-1}\mathbf{H}\boldsymbol{\mu} + \mathbf{V_0}^{-1}\boldsymbol{\mu})$$

If $\boldsymbol{\mu}$ is factored out of the terms in the second parentheses, it is clear that the expected value of $\hat{\boldsymbol{\theta}}$ is exactly $\boldsymbol{\mu}$.

Even though the expression in Eq. (9.1-11) appears somewhat complex, it is actually very simple to compute. Note that except for the vector $\mathbf{z}$, all the quantities are known and constant. Therefore, it is possible to evaluate them all before any observations are made. The only operations that are required on the observations are linear combinations. Such an estimation algorithm can be viewed as a linear filter on the observations.

Additional insight into the behavior of this estimator can be gained with some manipulations on the expression in Eq. (9.1-11). If the term $\mathbf{H}^T\mathbf{V}_n^{-1}\mathbf{H}\boldsymbol{\mu}$ is added and subtracted inside the second parentheses, the expression can be rewritten as

$$\hat{\boldsymbol{\theta}} = \boldsymbol{\mu} + (\mathbf{H}^T\mathbf{V}_n^{-1}\mathbf{H} + \mathbf{V}_0^{-1})^{-1}\mathbf{H}^T\mathbf{V}_n^{-1}(\mathbf{z} - \mathbf{H}\boldsymbol{\mu}) \qquad (9.1\text{-}12)$$

The first term in this expression is simply the expected value of $\boldsymbol{\theta}$, which represents the information available before any observations are made. The second term represents the departure from this estimate that is due to the difference between the actual observation and its expected value.

If we had used the method of finding the complete conditional density of $\boldsymbol{\theta}$ in order to find the conditional mean estimate, the variance in the estimate would have been apparent immediately. With the method used, however, the variance is not obvious, but it is easy to obtain. Using Eq. (9.1-11) to represent $\hat{\boldsymbol{\theta}}$, the estimation error can be written as

$$\tilde{\boldsymbol{\theta}} = \boldsymbol{\theta} - \hat{\boldsymbol{\theta}} = (\mathbf{H}^T\mathbf{V}_n^{-1}\mathbf{H} + \mathbf{V}_0^{-1})^{-1}[(\mathbf{H}^T\mathbf{V}_n^{-1}\mathbf{H} + \mathbf{V}_0^{-1})\boldsymbol{\theta} - \mathbf{H}^T\mathbf{V}_n^{-1}(\mathbf{z} - \mathbf{V}_0^{-1}\boldsymbol{\mu})]$$

Then, using the fact that $\mathbf{z}$ is the sum $\mathbf{H}\boldsymbol{\theta} + \mathbf{n}$ and canceling some terms, the estimation error becomes

$$\boldsymbol{\theta} - \hat{\boldsymbol{\theta}} = (\mathbf{H}^T\mathbf{V}_n^{-1}\mathbf{H} + \mathbf{V}_0^{-1})^{-1}[\mathbf{V}_0^{-1}(\boldsymbol{\theta} - \boldsymbol{\mu}) - \mathbf{H}^T\mathbf{V}_n^{-1}\mathbf{n})] \qquad (9.1\text{-}13)$$

Now, the variance of $\boldsymbol{\theta} - \hat{\boldsymbol{\theta}}$ is just the sum of the variances of the two independent terms in Eq. (9.1-13). Using this fact and noting that the variance matrices are symmetric, we have

$$\text{var } \{\boldsymbol{\theta} - \hat{\boldsymbol{\theta}}\} = (\mathbf{H}^T\mathbf{V}_n^{-1}\mathbf{H} + \mathbf{V}_0^{-1})^{-1}[\mathbf{V}_0^{-1}\mathbf{V}_0\mathbf{V}_0^{-1} + \mathbf{H}^T\mathbf{V}_n^{-1}\mathbf{V}_n\mathbf{V}_n^{-1}\mathbf{H}]$$

$$\times (\mathbf{H}^T\mathbf{V}_n^{-1}\mathbf{H} + \mathbf{V}_0^{-1})^{-1}$$

Finally, letting matrices cancel their inverses, the expression for the variance of estimation error becomes

$$\text{var } \{\boldsymbol{\theta} - \hat{\boldsymbol{\theta}}\} = (\mathbf{H}^T\mathbf{V}_n^{-1}\mathbf{H} + \mathbf{V}_0^{-1})^{-1} \qquad (9.1\text{-}14)$$

An alternative method for deriving $\hat{\boldsymbol{\theta}}$ and the variance of the estimation error is to note that the conditional probability density of $\boldsymbol{\theta}$, $p(\boldsymbol{\theta}|\mathbf{z})$, is a gaussian density. Therefore, since $\hat{\boldsymbol{\theta}}$ is the conditional mean of $\boldsymbol{\theta}$, this density can be written as

$$p(\boldsymbol{\theta}|\mathbf{z}) = C \exp\left[-\tfrac{1}{2}(\boldsymbol{\theta} - \hat{\boldsymbol{\theta}})^T\mathbf{P}^{-1}(\boldsymbol{\theta} - \hat{\boldsymbol{\theta}})\right]$$

where C is the normalizing constant and $\mathbf{P}$ is used as the conditional variance of $\boldsymbol{\theta}$. Writing out the terms in the exponent yields

$$p(\boldsymbol{\theta}|\mathbf{z}) = C \exp\left\{-\tfrac{1}{2}[\boldsymbol{\theta}^T\mathbf{P}^{-1}\boldsymbol{\theta} - \boldsymbol{\theta}^T\mathbf{P}^{-1}\hat{\boldsymbol{\theta}} - \hat{\boldsymbol{\theta}}^T\mathbf{P}^{-1}\boldsymbol{\theta} + \hat{\boldsymbol{\theta}}^T\mathbf{P}^{-1}\hat{\boldsymbol{\theta}}]\right\} \qquad (9.1\text{-}15)$$

Now, using the Bayes rules and the expressions for the conditional density of $\mathbf{z}$

in Eq. (9.1-4) and the unconditional density of θ in Eq. (9.1-3), it is clear that this density can be written as

$$p(\theta|z) = C \exp\{-\tfrac{1}{2}[(z - H\theta)^T V_n^{-1}(z - H\theta) + (\theta - \mu)^T V_0^{-1}(\theta - \mu) + \cdots]\}$$

(9.1-16)

where the omitted terms in the exponent do not depend on θ. Now, if the indicated multiplications in the exponent are carried out and if the terms are written to correspond to the terms in Eq. (9.1-15), we have

$$p(\theta|z) = C \exp\{-\tfrac{1}{2}[\theta^T H^T V_n^{-1} H\theta + \theta^T V_0^{-1}\theta - \theta^T H^T V_n^{-1}z - \theta^T V_0^{-1}\mu + \cdots]\}$$

(9.1-17)

where now the omitted terms in the exponent do not have θ^T which premultiplies the term. Therefore, the first two terms must correspond to the first term in the bracket in Eq. (9.1-15), so that P^{-1} is given by

$$P^{-1} = (H^T V_n^{-1} H + V_0^{-1})$$

(9.1-18)

By combining the third and fourth terms in Eq. (9.1-17) and inserting the product $P^{-1}P$, we have the second term in Eq. (9.1-15):

$$\theta^T P^{-1}\hat{\theta} = \theta^T P^{-1} P (H^T V_n^{-1}z + V_0^{-1}\mu)$$

(9.1-19)

It is easy to show that Eqs. (9.1-18) and (9.1-19) are equivalent to Eqs. (9.1-11) and (9.1-14.)

In order to illustrate the use of these results, consider the following example.

Example 9.1-1 Let θ be a three-dimensional gaussian vector with mean

$$\mu = \begin{bmatrix} 0 \\ 0 \\ 1 \end{bmatrix}$$

and variance matrix

$$V_0 = \begin{bmatrix} 1 & 0 & 0 \\ 0 & 2 & 1 \\ 0 & 1 & 1 \end{bmatrix}$$

The observation is given by

$$z = H\theta + n$$

where

$$H = \begin{bmatrix} 1 & 0 & 0 \\ 0 & 1 & 0 \end{bmatrix}$$

and the noise is white and gaussian with unit variance. Find the MAP estimate of θ.

The first step is to compute the variance matrix as given in Eq. (9.1-14). This is

$$\operatorname{var}\{\boldsymbol{\theta} - \hat{\boldsymbol{\theta}}\} = \left[\begin{bmatrix} 1 & 0 \\ 0 & 1 \\ 0 & 0 \end{bmatrix} \begin{bmatrix} 1 & 0 \\ 0 & 1 \end{bmatrix} \begin{bmatrix} 1 & 0 & 0 \\ 0 & 1 & 0 \end{bmatrix} + \begin{bmatrix} 1 & 0 & 0 \\ 0 & 2 & 1 \\ 0 & 1 & 1 \end{bmatrix}^{-1} \right]^{-1}$$

The inverse of the variance matrix $\mathbf{V}_0$ is

$$\mathbf{V}_0^{-1} = \begin{bmatrix} 1 & 0 & 0 \\ 0 & 2 & 1 \\ 0 & 1 & 1 \end{bmatrix}^{-1} = \begin{bmatrix} 1 & 0 & 0 \\ 0 & 1 & -1 \\ 0 & -1 & 2 \end{bmatrix}$$

so that

$$\operatorname{var}\{\boldsymbol{\theta} - \hat{\boldsymbol{\theta}}\} = \begin{bmatrix} 2 & 0 & 0 \\ 0 & 2 & -1 \\ 0 & -1 & 2 \end{bmatrix}^{-1} = \tfrac{1}{6} \begin{bmatrix} 3 & 0 & 0 \\ 0 & 4 & 2 \\ 0 & 2 & 4 \end{bmatrix}$$

Substituting this in Eq. (9.1-12), the estimate becomes

$$\hat{\boldsymbol{\theta}} = \begin{bmatrix} 0 \\ 0 \\ 1 \end{bmatrix} + \tfrac{1}{6} \begin{bmatrix} 3 & 0 & 0 \\ 0 & 4 & 2 \\ 0 & 2 & 4 \end{bmatrix} \begin{bmatrix} 1 & 0 \\ 0 & 1 \\ 0 & 0 \end{bmatrix} \begin{bmatrix} 1 & 0 \\ 0 & 1 \end{bmatrix} \begin{bmatrix} z_1 \\ z_2 \end{bmatrix} = \begin{bmatrix} \dfrac{z_1}{2} \\ \dfrac{2z_2}{3} \\ \dfrac{z_2}{3} + 1 \end{bmatrix}$$

This particular problem is easy to interpret. If the equation for **z** is written out, it is clear that its two components are

$$z_1 = \theta_1 + n_1$$

$$z_2 = \theta_2 + n_2$$

Therefore, since θ_1 and θ_2 are independent and since n_1 and n_2 are independent, the problem can be broken down into three parts: estimating θ_1 from z_1, estimating θ_2 from z_2, and estimating θ_3. The first two parts can be done using the methods of Chap. 8. The third part is not quite as obvious. It is interesting to note, however, that a constant 1 is added to $z_2/3$, so that the mean of $\hat{\theta}_3$ matches the mean of θ_3.

9.2 SEQUENTIAL ESTIMATION

In this section, we shall extend the idea of sequential decision making that was introduced in Chap. 6 to the gaussian estimation problem. However, in this case, our objective will be somewhat different. Instead of taking enough observations to achieve a specified performance, we shall require that the best estimate of θ be formed after each observation. Conceptually, this is trivial since we could simply reapply the results of Sec. 9.1 after each additional observation is received. Practically, however, we would like a system that produces the optimal estimates in an efficient way, which brings us to the topic of sequential estimation.

In this section we shall show that by exploiting the sequential nature of the problem, an optimal estimator can be designed that is far less complex than that implied by Sec. 9.1. In fact, instead of having to remember all the observations, the estimator will need only the prior estimate and current observation. In order to derive this procedure, we shall start with the simplest case—no observations—and gradually add observations. At each stage, we shall reduce our result to a standard form that will lend itself to generalization.

We shall assume that at each time unit an additional observation of the form

$$z_m = \mathbf{H}\theta + n_m \qquad m = 1, 2, \ldots \qquad (9.2\text{-}1)$$

is available at the receiver with cov $\{n_i, n_j\} = V_n \delta_{ij}$. Thus, to form the best estimate at time M, the estimator must base it on $\{z_1, z_2, \ldots, z_M\}$. Before any observations are made ($M = 0$), one can form an optimal estimate of θ. Clearly, this is just the mean

$$\hat{\theta}_0 = \mu$$

The variance of this estimate is V_0. As we shall see, these zero-level values form the basis of our iterative estimation procedure.

After a single observation, $M = 1$, we have the same problem treated in Sec. 9.1. The optimal estimate, from Eq. (9.1-12), was given by

$$\hat{\theta}_1 = \hat{\theta}_0 + V_1 \mathbf{H}^T V_n^{-1}(z_1 - \mathbf{H}\hat{\theta}_0) \qquad (9.2\text{-}2)$$

where V_1 is the error variance after the first observation. From Eq. (9.1-14), it is

$$V_1 = (\mathbf{H}^T V_n^{-1} \mathbf{H} + V_0^{-1})^{-1} \qquad (9.2\text{-}3)$$

The estimate based on two observations could be formed by using the results of Sec. 9.1 directly. However, if we restate the problem, the sequential nature of the data leads to a nice simplification. To find the MAP estimate, we must maximize the joint density of θ and the observations given by

$$p(\theta, z_1, z_2) = p(z_2|\theta, z_1)p(z_1, \theta) \qquad (9.2\text{-}4)$$

Since z_2 is independent of z_1 if θ is known, this becomes

$$p(\theta, z_1, z_2) = p(z_2|\theta)p(\theta|z_1)p(z_1)$$

Now, the last term in the product does not involve θ and will not influence the maximization. Therefore, we need maximize only the product $p(z_2|\theta)p(\theta|z_1)$. This, however, is essentially the same problem as maximizing

$p(\mathbf{z}|\boldsymbol{\theta})p(\boldsymbol{\theta})$, which was encountered in Sec. 9.1. The only difference is that the mean and variance of $\boldsymbol{\theta}$ are now the conditional mean and variance after the first observation. Note that $p(\boldsymbol{\theta}|z_1)$ is a gaussian density with mean $\hat{\boldsymbol{\theta}}_1$ and variance $\mathbf{V}_1$. In all other respects, it is equivalent to $p(\boldsymbol{\theta})$. The first terms in the products differ only in the subscript on $\mathbf{z}$. Thus, we have exactly the problem of Sec. 9.1 except that the mean of $\boldsymbol{\theta}$ is now equal to $\hat{\boldsymbol{\theta}}_1$ and its variance is now $\mathbf{V}_1$. Applying the solution from that section yields an optimal estimate of the form

$$\hat{\boldsymbol{\theta}}_2 = \hat{\boldsymbol{\theta}}_1 + \mathbf{V}_2\mathbf{H}^T\mathbf{V}_\mathbf{n}^{-1}(z_2 - \mathbf{H}\hat{\boldsymbol{\theta}}_1) \tag{9.2-5}$$

where the estimation variance is

$$\mathbf{V}_2 = (\mathbf{H}^T\mathbf{V}_\mathbf{n}^{-1}\mathbf{H} + \mathbf{V}_1^{-1})^{-1} \tag{9.2-6}$$

It is clear that these arguments generalize and that after $m + 1$ observations, the optimal estimate of $\boldsymbol{\theta}$ is

$$\hat{\boldsymbol{\theta}}_{m+1} = \hat{\boldsymbol{\theta}}_m + \mathbf{V}_{m+1}\mathbf{H}^T\mathbf{V}_\mathbf{n}^{-1}(z_{m+1} - \mathbf{H}\hat{\boldsymbol{\theta}}_m) \tag{9.2-7}$$

and the variance is

$$\mathbf{V}_{m+1} = (\mathbf{H}^T\mathbf{V}_\mathbf{n}^{-1}\mathbf{H} + \mathbf{V}_m^{-1})^{-1} \tag{9.2-8}$$

The expressions in Eqs. (9.2-7) and (9.2-8) give a recursive expression for the optimal estimate of $\boldsymbol{\theta}$. Note that it is not necessary to retain any of the prior observations. All that is required is that the immediate prior estimate of $\boldsymbol{\theta}$ be available. The bulk of the computation in forming this estimate is the matrix inversion in Eq. (9.2-8). It is possible to use matrix operations to minimize the degree of this matrix; these methods are presented in Chap. 11. In addition, the matrix inversion does not depend on the data and therefore can be precomputed and stored for later use. This estimation is actually a simple form of the Kalman filter, which is discussed at length in Chap. 11. For ease of reference, the sequential estimator equations are summarized in Table 9.2-1.

To illustrate the effectiveness of the sequential approach, consider the following example.

Example 9.2-1 Let θ be one-dimensional, and let the sequence of observations be

$$z_m = \theta + n_m$$

Table 9.2-1 Sequential Estimator Equations

Problem	$z_m = \mathbf{H}\theta + n_m \qquad m = 1, 2, \ldots$
Estimate	$\hat{\boldsymbol{\theta}}_{m+1} = \hat{\boldsymbol{\theta}}_m + \mathbf{V}_{m+1}\mathbf{H}^T\mathbf{V}_\mathbf{n}^{-1}(z_{m+1} - \mathbf{H}\hat{\boldsymbol{\theta}}_m)$
Error variance	$\text{var}\{\theta - \hat{\boldsymbol{\theta}}_{m+1}\} = \mathbf{V}_{m+1} = (\mathbf{H}^T\mathbf{V}_\mathbf{n}^{-1}\mathbf{H} + \mathbf{V}_m^{-1})^{-1}$
Initial conditions	$\hat{\boldsymbol{\theta}}_0 = \mu$

where the n_m are independent gaussian variables with variance σ^2. For simplicity, let θ have zero mean and unit variance. Find the sequential estimation procedure and determine how variance varies as a function of m.

It is clear that **H** is unity, and therefore Eqs. (9.2-7) and (9.2-8) reduce to

$$\hat{\theta}_{m+1} = \hat{\theta}_m + \frac{V_{m+1}}{\sigma^2}(z_{m+1} - \hat{\theta}_m)$$

$$V_{m+1} = [\frac{1}{\sigma^2} + \frac{1}{V_m}]^{-1}$$

Solving for V_{m+1} gives

$$V_{m+1} = \frac{\sigma^2}{m+1}$$

and $\hat{\theta}_{m+1}$ becomes

$$\hat{\theta}_{m+1} = \frac{m}{m+1}\hat{\theta}_m + \frac{1}{m+1}z_{m+1}$$

Clearly the variance decreases as $1/m$. It is interesting to note that as m increases, successive z_m have less and less influence on $\hat{\theta}_m$. If the recursive expression for $\hat{\theta}_{m+1}$ is solved, $\hat{\theta}_{m+1}$ can be written as

$$\hat{\theta}_{m+1} = \frac{1}{m+1}\sum_{i=1}^{m+1} z_i$$

The reader may wish to verify that this is the same answer that a nonrecursive solution would give.

9.3 NONLINEAR ESTIMATION

Throughout this chapter it has been assumed that the observation is a linear function of the message. When it is a nonlinear function of the message, the problem of forming an optimal estimate becomes quite complex. In this section, the general structure of such a problem will be introduced and evaluated. Expressions for both MAP and conditional mean estimates will be derived. Since there is generally no nice way to evaluate these expressions, one method of finding good, but not necessarily optimal, estimates will be be presented. It turns out that this procedure can be used in many situations where direct evaluation of the optimal estimate would be too costly.

The general problem to be addressed in this section is summarized in Eq. (9.3-1):

$$\mathbf{z} = \mathbf{h}(\boldsymbol{\theta}) + \mathbf{n} \tag{9.3-1}$$

The function $\mathbf{h}(\boldsymbol{\theta})$ is assumed to be known to the receiver and, in general, nonlinear. An example of such a situation might be the problem of estimating the destination of a projectile by observing its position at a sequence of times. Presumably the receiver knows the equations of motion which govern the behavior of the projectile. Since these equations involve such nonlinear effects as gravity, friction, and the curvature of the earth, they will be nonlinear.

Even though the observation is a nonlinear function of $\boldsymbol{\theta}$, the result from Chap. 8 that the minimum-variance estimate is the conditional mean of $\boldsymbol{\theta}$ is still valid. Thus, the general expression for this estimate is

$$\hat{\boldsymbol{\theta}} = \frac{\int_{-\infty}^{\infty} \boldsymbol{\theta} p(\mathbf{z}|\boldsymbol{\theta}) p(\boldsymbol{\theta})\, d\boldsymbol{\theta}}{\int_{-\infty}^{\infty} p(\mathbf{z}|\boldsymbol{\theta}) p(\boldsymbol{\theta})\, d\boldsymbol{\theta}} \tag{9.3-2}$$

If $\mathbf{n}$ and $\boldsymbol{\theta}$ are gaussian, then since the conditional mean of $\mathbf{z}$ is $\mathbf{h}(\boldsymbol{\theta})$, the density functions are

$$p(\mathbf{z}|\boldsymbol{\theta}) = \frac{1}{(2\pi)^{l/2}(\det \mathbf{V}_{\mathbf{n}})^{1/2}} \exp\left\{-\frac{1}{2}[\mathbf{z} - \mathbf{h}(\boldsymbol{\theta})]^T \mathbf{V}_{\mathbf{n}}^{-1}[\mathbf{z} - \mathbf{h}(\boldsymbol{\theta})]\right\} \tag{9.3-3}$$

$$p(\boldsymbol{\theta}) = \frac{1}{(2\pi)^{K/2}(\det \mathbf{V}_0)^{1/2}} \exp\left[-\frac{1}{2}(\boldsymbol{\theta} - \boldsymbol{\mu})^T \mathbf{V}_0^{-1}(\boldsymbol{\theta} - \boldsymbol{\mu})\right] \tag{9.3-4}$$

If these density functions are used in Eq. (9.3-2), the expression can be evaluated by numerical integration techniques. This is not a very satisfactory answer, but it is the type frequently encountered in nonlinear estimation problems.

In order to establish that not all nonlinear problems are complex, consider the following one-dimensional example.

Example 9.3-1 Suppose that a message has probability density

$$p(\theta) = \begin{cases} 1 & 0 \leq \theta \leq 1 \\ 0 & \text{elsewhere} \end{cases}$$

and that it is observed by the observation

$$z = \ln \frac{1}{\theta} + n$$

where the noise has probability density

$$p(n) = \begin{cases} e^{-n} & n \geq 0 \\ 0 & n < 0 \end{cases}$$

Find the conditional mean estimate.

The conditional density of z is just the density of n shifted by $\ln (1/\theta)$:

$$p(z|\theta) = \begin{cases} e^{-[z - \ln (1/\theta)]} & z - \ln \frac{1}{\theta} \geq 0 \\ 0 & z - \ln \frac{1}{\theta} \leq 0 \end{cases}$$

or, simplifying,

$$p(z|\theta) = \begin{cases} \dfrac{1}{\theta} e^{-z} & \theta \geq e^{-z} \\ 0 & \theta \leq e^{-z} \end{cases}$$

Then, evaluating the expression in Eq. (9.3-2), the conditional mean estimate is

$$\theta_{CM} = \frac{\displaystyle\int_{e^{-z}}^{1} e^{-z}\, d\theta}{\displaystyle\int_{e^{-z}}^{1} \frac{1}{\theta} e^{-z}\, d\theta}$$

The lower limit on each of the integrals is e^{-z} since $p(z|\theta)$ is zero for all θ less than e^{-z}. Evaluating the integrals is quite easy, and we have

$$\hat{\theta}_{CM} = \frac{1 - e^{-z}}{z}$$

For a nonlinear observation, the MAP and conditional mean estimate are no longer the same because $p(\theta|z)$ is not necessarily gaussian. However, the MAP estimate is still the value of θ that maximizes $p(\theta|z)$. Unless the maximum of $p(\theta|z)$ occurs at a boundary, $\hat{\theta}$ must satisfy

$$\frac{\partial}{\partial \theta} p(\theta|z) \bigg|_{\theta = \hat{\theta}} = 0$$

For the case of a gaussian signal and gaussian noise this can be simplified by noting that the partial derivative of the logarithm of $p(\theta|z)$ must also be zero at $\hat{\theta}$. Therefore,

$$\frac{\partial}{\partial \theta} \{ [z - h(\theta)]^T V_n^{-1} [z - h(\theta)] + (\theta - \mu)^T V_0^{-1} (\theta - \mu) \} \bigg|_{\theta = \hat{\theta}} = 0$$

Using the differentiation rules of Lemma 8.4-1, this becomes

$$-2 \frac{\partial h^T(\theta)}{\partial \theta} \bigg|_{\theta = \hat{\theta}} V_n^{-1} [z - h(\hat{\theta})] + 2 V_0^{-1} (\hat{\theta} - \mu) = 0 \qquad (9.3\text{-}5)$$

For some $h(\theta)$ it may be possible to evaluate Eq. (9.3-5) explicitly; for others, numerical techniques will be required.

For the problem presented in Example 9.3-1, the MAP estimate is easy to find as the following demonstrates.

Example 9.3-2 For the problem statement of Example 9.3-1, find the MAP estimate.

The joint probability density of θ and z is

$$p(z, \theta) = p(z|\theta)p(\theta) = \begin{cases} \dfrac{1}{\theta} e^{-z} & e^{-z} \leq \theta \leq 1; z \geq 0 \\ 0 & \text{otherwise} \end{cases}$$

This is clearly maximized by setting θ as small as possible. Therefore, the MAP estimate is

$$\hat{\theta}_{\text{MAP}} = e^{-z}$$

Although this appears quite different than the expression for $\hat{\theta}_{\text{CM}}$, the use of the exponential expansion for e^{-z} shows that

$$\hat{\theta}_{\text{MAP}} = 1 - z + \frac{z^2}{2!} - \frac{z^3}{3} + \cdots$$

Similarly, $\hat{\theta}_{\text{CM}}$ can be written as

$$\hat{\theta}_{\text{CM}} = 1 - \frac{z}{2!} + \frac{z^2}{3!} - \frac{z^3}{4!} + \cdots$$

Frequently one might be willing to sacrifice some optimality to achieve an estimator that is easier to implement than either Eq. (9.3-5) or Eq. (9.3-2). Generally this is done when one wishes to keep error variance small. One way to do so is to expand $\mathbf{h}(\boldsymbol{\theta})$ in a Taylor series and retain only the first two terms. The resulting approximation is linear, and the methods for linear problems can be applied.

In order for the Taylor series to be good approximation, two things must be true: $\mathbf{h}(\boldsymbol{\theta})$ must be well behaved, and the expansion should be about a value close to the actual value of $\boldsymbol{\theta}$. The approximation can be improved by iterating the procedure; the estimate of $\boldsymbol{\theta}$ from one step is used as the expansion point for the next step.

Before any observations are made, the best estimate of $\boldsymbol{\theta}$ in the mean-square-error sense is its mean $\boldsymbol{\mu}$. Therefore, the *zeroth-order estimate* can be defined as

$$\hat{\boldsymbol{\theta}}_0 = \boldsymbol{\mu}$$

Using a Taylor series to expand $\mathbf{h}(\boldsymbol{\theta})$, the observation can be written

$$\mathbf{z} = \mathbf{h}(\hat{\boldsymbol{\theta}}_0) + \left.\frac{\partial \mathbf{h}(\boldsymbol{\theta})}{\partial \boldsymbol{\theta}}\right|_{\boldsymbol{\theta}=\hat{\boldsymbol{\theta}}_0} (\boldsymbol{\theta} - \hat{\boldsymbol{\theta}}_0) + \text{HOT} + \mathbf{n} \qquad (9.3\text{-}6)$$

where HOT is used to denote higher-order terms in $(\boldsymbol{\theta} - \hat{\boldsymbol{\theta}}_0)$. The derivative term is a matrix whose elements are $\partial h_j(\boldsymbol{\theta})/\partial \theta_i$ evaluated at $\hat{\boldsymbol{\theta}}_0$. For simplicity, it will be denoted $\mathbf{H}_0$.

Suppose that a *first-order observation* is defined as

$$\mathbf{z}_1 = \mathbf{H}_0\boldsymbol{\theta} + \mathbf{n} \qquad (9.3\text{-}7)$$

Then, if $\mathbf{z}_1$ existed, it would be a linear observation of $\boldsymbol{\theta}$ and the methods of Sec. 9.1 could be applied. Although $\mathbf{z}_1$ is not known, it can be approximated by $\mathbf{z} - \mathbf{h}(\hat{\boldsymbol{\theta}}_0) + \mathbf{H}_0\hat{\boldsymbol{\theta}}_0$. Therefore, a *first-order estimate* of $\boldsymbol{\theta}$ can be formed by using this approximation and the results of Sec. 9.1:

$$\hat{\boldsymbol{\theta}}_1 = \boldsymbol{\mu} + (\mathbf{H}_0^T\mathbf{V}_n^{-1}\mathbf{H}_0 + \mathbf{V}_0^{-1})\mathbf{H}_0^T\mathbf{V}_n^{-1}[\mathbf{z} - \mathbf{h}(\hat{\boldsymbol{\theta}}_0) + \mathbf{H}_0(\hat{\boldsymbol{\theta}}_0 - \boldsymbol{\mu})] \qquad (9.3\text{-}8)$$

Now we are ready to iterate the procedure. Instead of expanding $\mathbf{h}(\boldsymbol{\theta})$ about $\hat{\boldsymbol{\theta}}_0$, we shall use $\hat{\boldsymbol{\theta}}_1$. Thus, $\mathbf{z}$ can be written as

$$\mathbf{z} = \mathbf{h}(\hat{\boldsymbol{\theta}}_1) + \mathbf{H}_1(\boldsymbol{\theta} - \hat{\boldsymbol{\theta}}_1) + \text{HOT} + \mathbf{n} \qquad (9.3\text{-}9)$$

and $\mathbf{z}_2$ can be defined as

$$\mathbf{z}_2 = \mathbf{H}_1 \boldsymbol{\theta} + \mathbf{n}$$

$$\simeq \mathbf{z} - \mathbf{h}(\hat{\boldsymbol{\theta}}_1) + \mathbf{H}_1 \hat{\boldsymbol{\theta}}_1$$

Since $\hat{\boldsymbol{\theta}}_1$ is supposed to be a better estimate of $\boldsymbol{\theta}$ than $\hat{\boldsymbol{\theta}}_0$, the higher-order terms in Eq. (9.3-9) should be smaller than those in Eq. (9.3-6). Therefore, we have a better estimate of $\mathbf{z}_2$ than we had of $\mathbf{z}_1$. Consequently, the estimate of $\boldsymbol{\theta}$ based on $\mathbf{z}_2$ should be better than the one based on $\mathbf{z}_1$. Again using Sec. 9.1, we have

$$\hat{\boldsymbol{\theta}}_2 = \boldsymbol{\mu} + (\mathbf{H}_1^T \mathbf{V}_\mathbf{n}^{-1} \mathbf{H}_1 + \mathbf{V}_0)^{-1} \mathbf{H}_1^T \mathbf{V}_\mathbf{n}^{-1} [\mathbf{z} - \mathbf{h}(\hat{\boldsymbol{\theta}}_1) + \mathbf{H}_1(\hat{\boldsymbol{\theta}}_1 - \boldsymbol{\mu})] \quad (9.3\text{-}10)$$

Clearly, we can continue this procedure as long as we want. The general form of the estimator is listed in Table 9.3-1.

Although this estimation procedure appears to be very nice, it has one significant flaw: There is no guarantee that it will converge. It is possible that at each successive step the estimate will get worse rather than better. Unfortunately, there is no general way of determining whether the estimate will converge for a specific example except to try it. If, however, $\mathbf{h}(\boldsymbol{\theta})$ is a relatively smooth function, the algorithm has a good chance of converging. In fact, there are many practical situations where it has proved quite useful.

If the algorithm does converge, one is left with the problem of determining the variance of the estimation error. To do so, the expression for $\hat{\boldsymbol{\theta}}_{m+1}$ can be rewritten with $\mathbf{z}$ replaced by its expansion about $\hat{\boldsymbol{\theta}}_m$:

$$\hat{\boldsymbol{\theta}}_{m+1} = \boldsymbol{\mu} + (\mathbf{H}_m^T \mathbf{V}_\mathbf{n}^{-1} \mathbf{H}_m + \mathbf{V}_0^{-1})^{-1} \mathbf{H}_m^T \mathbf{V}_\mathbf{n}^{-1} [\mathbf{H}_m(\hat{\boldsymbol{\theta}}_m - \boldsymbol{\mu}) + \text{HOT} + \mathbf{n}] \quad (9.3\text{-}11)$$

where the higher-order terms involve powers of $(\boldsymbol{\theta} - \hat{\boldsymbol{\theta}}_m)$. Since we have assumed that the estimate converges, these terms should be small. If they are neglected, an approximation to the error variance can be easily found. Note that without the HOT, the mean of $\hat{\boldsymbol{\theta}}_m$ is $\boldsymbol{\mu}$, and therefore, as in Sec. 9.1,

$$\text{var}\,\{\boldsymbol{\theta} - \hat{\boldsymbol{\theta}}_{m+1}\} \simeq (\mathbf{H}_m^T \mathbf{V}_\mathbf{n}^{-1} \mathbf{H}_m + \mathbf{V}_0^{-1})^{-1} \qquad (9.3\text{-}12)$$

Table 9.3-1 Extended Linear Estimator

Problem	$\mathbf{z} = \mathbf{h}(\boldsymbol{\theta}) + \mathbf{n}$
Estimate	$\hat{\boldsymbol{\theta}}_{m+1} = \boldsymbol{\mu} + \mathbf{V}_{m+1} \mathbf{H}_m^T \mathbf{V}_\mathbf{n}^{-1} [\mathbf{z} - \mathbf{h}(\hat{\boldsymbol{\theta}}_m) + \mathbf{H}_m(\hat{\boldsymbol{\theta}}_m - \boldsymbol{\mu})]$
Error variance	$\text{var}\,\{\boldsymbol{\theta} - \hat{\boldsymbol{\theta}}_{m+1}\} \simeq \mathbf{V}_{m+1} = (\mathbf{H}_m^T \mathbf{V}_\mathbf{n}^{-1} \mathbf{H}_m + \mathbf{V}_0^{-1})^{-1}$
Definition	$\mathbf{H}_m = \dfrac{\partial}{\partial \boldsymbol{\theta}} \mathbf{h}(\boldsymbol{\theta}) \Big|_{\boldsymbol{\theta} = \hat{\boldsymbol{\theta}}_m}$
Initial condition	$\boldsymbol{\theta}_0 = \boldsymbol{\mu}$

It is worth noting carefully the difference between the sequential estimation procedure described in Sec. 9.2 and the extended linear estimator presented here. In both cases, a succession of estimates were obtained. For the sequential case, however, each successive estimate was based on an additional observation; for the extended linear case, no new observations were available. Also, in the sequential case, each observation was linearly related to the unknown. In the extended linear case, the observation was nonlinear and linearization techniques were used. This resulted in a good, but not necessarily optimum, estimate. One could certainly have a problem involving a sequence of nonlinear observations. Such a problem could be solved by combining the sequential and extended linear procedures.

9.4 SUMMARY

In this chapter we have been concerned with the problem of estimating a gaussian parameter in the presence of additive gaussian noise. Three versions of the problem have been examined. First, a simple case with linear observations was developed. This material is a direct extension of the work in Chap. 8. Next a sequential estimation problem was discussed. This result made use of the results of Sec. 9.1 in an iterative fashion to develop a sequential estimation algorithm. Finally, a simple class of nonlinear estimation problems was considered. The results developed here again made use of the results of Sec. 9.1 in an iterative manner. In this case, however, the iteration regarded successive approximation of the optimal estimate.

9.5 PROBLEMS

9.5-1 For the general gaussian problem, assume that you have two observations:

$$\mathbf{z}_1 = \mathbf{H}_1 \boldsymbol{\theta} + \mathbf{n}_1$$

$$\mathbf{z}_2 = \mathbf{H}_2 \boldsymbol{\theta} + \mathbf{n}_2$$

Assuming that $\mathbf{n}_1$ and $\mathbf{n}_2$ are independents, show that the estimate $\hat{\boldsymbol{\theta}}$ based on $[\mathbf{z}_1 \ \mathbf{z}_2]^T$ can be written as

$$\hat{\boldsymbol{\theta}} = \mathbf{A}\hat{\boldsymbol{\theta}}_1 + \mathbf{B}\hat{\boldsymbol{\theta}}_2$$

where
$$\hat{\boldsymbol{\theta}}_1 = E\{\boldsymbol{\theta}|\mathbf{z}_1\}$$

$$\hat{\boldsymbol{\theta}}_2 = E\{\boldsymbol{\theta}|\mathbf{z}_2\}$$

and
$$\mathbf{A} + \mathbf{B} = \mathbf{I}$$

9.5-2 If an observation z is given by

$$\mathbf{z} = \boldsymbol{\theta} + \mathbf{n}$$

and if $\boldsymbol{\theta}$ and $\mathbf{n}$ are independent zero-mean gaussian random processes with variance matrices $\mathbf{V}_{\boldsymbol{\theta}}$ and $\mathbf{V}_{\mathbf{n}}$ respectively, find the probability density function $p(\boldsymbol{\theta}|\mathbf{z})$. Use this density function to find the MAP estimate.

9.5-3 Suppose that θ is a zero-mean unit-variance gaussian random variable and

$$\mathbf{z} = \mathbf{H}\theta + \mathbf{n}$$

where

$$\mathbf{H} = \begin{bmatrix} 1 \\ 1 \\ 1 \end{bmatrix}$$

and $\mathbf{n}$ is gaussian with variance matrix

$$\mathbf{V_n} = \begin{bmatrix} J_1^2 & 0 & 0 \\ 0 & J_2^2 & 0 \\ 0 & 0 & J_3^2 \end{bmatrix}$$

Find the MAP estimate of θ and verify that your answer makes sense when J_1^2, J_2^2, and J_3^2 are not equal.

9.5-4 Given the nonlinear observation

$$z = \theta + \theta^2 + n$$

with

$$p(\theta) = \frac{1}{\sqrt{2\pi}} e^{-\theta^2/2}$$

and

$$p(n) = \frac{1}{\sqrt{2\pi}} e^{-n^2/2}$$

use the extended linear estimator of Table 9.3-1 to find $\hat{\theta}$ if $z = 3$. Carry out only the first three iterations of the filter.

9.5-5

(a) Find the MAP estimate of θ based on

$$\mathbf{z} = \mathbf{H}\theta + \mathbf{n}$$

if

$$\mathbf{H} = \begin{bmatrix} 1 \\ 1 \end{bmatrix}$$

and $\mathbf{n}$ is gaussian with zero mean and

$$\text{var } \{\mathbf{n}\} = \begin{bmatrix} \sigma^2 & \rho\sigma^2 \\ \rho\sigma^2 & \sigma^2 \end{bmatrix}$$

assuming that θ is also gaussian with zero mean and variance V.

(b) Repeat part (a) but use a sequential procedure like that derived in Sec. 9.2. First find $\hat{\theta}_1$, the estimate based on z_1 alone. Then use $\hat{\theta}_1$ and z_2 to find $\hat{\theta}_{\text{MAP}}$.

9.5-6

(a) Find the maximum-likelihood estimate of $\boldsymbol{\theta} = [a \ b]^T$ for the observation

$$z_i = \sqrt{a}\, n_i + b \qquad i = 1, 2, \ldots, I$$

Where n_i are independent zero-mean, unit-variance gaussian random variables

(b) Show that your answers can be written in the following sequential form:

$$\hat{b}_i = \frac{i-1}{i} \hat{b}_{i-1} + z_i$$

$$\hat{a}_i = \frac{i-1}{i} \hat{a}_{i-1} + \frac{1}{i-1}(z_i - \hat{b}_i)^2$$

9.5-7 The autoregressive model introduced in Chap. 8

$$z_i = \sum_{k=1}^{K} \theta_k z_{i-k} + n_i$$

can also be solved using the sequential procedure. The only trick is to let $\mathbf{H}$ vary with i. Show how the estimate given in Table 9.2-1 applies to this case. Be sure to state what assumptions on $\mathbf{n}$ and θ are needed.

TEN

PROPERTIES OF ESTIMATORS

One of the major differences between the estimation problem and the decision problem is the difficulty in describing how "good" a given estimation algorithm is. In a decision problem, the various probabilities of error form a compact description of the effectiveness of the decision algorithm. No such simple measure exists, however, for an estimation problem. As we shall see, the only complete description is the conditional probability density $p(\hat{\boldsymbol{\theta}}|\boldsymbol{\theta})$. Since this function can differ for every value of $\hat{\boldsymbol{\theta}}$, it is quite a cumbersome description.

In an effort to simplify the problem of describing how good a given estimation procedure is, a number of classes of estimation algorithms have been defined. In this chapter we shall review these definitions and show how they can be used to describe estimation algorithms.

10.1 UNBIASED ESTIMATORS

Any estimation algorithm can be characterized as a mapping from the message $\boldsymbol{\theta}$ to the estimate $\hat{\boldsymbol{\theta}}$. This is a probabilistic mapping and therefore must be described by the probability density function $p(\hat{\boldsymbol{\theta}}|\boldsymbol{\theta})$. One typical example of such a density function for the one-dimensional case is given in Fig. 10.1-1, which shows the actual value of the parameter θ.

The "goodness" of the receiver is characterized by how likely it is that the estimate $\hat{\boldsymbol{\theta}}$ is "close" to the actual value of $\boldsymbol{\theta}$. Therefore, if the density function is closely clustered about $\boldsymbol{\theta}$, it is probably a good estimation procedure; if the density function is not clustered or if it is clustered about some other point, it is a less good estimation procedure.

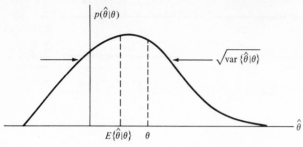

Figure 10.1-1 Typical conditional probability density $p(\hat{\theta}|\theta)$.

The variance of a density function of a scalar is a good measure of how clustered it is, and the mean of the density tells where it is clustered. In the instrumentation business, the effectiveness of a measuring instrument is specified by its *accuracy* and *precision*. Accuracy is a measure of how well the conditional mean of $\hat{\theta}$ matches θ, and precision measures the conditional variance. Clearly, then, a good estimation algorithm is one for which the mean of $\hat{\theta}$, when conditioned on θ, is close to θ and for which the conditional variance of $\hat{\theta}$ is small.

As we shall see, it is sometimes possible to design estimators for which the conditional mean of $\hat{\theta}$ is *always* exactly *equal* to θ, which is generally a desirable property. When this is true for all values of θ, such an estimator is referred to as *conditionally unbiased*. In other words, an estimator is conditionally unbiased when

$$E\{\hat{\theta}|\theta\} = \theta \qquad (10.1\text{-}1)$$

One example of such an estimator is as follows.

Example 10.1-1 Consider forming the maximum-likelihood estimate of a parameter θ from the set of observations

$$z_i = \theta + n_i \qquad i = 1, 2, \ldots, I$$

where the noise terms n_i are independent zero-mean, gaussian random variables of variance σ^2. The conditional density function is

$$p(\mathbf{z}|\theta) = (2\pi\sigma^2)^{-I/2}\exp\left\{-\frac{1}{2\sigma^2}\sum_{i=1}^{I}(z_i - \theta)^2\right\}$$

The derivative of the log of this function is

$$\frac{\partial}{\partial\theta}\ln p(\mathbf{z}|\theta) = \frac{1}{\sigma^2}\sum_{i=1}^{I}(z_i - \theta)$$

Therefore, the maximum-likelihood estimate is

$$\hat{\theta}_{\text{ML}} = \frac{1}{I}\sum_{i=1}^{I}z_i$$

Since the expected value of each z_i given θ is always θ, the estimate is unbiased.

To determine the precision of the estimate, we must compute the conditional variance of $\hat{\theta}_{ML}$:

$$\text{var}\,\{\hat{\theta}_{ML}|\theta\} = E\left\{\left(\frac{1}{I}\sum_{i=1}^{I} z_i - \theta\right)^2 |\theta\right\}$$

$$= E\left\{\left(\frac{1}{I}\sum_{i=1}^{I} n_i\right)^2\right\}$$

$$= \frac{\sigma^2}{I}$$

Clearly the precision improves as I increases.

Note that for an *unbiased* estimate of a scalar, the conditional variance of $\hat{\theta}$ is the same as the conditional mean square error $E\{(\hat{\theta} - \theta)^2|\theta\}$. This is not true in general, and minimizing the conditional variance may not minimize the conditional mean square error.

For those estimation situations in which the density function of θ is known, it is possible to define the unconditional expected value of $\hat{\theta}$, as well as the conditional expected value. If this quantity is equal to the expected value of θ, the estimator is called *unconditionally unbiased*. In other words, an estimator is unconditionally unbiased if

$$E\{E(\hat{\theta}|\theta)\} = E\{\hat{\theta}\} = E\{\theta\} \qquad (10.1\text{-}2)$$

It is clear that any conditionally unbiased estimator is also unconditionally unbiased. The converse, however, is not necessarily true. It is possible to have an estimate that is not conditionally unbiased but that is unconditionally unbiased, as the following example demonstrates.

Example 10.1-2 An observation z is the product of a parameter θ and a noise term n. The probability density function of the noise is

$$p(n) = \begin{cases} 2n & 0 \le n \le 1 \\ 0 & \text{otherwise} \end{cases}$$

This density function is shown in Fig. 10.1-2a. The conditional density function of z given θ is just the scaled version of $p(n)$, as shown in Fig. 10.1-2b. Therefore, the value of θ which would maximize $p(z|\theta)$ is just z, and

$$\hat{\theta}_{ML} = z = n\theta$$

Clearly this is a conditionally biased estimate since

$$E\{\hat{\theta}_{ML}|\theta\} = \frac{2\theta}{3}$$

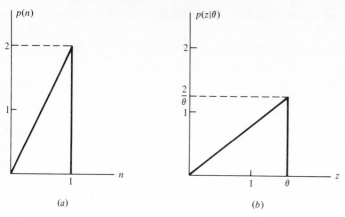

Figure 10.1-2 Density functions for Example 10.1-2. (*a*) Density of n; (*b*) conditional density of z.

However, if θ had a mean of zero, the estimate would be unconditionally unbiased. In fact, the estimator

$$\hat{\theta} = 0$$

would be conditionally biased but unconditionally unbiased. It also would not be very good.

Occasionally, the familiar maximum-likelihood estimate will not be unbiased, but there may be another estimate which is. Consider, for example, estimating the mean and variance from a set of independent samples of a gaussian process.

Example 10.1-3 Assume we have a set of observations

$$z_i = \sqrt{a}\, n_i + b \qquad i = 1, 2, \ldots, I$$

where n_i are independent zero-mean, unit-variance gaussian random variables. We wish to estimate $\boldsymbol{\theta} = [a\ b]^T$.

We know from Chap. 8 that the maximum-likelihood estimate of the mean is

$$\hat{b}_{\mathrm{ML}} = \frac{1}{I} \sum_{i=1}^{I} z_i$$

and the maximum-likelihood estimate of the variance is

$$\hat{a}_{\mathrm{ML}} = \frac{1}{I} \sum_{i=1}^{I} (z_i - \hat{b}_{\mathrm{ML}})^2$$

Clearly, the estimate of b is conditionally unbiased, but the conditional expected value of $\hat{a}_{ML}$ is

$$E\{\hat{a}_{ML}|a, b\} = E\left\{\frac{1}{I} \sum_{i=1}^{I} \left[\sqrt{a}\, n_i + b - \frac{1}{I} \sum_{j=1}^{I} (\sqrt{a}\, n_j + b) \right]^2 \right\}$$

$$= E\left\{ \frac{a}{I} \sum_{i=1}^{I} n_i^2 - \frac{a}{I^2} \sum_{i=1}^{I} \sum_{j=1}^{I} n_i n_j \right\}$$

$$= \frac{I-1}{I}\, a$$

and $\hat{a}_{ML}$ is *not* an unbiased estimate (ub).

It is possible to form an unbiased estimate by simply scaling $\hat{a}_{ML}$ as follows:

$$\hat{a}_{ub} = \frac{I}{I-1}\, \hat{a}_{ML} = \frac{1}{I-1} \sum_{i=1}^{I} (z_i - \hat{b}_{ML})^2$$

Although this estimate is unbiased, it is not necessarily better than the maximum-likelihood estimate. Note that the conditional variance of the unbiased estimate is

$$\text{var}\,\{\hat{a}_{ub}\} = \frac{1}{(I-1)^2}\, E\left\{ \left[\sum_{i=1}^{I} (z_i - \hat{b}_{ML})^2 - (I-1)a \right]^2 \right\}$$

whereas the variance of $\hat{a}_{ML}$ is

$$\text{var}\,\{\hat{a}_{ML}\} = \frac{1}{I^2}\, E\left\{ \left[\sum_{i=1}^{I} (z_i - \hat{b}_{ML})^2 - (I-1)a \right]^2 \right\}$$

Thus, the variance of the maximum-likelihood estimate is lower than that of the unbiased estimate.

10.2 EFFICIENT ESTIMATORS

We have seen that when estimating a scalar, the conditional mean and conditional variance let us determine whether we have a good estimator. If we restrict our attention to only those estimators that are unbiased, we shall reduce our measure of goodness to one dimension. Therefore, it will be possible to define the "best" estimator in this class as the one that minimizes the conditional variance. Such estimators are formally referred to as *minimum-variance conditionally unbiased estimators*.

At first, such a concept does not seem particularly useful since it appears that we would have to look at *all* unbiased estimators to determine which one is best. Fortunately, this is not always the case. As we shall see, we can establish a lower bound on the conditional variance for *any* unbiased estimator. Clearly, then, any estimator whose variance equals this bound must be the best in the sense that we have defined it. We shall see also that if any estimator meets the bound, then the maximum-likelihood estimator does.

Although the bound is easily stated, it definitely is not intuitively obvious. In fact, it looks rather strange. The bound was first stated by Fisher and proved by Duqué but is generally attributed to Cramér (1944) and Rao (1945). It is stated as follows:

Theorem 10.2-1 (The Cramér-Rao bound) For any unbiased estimate $\hat{\theta}$ of a scalar θ, the conditional variance is bounded by

$$\text{var}\,\{\hat{\theta}|\theta\} \geq \left(E\left\{\left[\frac{\partial}{\partial\theta}\ln p(z|\theta)\right]^2\right\}\right)^{-1} \qquad (10.2\text{-}1a)$$

or, alternatively,

$$\text{var}\,\{\hat{\theta}|\theta\} \geq \left[-E\left\{\frac{\partial^2}{\partial\theta^2}\ln p(z|\theta)\right\}\right]^{-1} \qquad (10.2\text{-}1b)$$

The critical feature of these bounds is that they depend only on $p(z|\theta)$. The two forms are given since one may be easier to evaluate than the other. To prove the theorem, note that since $\hat{\theta}$ is required to be unbiased, we can write

$$\int_{-\infty}^{\infty} [\hat{\theta}(z) - \theta]p(z|\theta)\,dz = 0$$

where we have indicated explicitly that $\hat{\theta}$ is a function of z. Now, if we differentiate both sides with respect to θ, we can interchange the differentiation with the integration to obtain

$$\int_{-\infty}^{\infty} \left[-p(z|\theta) + [\hat{\theta}(z) - \theta]\frac{\partial p(z|\theta)}{\partial\theta}\right] dz = 0 \qquad (10.2\text{-}2)$$

Using the fact that the integral of any probability density is 1 and that

$$\frac{\partial x}{\partial\theta} = x\frac{\partial\ln x}{\partial\theta} \qquad (10.2\text{-}3)$$

the equation can be written

$$\int_{-\infty}^{\infty} [\hat{\theta}(z) - \theta]p(z|\theta)\frac{\partial\ln p(z|\theta)}{\partial\theta}\,dz = 1 \qquad (10.2\text{-}4)$$

Now we shall need the Schwartz inequality. It states that for any two functions $f(x)$ and $g(x)$,

$$\left[\int_a^b f(x)g(x)\,dx\right]^2 \leq \int_a^b f^2(x)\,dx \int_a^b g^2(x)\,dx \qquad (10.2\text{-}5a)$$

with equality if and only if

$$g(x) = cf(x) \qquad (10.2\text{-}5b)$$

If Eq. (10.2-4) is squared we can use Eqs. (10.2-5) to show that

$$1 = \left[\int_{-\infty}^{\infty} \{ (\hat{\theta}(z) - \theta) \sqrt{p(z|\theta)} \} \sqrt{p(z|\theta)} \frac{\partial \ln p(z|\theta)}{\partial \theta} \, dz \right]^2$$

$$\leq \int_{-\infty}^{\infty} [\hat{\theta}(z) - \theta]^2 p(z|\theta) \, dz \int_{-\infty}^{\infty} \left\{ \frac{\partial \ln p(z|\theta)}{\partial \theta} \right\}^2 p(z|\theta) \, dz$$

which is the same as Eq. (10.2-1a). It holds with equality if and only if

$$\frac{\partial}{\partial \theta} \ln p(z|\theta) = c[\hat{\theta}(z) - \theta] \tag{10.2-6}$$

for some constant c. Note that c can depend on θ, but it cannot be zero for any θ. If it were zero, the left side of Eq. (10.2-4) would be zero and would not be consistent with the right side.

To establish the alternative form of the bound shown in Eq. (10.2-1b), we need first to differentiate the equality

$$\int_{-\infty}^{\infty} p(z|\theta) \, dz = 1$$

with respect to θ and use Eq. (10.2-3) to give

$$\int_{-\infty}^{\infty} \frac{\partial \ln p(z|\theta)}{\partial \theta} p(z|\theta) \, dz = 0$$

A second round of differentiation and substitution with Eq. (10.2-3) yields

$$\int_{-\infty}^{\infty} \frac{\partial^2 \ln p(z|\theta)}{\partial \theta^2} p(z|\theta) \, dz + \int_{-\infty}^{\infty} \left[\frac{\partial \ln p(z|\theta)}{\partial \theta} \right]^2 p(z|\theta) \, dz = 0$$

But this is just

$$E\left\{ \frac{\partial^2}{\partial \theta^2} \ln p(z|\theta) \right\} = -E\left\{ \left[\frac{\partial}{\partial \theta} \ln p(z|\theta) \right]^2 \right\}$$

which, together with Eq. (10.2-1a), establishes Eq. (10.2-1b).

The true beauty of the Cramér-Rao bound is that it lets us define and find an *efficient estimate*.

Definition 10.2-1 An *efficient estimate* is an unbiased estimate whose conditional variance satisfies the Cramér-Rao bound with equality.

There is no guarantee that an efficient estimate exists for a given problem; it may not. However, we can show that if one does exist, the maximum-likelihood estimate will be efficient. This result is important enough to state as a separate theorem.

Theorem 10.2-2 If an efficient estimate exists, the maximum-likelihood estimate is efficient.

Recall that the maximum-likelihood estimate was the one which satisfied

$$\frac{\partial}{\partial \theta} \ln p(z|\theta) \bigg|_{\theta = \hat{\theta}_{\text{ML}}} = 0$$

However, if an efficient estimate $\hat{\theta}_{\text{eff}}$ exists, Eq. (10.2-6) says that for $\hat{\theta}_{\text{eff}}$

$$\frac{\partial}{\partial \theta} \ln p(z|\theta) = c(\hat{\theta}_{\text{eff}} - \theta)$$

Evaluating this for $\theta = \hat{\theta}_{\text{ML}}$, the left side is zero, so the right side must be zero. But, since c cannot be zero, $\hat{\theta}_{\text{eff}}$ must be the same as $\hat{\theta}_{\text{ML}}$.

As an example of an efficient estimate, consider the problem presented in Example 10-1.1.

Example 10.2-1 (Example 10.1-1 revisited) From Sec. 10.1, the maximum-likelihood estimate was unbiased and the condition variance was

$$\text{var} (\hat{\theta}_{\text{ML}}|\theta) = \frac{\sigma^2}{I} \tag{10.2-7}$$

To find the Cramér-Rao bound, we must compute the expected value of the square of

$$\frac{\partial}{\partial \theta} \ln p(z|\theta) = \frac{1}{\sigma^2} \sum_{i=1}^{I} (z_i - \theta) \tag{10.2-8}$$

or the expected value of

$$\frac{\partial^2}{\partial \theta^2} \ln p(z|\theta) = -\frac{I}{\sigma^2} \tag{10.2-9}$$

Clearly, the second option is easier, and it is obvious that

$$\left[-E\left\{ \frac{\partial^2}{\partial \theta^2} \ln p(z|\theta) \right\} \right]^{-1} = \text{var} \{\hat{\theta}_{\text{ML}}|\theta\} \tag{10.2-10}$$

Thus, the estimate is efficient. Note that since Eq. (10.2-8) can be put into the same form as Eq. (10.2-6), we could have known at that point that the estimate was efficient. In fact, if we had noticed this, we could have used Eq. (10.2-9) to determine the variance.

As we have stated it, the Cramér-Rao bound applies only to estimates of scalars. There is a form of the bound for estimating vectors, but it is even more complex and not as useful. We shall state the theorem without proof.

Theorem 10.2-3 The diagonal elements of the conditional variance matrix var $\{\hat{\boldsymbol{\theta}}|\boldsymbol{\theta}\}$ are each greater than or equal to the corresponding diagonal elements of $\mathbf{J}^{-1}$ where the matrix $\mathbf{J}$ is

$$\mathbf{J} = E\left[\frac{\partial \ln p(\mathbf{z}|\boldsymbol{\theta})}{\partial \boldsymbol{\theta}}\left(\frac{\partial \ln p(\mathbf{z}|\boldsymbol{\theta})}{\partial \boldsymbol{\theta}}\right)^T\right] \tag{10.2-11a}$$

$$= -E\left[\frac{\partial}{\partial \boldsymbol{\theta}}\left(\frac{\partial}{\partial \boldsymbol{\theta}}\ln p(\mathbf{z}|\boldsymbol{\theta})\right)^T\right] \tag{10.2-11b}$$

The equality for the jjth element holds if and only if

$$\hat{\theta}_j - \theta_j = \mathbf{C}_j^T\frac{\partial}{\partial \boldsymbol{\theta}}\ln p(\mathbf{z}|\boldsymbol{\theta}) \tag{10.2-12}$$

where $\mathbf{C}_j$ can depend on $\boldsymbol{\theta}$.

Thus, there is a bound on the terms of the form var $\{\hat{\theta}_j|\boldsymbol{\theta}\}$ but not on the off-diagonal terms, which are cov $\{\hat{\theta}_j, \hat{\theta}_k|\boldsymbol{\theta}\}$. In the one-dimensional case, Theorem 10.2-3 obviously reduces to the Cramér-Rao bound.

The maximum-likelihood estimate for the general gaussian case satisfies Eq. (10.2-12) for all j, and therefore the conditional variance of each $\hat{\theta}_j$ is minimized.

Example 10.2-2 (General gaussian problem) Let the observation

$$\mathbf{z} = \mathbf{H}\boldsymbol{\theta} + \mathbf{n}$$

where $\mathbf{n}$ is a gaussian process. The conditional density function of $\mathbf{z}$ is

$$p(\mathbf{z}|\boldsymbol{\theta}) = \frac{1}{(2\pi)^{l/2}(\det \mathbf{V})^{1/2}}\exp\left\{-\frac{1}{2}(\mathbf{z} - \mathbf{H}\boldsymbol{\theta})^T\mathbf{V}^{-1}(\mathbf{z} - \mathbf{H}\boldsymbol{\theta})\right\}$$

and the derivative of the log of this is

$$\frac{\partial}{\partial \boldsymbol{\theta}}\ln p(\mathbf{z}|\boldsymbol{\theta}) = \mathbf{H}^T\mathbf{V}^{-1}(\mathbf{z} - \mathbf{H}\boldsymbol{\theta})$$

Since this derivative has the form required by Eq. (10.2-12) for equality in the Schwartz inequality, the Cramér-Rao bound also must be satisfied with equality. Therefore, we can compute the conditional variance from

$$\text{var }\{\hat{\boldsymbol{\theta}}_{\text{ML}}\} = [\mathbf{H}^T\mathbf{V}^{-1}\mathbf{H}]^{-1}$$

In addition to the bound on conditional variance for conditionally unbiased estimators, there is a similar bound on the mean-square error for estimating a random variable. It is stated as the following theorem.

Theorem 10.2-4 The mean-square error in estimating a random variable θ

can be bounded by

$$E\{(\hat{\theta} - \theta)^2\} \geq \left(E\left\{ \left[\frac{\partial}{\partial\theta} \ln p(z, \theta) \right]^2 \right\} \right)^{-1} \tag{10.2-13a}$$

$$\geq \left[-E\left\{ \frac{\partial^2}{\partial\theta^2} \ln p(z, \theta) \right\} \right]^{-1} \tag{10.2-13b}$$

if the following conditions are met:

(a) $\dfrac{\partial}{\partial\theta} p(z, \theta)$ and $\dfrac{\partial^2}{\partial\theta^2} p(z, \theta)$ are both absolutely integrable with respect to z and θ.

(b) $\displaystyle\lim_{\theta\to\infty} p(\theta) \, E\{\hat{\theta} - \theta|\theta\} = 0.$

(c) $\displaystyle\lim_{\theta\to-\infty} p(\theta) \, E\{\hat{\theta} - \theta|\theta\} = 0.$

The proof is quite similar to that for the Cramér-Rao bound. Consider differentiating $p(\theta) \, E\{\hat{\theta} - \theta|\theta\}$ with respect to θ:

$$\frac{d}{d\theta} p(\theta) E\{\hat{\theta} - \theta|\theta\} = \int_{-\infty}^{\infty} \left[-p(z, \theta) + \frac{\partial p(z, \theta)}{\partial\theta} (\hat{\theta} - \theta) \right] dz$$

If this is integrated with respect to θ from $-\infty$ to ∞, we have

$$p(\theta) E\{\hat{\theta} - \theta|\theta\} \Big|_{-\infty}^{\infty} = \int_{-\infty}^{\infty} \int_{-\infty}^{\infty} \left[-p(z, \theta) + (\hat{\theta}(z) - \theta) \frac{\partial p(z, \theta)}{\partial\theta} \right] dz \, d\theta \tag{10.2-14}$$

Conditions (b) and (c) ensure that the left side is zero; therefore, Eq. (10.2-14) is essentially the same as Eq. (10.2-2). From this point, the derivation is essentially unchanged. The major difference is that when the Schwartz inequality is used, the variable of integration includes θ as well as z. Therefore, the condition for equality is

$$\frac{\partial}{\partial\theta} \ln p(z, \theta) = c[\hat{\theta}(z) - \theta] \tag{10.2-15}$$

and c cannot depend on θ and cannot be zero. An estimator which satisfies the bound with equality is again called an *efficient estimator*. Therefore, since the definition of the MAP estimate requires that

$$\frac{\partial}{\partial\theta} \ln p(z, \theta) \Big|_{\theta=\hat{\theta}_{\mathrm{MAP}}} = 0$$

then if an efficient estimate exists, the MAP estimate is efficient. In addition, since $\hat{\theta}_{\mathrm{MAP}}$ has minimum mean-square error, it must equal $\hat{\theta}_{\mathrm{CM}}$.

That is not all we can say. Replacing $p(z, \theta)$ by $p(\theta|z)p(z)$ in Eq. (10.2-15) and taking another derivative gives

$$\frac{\partial^2}{\partial\theta^2} \ln p(\theta|z) = -c \tag{10.2-15}$$

Therefore, $p(\theta|z)$ must be of the form

$$p(\theta|z) = K \exp\left(-c\theta^2 + c_1\theta + c_2\right) \qquad (10.2\text{-}16)$$

which is just a gaussian density.

10.3 ASYMPTOTIC PROPERTIES

In many estimation problems, the observation actually consists of a sequence of observations. In such cases, the number of observations in the sequence may be a parameter of the receiver design. The more observations taken, the more costly the receiver. It is important, therefore, to examine the behavior of an estimator as a function of the number of observations. In general, we shall expect the receiver to get better as the number of observations increases. We shall use $\hat{\theta}_I$ to denote the estimate of θ based on the first I observations.

As an illustration, recall Example 10.1-3 where we computed the variance of a gaussian process from a set of samples. The maximum-likelihood estimate was

$$\hat{a}_{\mathrm{ML}} = \frac{1}{I}\sum_{i=1}^{I}\left(z_i - \frac{1}{I}\sum_{j=1}^{I} z_j\right)^2 \qquad (10.3\text{-}1)$$

The conditional mean of this estimate was

$$E\{\hat{a}_{\mathrm{ML}}|a\} = \frac{I-1}{I}\,a \qquad (10.3\text{-}2)$$

and the estimate was biased. However, in the limit of large I, $E\{\hat{a}_{\mathrm{ML}}|a\}$ becomes a, and the estimate becomes unbiased. Such an estimator is called *asymptotically unbiased* and is defined as follows.

Definition 10.3-1 An estimate $\hat{\theta}_I$ is *asymptotically unbiased* if

$$\lim_{I\to\infty} E\{\hat{\theta}_I|\theta\} = \theta$$

Generally, one would expect a good estimate to get better as I increases. In fact, $\hat{\theta}_I$ should be essentially the same as θ in the limit. There are two simple ways to state this formally: An estimate can be *simple consistent* or *mean-square consistent*. As with unbiased estimators, a consistent estimator can be *conditionally consistent* or, if $p(\theta)$ is defined, *unconditionally consistent*, which leads to four definitions.

Definition 10.3-2 An estimate is *conditionally simple consistent* (or *conditionally convergent with probability 1*) if for all $\epsilon > 0$

$$\lim_{I\to\infty} P\{\|\theta_I - \theta\| < \epsilon|\theta\} = 1$$

Definition 10.3-3 An estimate of a random vector $\boldsymbol{\theta}$ is *unconditionally simple consistent* if for any $\epsilon > 0$

$$\lim_{I \to \infty} P\{\|\hat{\boldsymbol{\theta}}_I - \boldsymbol{\theta}\| < \epsilon\} = 1$$

Definition 10.3-4 An estimate is *conditionally mean-square-consistent* (or *mean-square-convergent*) if

$$\lim_{I \to \infty} E\{(\hat{\boldsymbol{\theta}}_I - \boldsymbol{\theta})(\hat{\boldsymbol{\theta}}_I - \boldsymbol{\theta})^T | \boldsymbol{\theta}\} = 0$$

Definition 10.3-5 An estimate of a random variable is *unconditionally mean-square-consistent* if

$$\lim_{I \to \infty} E\{(\hat{\boldsymbol{\theta}}_I - \boldsymbol{\theta})(\hat{\boldsymbol{\theta}}_I - \boldsymbol{\theta})^T\} = 0$$

Implicit in Definitions 10.3-4 and 10.3-5 is the concept of an inequality between variance matrices. When we say that

$$\mathbf{V}_1 \leq \mathbf{V}_2$$

we mean that $\mathbf{V}_2 - \mathbf{V}_1$ is nonnegative definite. This concept lets us compare two mean-square-consistent estimators and determine which is better. Therefore, we can define an *asymptotically efficient* estimate as follows.

Definition 10.3-6 An unconditionally mean-square-consistent estimator θ_I is *unconditionally asymptotically efficient* if there is some I_0 such that for any other unconditionally mean-square-consistent estimator $\hat{\theta}_I'$

$$E\{(\hat{\boldsymbol{\theta}}_I - \boldsymbol{\theta})(\hat{\boldsymbol{\theta}}_I - \boldsymbol{\theta})^T\} \leq E\{(\hat{\boldsymbol{\theta}}_I' - \boldsymbol{\theta})(\hat{\boldsymbol{\theta}}_I' - \boldsymbol{\theta})^T\} \qquad \text{for all } I > I_0$$

A similar definition holds for a *conditionally asymptotically efficient* estimator.

Finally, we can define an *asymptotically normal* estimate as one for which the distribution of $\sqrt{I}\,(\hat{\boldsymbol{\theta}}_I - \boldsymbol{\theta})$ approaches the gaussian distribution. The *best asymptotically normal* estimator would be the one for which the mean of $\sqrt{I}\,(\hat{\boldsymbol{\theta}}_I - \boldsymbol{\theta})$ would be zero, and its variance would be a minimum over all asymptotically normal estimators.

10.4 SENSITIVITY AND ERROR ANALYSIS

In almost everything we have done so far, we have assumed that we have had perfect knowledge of our source and channel models when designing our receiver. This assumption frequently will be invalid. We may know a lot about the source and the channel, but generally we shall not know everything. In this section we shall examine how the performance measures of estimators vary when the actual situation differs from the assumed model.

We wish to distinguish between three different values of a performance measure: ideal, computed, and actual. The *ideal* measure is the best performance that could be obtained if the system designer had perfect knowledge of the system; it is the quantity that we are familiar with. The *computed* performance is what the designer *thinks* will happen based on imperfect knowledge; it is computed in the same way as the ideal measure using the assumed system model rather than the actual model. The *actual* performance is a measure of how well the system actually works; it is the result of using an imperfectly designed estimator on the actual channel.

It is interesting to compare the relative values of these three measures. Clearly, the actual performance cannot be better than the ideal performance. If it were, it would contradict the definition of ideal. Care must be taken, however, since our performance measures for estimators are not simple. As we shall illustrate, it may seem possible for the actual performance to be better than the ideal.

Of course, it is possible for the computed performance to be better than the ideal performance. Suppose, for example, an optimistic designer thought that there was very little noise on a channel. The computed performance would be very good. If actually the channel was quite noisy, the best performance obtainable would not be as good. In fact, it is not uncommon for the designer of a system to think that it will perform much better than is actually possible, as illustrated by the following example.

Example 10.4-1 Consider the scalar estimation problem

$$z = h\theta + n \tag{10.4-1}$$

where n is normal with zero mean and variance V. We know that the maximum-likelihood estimate of θ is

$$\hat{\theta}_{ML} = \frac{z}{h} \tag{10.4-2}$$

which is conditionally unbiased and has conditional variance

$$\text{var } \{\hat{\theta}_{ML}|\theta\} = \frac{V}{h^2} \tag{10.4-3}$$

This is the ideal performance for the model.

Now the receiver who thought that the model was

$$z = \bar{h}\theta + n$$

and that the variance of n was $\bar{V}$ would use

$$\hat{\theta} = \frac{z}{\bar{h}} \tag{10.4-4}$$

as an estimate. The receiver would think this estimate was unbiased and that its variance was

$$\text{var}\,\{\hat{\theta}|\theta\} = \frac{\bar{V}}{\bar{h}^2} \tag{10.4-5}$$

Depending on the values of $\bar{V}$ and $\bar{h}$, this computed variance could be larger or smaller than the ideal variance given in Eq. (10.4-3).

The actual performance would be another story. Unless $\bar{h}$ was actually h, the estimate would be biased:

$$E\{\hat{\theta}|\theta\} = \frac{\theta h}{\bar{h}} \tag{10.4-6}$$

The actual variance would be

$$\text{var}\,\{\hat{\theta}|\theta\} = \frac{V}{\bar{h}^2} \tag{10.4-7}$$

This, too, could be larger or smaller than the ideal and computed variances given in Eqs. (10.4-3) and (10.4-5) because the computed estimate is not unbiased.

In general, we have talked about using maximum-likelihood estimators when the unknown was not random or random with unknown statistics. Sometimes, however, it is better to use this procedure if the problem is imperfectly known. Consider the simple scalar problem in the following example.

Example 10.4-2 For the scalar observation

$$z = \theta + n$$

we wish to estimate θ if we know it is normal with zero mean and variance V. We know n is also zero-mean and normal, but we do not know its variance.

If we use a maximum-likelihood procedure, we have

$$\hat{\theta}_{\text{ML}} = z$$

which is unbiased, and the error variance is

$$\text{var}\,\{\hat{\theta}_{\text{ML}} - \theta\} = \sigma^2$$

where we have denoted the actual noise variance by σ^2. Suppose, now, that we guess the variance of n to be σ_1^2 and form the corresponding MAP estimate

$$\hat{\theta}_{\text{MAP}} = \frac{V}{V + \sigma_1^2}\,z$$

The error variance is

$$\text{var } \{\hat{\theta}_{\text{MAP}} - \theta\} = \frac{\sigma_1^4 V + V^2 \sigma^2}{(V + \sigma_1^2)^2}$$

If the assumed value of σ_1^2 is too big, the maximum-likelihood estimate will be better than the MAP. In particular, if

$$\sigma_1^2 > \left[\frac{1}{2} \left(\frac{1}{\sigma^2} - \frac{1}{V} \right) \right]^{-1}$$

then the MAP estimate will be worse.

10.5 SUMMARY

In this chapter we have examined some of the properties of estimators and have seen that the mean and variance of the estimate can serve to categorize estimators. Frequently it was possible to find an estimator whose mean matched the unknown or at least the mean of the unknown. Such an unbiased estimator is often desirable. In addition, it is possible to bound the performance of unbiased estimators and sometimes find estimates that match the bound. For those estimators that use a sequence of observation, we defined a number of desirable properties in the limit as the number of observations became large. Finally, we investigated the performance of estimators when imperfect source and/or channel models were used.

10.6 PROBLEMS

10.6-1 Let θ be the mean of a Poisson process, and consider estimating θ from the number of observations n. Recalling that

$$P\{n \text{ events} \,|\, \theta\} = \frac{\theta^n}{n!} e^{-\theta} \qquad n = 0, 1, 2, \ldots$$

determine whether there is an efficient estimate of θ.

10.6-2 It is possible to show that the ML estimator of θ given the observation

$$z = \ln \theta + n$$

is

$$\hat{\theta}_{\text{ML}} = e^z$$

if the density of the noise $p(n)$ is such that $p(0) > p(n)$ for $n \neq 0$. One of your practically minded friends studied this problem and decided to employ an approximate estimator given by

$$\hat{\theta}_{\text{approx}} = 1 + z$$

if

$$p(n) = \begin{cases} 2(1 - n) & \leq n \leq 1 \\ 0 & \text{otherwise} \end{cases}$$

Find the *mean* and *variance* of the estimation error for the optimal and approximate estimators.

10.6-3 For the observation

$$z_i = \theta + n_i \qquad i = 1, 2, \ldots, I$$

where $\theta = N(\mu_0, V_0)$, $n_i = N(0, V)$, and $E\{n_i n_j\} = 0$ for $i \neq j$, find the expected value and variance of the optimal, actual, and computed error when $\mu_0 = V_0 = V = 1$ but $\bar\mu_0 = \bar V_0 = \bar V = 2$ is used. Do the work for both the ML and MAP estimators. Plot the results versus I for $I = 1, 2, \ldots, 10$.

10.6-4 Suppose that we are given a single scalar observation

$$z = \theta + n$$

of a parameter θ. We wish to study the relative merits of ML and MAP estimators (with the usual gaussian assumptions). We know that n is zero-mean and has variance V. We also know that θ is zero-mean but its variance V_θ is unknown. Assume that we use $\bar V_\theta$ for the unknown V_θ in the MAP estimator.

(*a*) Show that both estimators are unbiased.

(*b*) Find the range of values for $\bar V_\theta$ in terms of V_0 and V for which the ML estimator has smaller actual error variance than the MAP estimator.

10.6-5 Suppose you have a binary source generating a sequence of 1s and 0s. After I observations, you wish to estimate

$$\theta = P\{\text{source output} = 1\}$$

Find a maximum-likelihood estimate of θ and compute its variance. Is this estimate unbiased? Is it efficient?

10.6-6 Show that the linear minimum-variance estimate of the autoregressive parameter vector $\boldsymbol\theta$ in the observation model

$$z_i = \sum_{k=1}^{K} \theta_k z_{i-k} + n_i \qquad i = 1, 2, \ldots, I$$

is unbiased. Assume that the noise samples n_i are uncorrelated, identically distributed, and zero-mean. (See Example 8.4-3.)

10.6-7 Consider, again, Prob. 10.6-6, but assume that the estimate must be based on a noisy observation. The model now becomes

$$s_i = \sum_{k=1}^{K} \theta_k s_{i-k} + n_i$$

$$z_i = s_i + v_i$$

where v_i is also uncorrelated, identically distributed, and zero-mean. The noise processes n_i and v_i are independent. Show that the linear minimum-variance estimate is now biased.

10.6-8 Let θ be a gaussian random variable with variance σ^2. Does an efficient estimate of σ^2 exist? Does an efficient estimate of the standard deviation σ exist?

10.6-9 For the gaussian problem

$$z_i = \theta + n_i \qquad i = 1, 2, \ldots, I$$

let θ have mean μ. Assume, however, that the MAP estimation algorithm was designed assuming that θ was zero-mean. Show that $\hat\theta_I$ is biased but asymptotically unbiased.

STATE ESTIMATION

In this chapter, we shall consider a new variety of estimation problems known as *state estimation*. In the preceding chapters, we estimated a constant parameter θ; now we wish to estimate the time-varying state of a dynamic system $\mathbf{x}(k)$. In particular, our interest is in a class of linear unbiased minimum-error-variance sequential-state estimation algorithms referred to as *Wiener-Kalman filters*, *Kalman Bucy filters*, or more commonly, *Kalman filters*. Kalman filter algorithms or one of the many extensions and variations of them have been applied in numerous practical situations, including navigation, space guidance, and orbit determination.

Section 11.1 gives a formulation of the state estimation problem, while Sec. 11.2 develops the Kalman filter algorithm. We shall treat only one of the simpler forms of the Kalman filter in this text. For additional derivations and extensions, the interested reader is directed to the literature (Sage and Melsa, 1971; and Jazwinski, 1970).

11.1 PROBLEM STATEMENT

As mentioned previously, we wish to consider the development of a linear un-biased minimum-error-variance algorithm for state estimation. The state that we wish to estimate is described by the following linear vector equation:

$$\mathbf{x}(k + 1) = \mathbf{\Phi}(k + 1)\mathbf{x}(k) + \mathbf{\Gamma}(k)\mathbf{w}(k) \tag{11.1-1}$$

Here $\mathbf{w}(k)$ is the *input* or *plant* noise and is a zero-mean white-noise process with covariance

$$\operatorname{cov}\{\mathbf{w}(k), \mathbf{w}(j)\} = \mathbf{V}_w(k)\delta_K(k - j) \tag{11.1-2}$$

Equation (11.1-1) is often referred to as the *message model* since it describes the basic information that we are trying to determine.

The state $\mathbf{x}(k)$ is observed by means of a noisy mechanism of the form

$$\mathbf{z}(k) = \mathbf{H}(k)\mathbf{x}(k) + \mathbf{v}(k) \tag{11.1-3}$$

where the measurement noise $\mathbf{v}(k)$ is a zero-mean white-noise process with

$$\text{cov } \{\mathbf{v}(k), \mathbf{v}(j)\} = \mathbf{V}_v(k)\delta_K(k - j) \tag{11.1-4}$$

Equation (11.1-3) is called the *measurement model.*

For simplicity in our initial development, we shall assume that $\mathbf{w}$ and $\mathbf{v}$ are uncorrelated, so that

$$\text{cov } \{\mathbf{w}(k), \mathbf{v}(j)\} = \mathbf{0} \qquad \text{for all } j, k \tag{11.1-5}$$

The initial value of $\mathbf{x}$ is a random variable with mean equal to $\boldsymbol{\mu}_x(0)$ and variance $\mathbf{V}_x(0)$; in other words,

$$E\{\mathbf{x}(0)\} = \boldsymbol{\mu}_x(0) \qquad \text{var } \{\mathbf{x}(0)\} = \mathbf{V}_x(0) \tag{11.1-6}$$

Also, we shall assume that cov $\{\mathbf{x}(0), \mathbf{w}(k)\} = \mathbf{0}$ for all $k > 0$.

Based on a set of sequential observations $\mathbf{Z}(k) = \{\mathbf{z}(1), \mathbf{z}(2), \dots, \mathbf{z}(k)\}$, we wish to determine an estimate of $\mathbf{x}(j)$, which we shall symbolically represent by $\hat{\mathbf{x}}(j|k)$. The estimation error will be denoted by

$$\tilde{\mathbf{x}}(j|k) = \mathbf{x}(j) - \hat{\mathbf{x}}(j|k) \tag{11.1-7}$$

Depending on the relative values of j and k, the estimation is referred to as *prediction* or *extrapolation* ($j > k$), *filtering* ($j = k$), or *smoothing* or *interpolation* ($j < k$). This division should be intuitively appealing since *prediction* ($j > k$), for example, implies the estimate of the state at the jth sample based on observations to the kth sample. We shall treat only the filtering problem here.

In the derivation of the Kalman filter we shall assume and require that the observations be processed sequentially. Regardless of whether the estimator is sequential or nonsequential, the values of the resulting state estimates are unaltered. However, the computational feasibility of the technique is of fundamental importance. Probably the most significant contribution of Kalman and Bucy was to put the linear minimum-variance estimator into a state-variable sequential framework. The problem of linear minimum-variance sequential filtering has long been solved by Wiener and others for single input-output systems. The principal contribution of Kalman was to extend the Wiener filter to nonconstant coefficient multivariable systems with nonstationary finite-time noise records and to obtain a sequential form for the solution.

11.2 KALMAN FILTER

To obtain a linear minimum-variance estimator, we may use one of two procedures: The first approach is to specify a linear conditional mean and find the best linear form (this approach was used in Sec. 8.4). The second approach is to assume gaussian amplitude distribution for **x**, **w**, and **v**. Because of the repeatability property associated with linear systems and gaussian distribution, the exact conditional mean in this case will be linear. The linear minimum-variance estimate must be equal to the minimum-variance estimate if the minimum-variance estimate is, in fact, linear. This is the case if gaussian distributions are assumed.

Note that if we require that the estimator be linear in the observations, then the actual distributions of **x**, **w**, and **v** are unimportant. However, if the distributions are, in fact, gaussian, as is often the case, then the conditional mean is actually linear. In other words, the Kalman filter is the best (minimum-error variance) linear filter for any distribution; it is the best filter of all possible linear and nonlinear estimators if the plant and measurement noises as well as the initial state are gaussian.

We shall make use of the second approach here. As a result, our development will follow closely the development in Sec. 9.2. Because of the gaussian assumption, we know that the maximum a posteriori (MAP) and conditional mean (minimum-variance) estimators are identical. The MAP procedure is simpler, and we shall employ it. The MAP estimate of $\mathbf{x}(k)$ given $\mathbf{Z}(k)$ is given by the value of $\mathbf{x}(k)$ with maximizes $p[\mathbf{x}(k)|\mathbf{Z}(k)]$.

We make use of Bayes' rule to write the expression for $p[\mathbf{x}(k)|\mathbf{Z}(k)]$ as

$$p[\mathbf{x}(k)|\mathbf{Z}(k)] = \frac{p[\mathbf{x}(k), \mathbf{Z}(k)]}{p[\mathbf{Z}(k)]} \tag{11.2-1}$$

If we think of $\mathbf{Z}(k)$ as the combination of the new observation $\mathbf{z}(k)$, with the previous observations $\mathbf{Z}(k-1)$, then Eq. (11.2-1) becomes

$$p[\mathbf{x}(k)|\mathbf{Z}(k)] = \frac{p[\mathbf{x}(k), \mathbf{z}(k), \mathbf{Z}(k-1)]}{p[\mathbf{z}(k), \mathbf{Z}(k-1)]} \tag{11.2-2}$$

Let us consider the numerator of this expression by itself. Using the theorem of joint probability, we may write

$$p[\mathbf{x}(k), \mathbf{z}(k), \mathbf{Z}(k-1)] = p[\mathbf{z}(k)|\mathbf{x}(k), \mathbf{Z}(k-1)]p[\mathbf{x}(k), \mathbf{Z}(k-1)] \tag{11.2-3}$$

If now we use the joint probability law on the second term on the right-hand side, we have

$$p[\mathbf{x}(k), \mathbf{z}(k), \mathbf{Z}(k-1)] = p[\mathbf{z}(k)|\mathbf{x}(k), \mathbf{Z}(k-1)]p[\mathbf{x}(k)|\mathbf{Z}(k-1)]p[\mathbf{Z}(k-1)]$$

This expression may be written

$$p[\mathbf{x}(k), \mathbf{z}(k), \mathbf{Z}(k-1)] = p[\mathbf{z}(k)|\mathbf{x}(k)]p[\mathbf{x}(k)|\mathbf{Z}(k-1)]\,p[\mathbf{Z}(k-1)] \tag{11.2-4}$$

since if $\mathbf{x}(k)$ is given, then the only random variable in $\mathbf{z}(k)$ is $\mathbf{v}(k)$, which does not depend on either $\mathbf{x}(k)$ or $\mathbf{Z}(k-1)$.

If we substitute Eq. (11.2-4) into Eq. (11.2-2), we obtain

$$p[\mathbf{x}(k)|\mathbf{Z}(k)] = \frac{p[\mathbf{z}(k)|\mathbf{x}(k)]p[\mathbf{x}(k)|\mathbf{Z}(k-1)]p[\mathbf{Z}(k-1)]}{p[\mathbf{z}(k), \mathbf{Z}(k-1)]}$$

An application of the joint probability theorem on the denominator of this expression yields

$$p[\mathbf{x}(k)|\mathbf{Z}(k)] = \frac{p[\mathbf{z}(k)|\mathbf{x}(k)]p[\mathbf{x}(k)|\mathbf{Z}(k-1)]p[\mathbf{Z}(k-1)]}{p[\mathbf{z}(k)|\mathbf{Z}(k-1)]p[\mathbf{Z}(k-1)]}$$

which, upon cancelation of the common scalar probability function $p[\mathbf{Z}(k-1)]$, becomes

$$p[\mathbf{x}(k)|\mathbf{Z}(k)] = \frac{p[\mathbf{z}(k)|\mathbf{x}(k)]p[\mathbf{x}(k)|\mathbf{Z}(k-1)]}{p[\mathbf{z}(k)|\mathbf{Z}(k-1)]} \qquad (11.2\text{-}5)$$

This is the desired result, and we may now determine the conditional density of $\mathbf{x}(k)$, given $\mathbf{Z}(k)$, by evaluating each of the probability expressions on the right-hand side of the equation. Since each of these densities is gaussian, we need find only the mean and variance in each case.

Let us examine $p[\mathbf{z}(k)|\mathbf{x}(k)]$ first. The mean is

$$E\{\mathbf{z}(k)|\mathbf{x}(k)\} = E\{\mathbf{H}(k)\mathbf{x}(k) + \mathbf{v}(k)|\mathbf{x}(k)\} = \mathbf{H}(k)\mathbf{x}(k) \qquad (11.2\text{-}6)$$

since $\mathbf{v}(k)$ is zero-mean. The variance is

$$\text{var}\{\mathbf{z}(k)|\mathbf{x}(k)\} = \text{var}\{\mathbf{v}(k)\} = \mathbf{V}_v(k) \qquad (11.2\text{-}7)$$

so that $p[\mathbf{z}(k)|\mathbf{x}(k)]$ becomes

$$p[\mathbf{z}(k)|\mathbf{x}(k)] = K_1 \exp\{-\tfrac{1}{2}[\mathbf{z}(k) - \mathbf{H}(k)\mathbf{x}(k)]^T\mathbf{V}_v^{-1}(k)[\mathbf{z}(k) - \mathbf{H}(k)\mathbf{x}(k)]\} \quad (11.2\text{-}8)$$

Note that we do not need to compute the denominator density $p[\mathbf{z}(k)|\mathbf{Z}(k-1)]$ since it contains no $\mathbf{x}(k)$ terms and hence will serve only as a scale factor in Eq. (11.2-5).

The mean of the density $p[\mathbf{x}(k)|\mathbf{Z}(k-1)]$ is

$$\begin{aligned} E\{\mathbf{x}(k)|\mathbf{Z}(k-1)\} &= E\{\mathbf{\Phi}(k)\mathbf{x}(k-1) + \mathbf{\Gamma}(k-1)\mathbf{w}(k-1)|\mathbf{Z}(k-1)\} \\ &= \mathbf{\Phi}(k)\hat{\mathbf{x}}(k-1) = \hat{\mathbf{x}}(k|k-1) \end{aligned} \qquad (11.2\text{-}9)$$

The variance is

$$\begin{aligned} \text{var}\{\mathbf{x}(k)|\mathbf{Z}(k-1)\} &= \text{var}\{\mathbf{x}(k) - \hat{\mathbf{x}}(k|k-1)|\mathbf{Z}(k-1)\} \\ &= \text{var}\{\tilde{\mathbf{x}}(k|k-1)|\mathbf{Z}(k-1)\} = \mathbf{V}(k|k-1) \end{aligned} \qquad (11.2\text{-}10)$$

The variance $\mathbf{V}(k|k-1)$ remains to be determined. Then $p[\mathbf{x}(k)|\mathbf{Z}(k-1)]$ becomes

$$p[\mathbf{x}(k)|\mathbf{Z}(k-1)] =$$
$$K_2 \exp\{-\tfrac{1}{2}[\mathbf{x}(k) - \hat{\mathbf{x}}(k|k-1)]^T\mathbf{V}^{-1}(k|k-1)[\mathbf{x}(k) - \hat{\mathbf{x}}(k|k-1)]\} \quad (11.2\text{-}11)$$

If we substitute Eqs. (11.2-8) and (11.2-11) into Eq. (11.2-5), we obtain

$$\begin{aligned} p[\mathbf{x}(k)|\mathbf{Z}(k)] = K \exp\{&-\tfrac{1}{2}[\mathbf{z}(k) - \mathbf{H}(k)\mathbf{x}(k)]^T\mathbf{V}_v^{-1}(k)[\mathbf{z}(k) - \mathbf{H}(k)\mathbf{x}(k)] \\ &-\tfrac{1}{2}[\mathbf{x}(k) - \hat{\mathbf{x}}(k|k-1)]^T\mathbf{V}^{-1}(k|k-1)[\mathbf{x}(k) - \hat{\mathbf{x}}(k|k-1)]\} \quad (11.2\text{-}12) \end{aligned}$$

To determine the MAP estimate, we need find only the value of $\mathbf{x}(k)$ which maximizes $p[\mathbf{x}(k)|\mathbf{Z}(k)]$. Instead of maximizing $p[\mathbf{x}(k)|\mathbf{Z}(k)]$ directly, let us take the usual approach of maximizing the logarithm of $p[\mathbf{x}(k)|\mathbf{Z}(k)]$. The MAP estimate is then given by the expression

$$\frac{\partial \ln p[\mathbf{x}(k)|\mathbf{Z}(k)]}{\partial \mathbf{x}(k)}\bigg|_{\mathbf{x}(k)=\hat{\mathbf{x}}(k)} = \mathbf{0} \tag{11.2-13}$$

Using the form of Eq. (11.2-12) for $p[\mathbf{x}(k)|\mathbf{Z}(k)]$ in this expression yields

$$\mathbf{H}^T(k)\mathbf{V}_v^{-1}(k)[\mathbf{z}(k) - \mathbf{H}(k)\hat{\mathbf{x}}(k)] - \mathbf{V}^{-1}(k|k-1)[\hat{\mathbf{x}}(k) - \hat{\mathbf{x}}(k|k-1)] = \mathbf{0} \tag{11.2-14}$$

Solving for $\hat{\mathbf{x}}(k)$ yields the following expression:

$$\hat{\mathbf{x}}(k) = [\mathbf{H}^T(k)\mathbf{V}_v^{-1}(k)\mathbf{H}(k) + \mathbf{V}^{-1}(k|k-1)]^{-1}[\mathbf{V}^{-1}(k|k-1)\hat{\mathbf{x}}(k|k-1)$$
$$+ \mathbf{H}^T(k)\mathbf{V}_v^{-1}(k)\mathbf{z}(k)] \tag{11.2-15}$$

In order to put this result into a more convenient form, we need to make use of the following matrix inversion lemma.

Lemma 11.2-1 (Matrix inversion lemma) If $\mathbf{P}$ and $\mathbf{R}$ are nonsingular matrices of order $n \times n$ and $m \times m$, respectively, and $\mathbf{H}$ is a $m \times n$ matrix, then the following identity holds:

$$(\mathbf{H}^T\mathbf{R}^{-1}\mathbf{H} + \mathbf{P}^{-1})^{-1} = \mathbf{P} - \mathbf{P}\mathbf{H}^T(\mathbf{H}\mathbf{P}\mathbf{H}^T + \mathbf{R})^{-1}\mathbf{H}\mathbf{P}$$

The proof of this lemma, which involves a complicated sequence of simple matrix algebra, can be found in Sage and Melsa (1971). If we use this result in Eq. (11.2-15), with $\mathbf{R} = \mathbf{V}_v$ and $\mathbf{P} = \mathbf{V}$, then we have

$$[\mathbf{H}^T(k)\mathbf{V}_v^{-1}(k)\mathbf{H}(k) + \mathbf{V}^{-1}(k|k-1)]^{-1} = \mathbf{V}(k|k-1)$$
$$- \mathbf{V}(k|k-1)\mathbf{H}^T(k)[\mathbf{H}(k)\mathbf{V}(k|k-1)\mathbf{H}^T(k) + \mathbf{V}_v(k)]^{-1}\mathbf{H}(k)\mathbf{V}(k|k-1) \tag{11.2-16}$$

The advantage of this change is that the left side of Eq. (11.2-16) requires the inversion of a $K \times K$ matrix while the right side requires the inversion an $I \times I$ matrix. Here K is the dimension $\mathbf{x}(k)$ while I is the dimension of $\mathbf{z}(k)$. Since I is generally smaller than K, Eq. (11.2-16) can yield a considerable saving. If we substitute Eq. (11.2-16) into Eq. (11.2-15) and carry out some simple but lengthy algebraic reductions, we find that

$$\hat{\mathbf{x}}(k) = \hat{\mathbf{x}}(k|k-1) + \mathbf{K}(k)[\mathbf{z}(k) - \mathbf{H}(k)\hat{\mathbf{x}}(k|k-1)] \tag{11.2-17}$$

where the Kalman gain is defined as

$$\mathbf{K}(k) = \mathbf{V}(k|k-1)\mathbf{H}^T(k)[\mathbf{H}(k)\mathbf{V}(k|k-1)\mathbf{H}^T(k) + \mathbf{V}_v(k)]^{-1} \tag{11.2-18}$$

Note that Eq. (11.2-17) takes the interesting form of a prediction $\hat{\mathbf{x}}(k|k-1)$ as given by Eq. (11.2-9) plus a correction based on the residual observation error $\mathbf{z}(k) - \mathbf{H}(k)\hat{\mathbf{x}}(k|k-1)$. The weighting is optimally determined by the Kalman gain $\mathbf{K}(k)$. Before the algorithm is complete, we must have a method for computing $\mathbf{V}(k|k-1)$.

Since $\mathbf{V}(k|k-1) = \text{var } \{\tilde{\mathbf{x}}(k|k-1)\}$, let us determine an expression for $\tilde{\mathbf{x}}(k|k-1)$.

$$\tilde{\mathbf{x}}(k|k-1) = \mathbf{x}(k) - \hat{\mathbf{x}}(k|k-1)$$

$$= \mathbf{\Phi}(k)\mathbf{x}(k-1) + \mathbf{\Gamma}(k-1)\mathbf{w}(k-1) - \mathbf{\Phi}(k)\hat{\mathbf{x}}(k-1)$$

$$= \mathbf{\Phi}(k)\tilde{\mathbf{x}}(k-1) + \mathbf{\Gamma}(k-1)\mathbf{w}(k-1) \quad (11.2\text{-}19)$$

Therefore, $\mathbf{V}(k|k-1)$ is given by

$$\mathbf{V}(k|k-1) = \text{var } \{\tilde{\mathbf{x}}(k|k-1)\}$$

$$= \text{var } \{\mathbf{\Phi}(k)\tilde{\mathbf{x}}(k-1) + \mathbf{\Gamma}(k-1)\mathbf{w}(k-1)\} \quad (11.2\text{-}20)$$

$$= \mathbf{\Phi}(k)\mathbf{V}(k-1)\mathbf{\Phi}^T(k) + \mathbf{\Gamma}(k-1)\mathbf{V}_\mathbf{w}(k-1)\mathbf{\Gamma}^T(k-1)$$

where $\quad \mathbf{V}(k-1) = \text{var } \{\tilde{\mathbf{x}}(k-1)\} \quad (11.2\text{-}21)$

Although it may not seem so, we are, in fact, making progress. The filtering error is

$$\tilde{\mathbf{x}}(k) = \mathbf{x}(k) - \hat{\mathbf{x}}(k)$$

$$= \mathbf{x}(k) - \{\hat{\mathbf{x}}(k|k-1) + \mathbf{K}(k)[\mathbf{z}(k) - \mathbf{H}(k)\hat{\mathbf{x}}(k|k-1)]\} \quad (11.2\text{-}22)$$

But $\mathbf{z}(k) = \mathbf{H}(k)\mathbf{x}(k) + \mathbf{v}(k)$, so that Eq. (11.2-22) becomes

$$\tilde{\mathbf{x}}(k) = [\mathbf{I} - \mathbf{K}(k)\mathbf{H}(k)]\tilde{\mathbf{x}}(k|k-1) - \mathbf{K}(k)\mathbf{v}(k) \quad (11.2\text{-}23)$$

The error variance $\mathbf{V}(k)$ is, therefore,

$$\mathbf{V}(k) = \text{var } \{\tilde{\mathbf{x}}(k)\}$$

$$= [\mathbf{I} - \mathbf{K}(k)\mathbf{H}(k)]\mathbf{V}(k|k-1)[\mathbf{I} - \mathbf{K}(k)\mathbf{H}(k)]^T + \mathbf{K}(k)\mathbf{V}_\mathbf{v}(k)\mathbf{K}^T(k) \quad (11.2\text{-}24)$$

After a bit of algebraic reduction, Eq. (11.2-24) becomes

$$\mathbf{V}(k) = [\mathbf{I} - \mathbf{K}(k)\mathbf{H}(k)]\mathbf{V}(k|k-1) \quad (11.2\text{-}25)$$

The Kalman filter algorithm is now complete, consisting of Eqs. (11.2-9), (11.2-17) to (11.2-19), and (11.2-25). The algorithm is initialized with $\mathbf{V}(0) = \mathbf{V}_\mathbf{x}(0)$ and $\hat{\mathbf{x}}(0) = \boldsymbol{\mu}_\mathbf{x}(0)$.

Example 11.2-1 Let us consider a simple first-order problem to illustrate the use of the Kalman filter algorithm. The message model is

$$x(k+1) = x(k) + w(k)$$

while the observation model is

$$z(k) = x(k) + v(k)$$

with $\quad \mu_x(0) = 0, \qquad V_x(0) = 100, \qquad V_w = 1 \quad \text{and} \quad V_v = 2$

The filter equation is

$$x(k) = x(k-1) + K(k)[z(k) - x(k-1)]$$

where
$$K(k) = \frac{V(k|k-1)}{V(k|k-1)+2}$$

and
$$V(k|k-1) = V(k-1) + 1$$

$$V(k) = [1 - K(k)]V(k|k-1)$$

If we receive the observation sequence $Z(k) = \{1, 2, -1, 4, 2, 4, \dots\}$, then the following table lists the estimate and other quantities for this problem. (The quantities are listed in the order they are computed.)

k	$V(k\|k-1)$	$K(k)$	$z(k)$	$\hat{x}(k)$	$V(k)$
0				0	100
1	101	0.98	1	0.98	1.96
2	2.96	0.60	2	1.59	1.18
3	2.18	0.52	-1	0.24	1.05
4	2.05	0.51	4	2.16	1.01
5	2.01	0.50	2	2.08	1.00
6	2.00	0.50	4	3.04	1.00
∞	2	0.50			1.00

We see that the limiting form for the filter is

$$\hat{x}(k) = 0.5\hat{x}(k-1) + 0.5z(k)$$

so that the updated estimate is one-half of the previous estimate plus one-half of the current observation.

If the message and observation models contain known inputs **u** and **y** so that Eqs. (11.1-1) and (11.1-3) become

$$\mathbf{x}(k+1) = \mathbf{\Phi}(k+1)\mathbf{x}(k) + \mathbf{\Gamma}(k)\mathbf{w}(k) + \mathbf{u}(k)$$

$$\mathbf{z}(k) = \mathbf{H}(k)\mathbf{x}(k) + \mathbf{v}(k) + \mathbf{y}(k)$$

then the Kalman filter algorithm can be easily modified to include these items. The filter equation becomes

$$\hat{\mathbf{x}}(k) = \hat{\mathbf{x}}(k|k-1) + \mathbf{K}(k)[\mathbf{z}(k) - \mathbf{H}(k)\hat{\mathbf{x}}(k|k-1) - \mathbf{y}(k)] \quad (11.2\text{-}26)$$

where
$$\hat{\mathbf{x}}(k|k-1) = \mathbf{\Phi}(k)\hat{\mathbf{x}}(k-1) + \mathbf{u}(k-1) \quad (11.2\text{-}27)$$

The variance and gain equations remain unchanged.

It is quite easy to extend this algorithm to the case where $\mathbf{w}(k)$ and $\mathbf{v}(k)$ are nonzero-mean simply by treating the means as known inputs. To handle the case where $\mathbf{v}(k)$ and $\mathbf{w}(k)$ are correlated, that is

$$\text{cov } \{\mathbf{w}(j), \mathbf{v}(k)\} = \mathbf{S}(k)\delta_K(j - k)$$

we simply form a related but uncorrelated problem. This is easily accomplished by rewriting the message model by adding a term whose value is zero as

$$\mathbf{x}(k + 1) = \mathbf{\Phi}(k + 1)\mathbf{x}(k) + \mathbf{\Gamma}(k)\mathbf{w}(k) + \mathbf{D}(k)[\mathbf{z}(k) - \mathbf{H}(k)\mathbf{x}(k) - \mathbf{v}(k)] \quad (11.2\text{-}28)$$

The matrix $\mathbf{D}(k)$ can be anything we want. To see how to select it, we group terms to write a new message model as

$$\mathbf{x}(k + 1) = \mathbf{\Phi}^*(k + 1)\mathbf{x}(k) + \mathbf{w}^*(k) + \mathbf{u}^*(k) \quad (11.2\text{-}29)$$

where
$$\mathbf{\Phi}^*(k + 1) = \mathbf{\Phi}(k + 1) - \mathbf{D}(k)\mathbf{H}(k)$$

$$\mathbf{w}^*(k) = \mathbf{\Gamma}(k)\mathbf{w}(k) - \mathbf{D}(k)\mathbf{v}(k)$$

$$\mathbf{u}^*(k) = \mathbf{D}(k)\mathbf{z}(k)$$

We now adjust $\mathbf{D}(k)$ such that the new plant and measurement noise are uncorrelated. We have

$$\text{cov } \{\mathbf{w}^*(k), \mathbf{v}(k)\} = \text{cov } \{\mathbf{\Gamma}(k)\mathbf{w}(k) - \mathbf{D}(k)\mathbf{v}(k), \mathbf{w}(k)\} = \mathbf{\Gamma}(k)\mathbf{S}(k) - \mathbf{D}(k)\mathbf{V}_v(k)$$

This will be zero if $\mathbf{D}(k) = \mathbf{\Gamma}(k)\mathbf{S}(k)\mathbf{V}_v^{-1}(k)$. Thus, we implement the standard Kalman filter algorithms with uncorrelated plant and measurement noise using the message model of Eq. (11.2-29) to obtain the result for correlated measurement and observation noise.

11.3 SUMMARY

In this chapter we have examined briefly the problem of state estimation. The Kalman filter for discrete-time problems was derived using a MAP approach. There are many other derivations of this result as well as extension to continuous-time systems, prediction, smoothing, and many other topics. Hopefully, the material presented in this chapter will serve to whet the appetite of the reader for further study of this vast and extremely important topic.

11.4 PROBLEMS

11.4-1 Show that if $\mathbf{V}_v = \mathbf{0}$, then $\mathbf{K}(k)$ will approach zero as k approaches infinity if the message model is stable.

11.4-2 Consider the following estimation problem:

$$\mathbf{x}(k + 1) = \begin{bmatrix} 0 & 1 \\ 1 & 1 \end{bmatrix}\mathbf{x}(k) + \begin{bmatrix} 0 \\ 1 \end{bmatrix}w(k)$$

$$z(k) = [1 \quad 0]\mathbf{x}(k) + v(k)$$

where $V_w = V_v = 2$ and $\mu_x(0) = 1$ and $\mathbf{V_x}(0) = 10\mathbf{I}$. Find the state estimate $\hat{\mathbf{x}}(k)$ if the observation sequence is $Z(k) = \{4, -1, 2, 3, \dots \}$. What is the steady-state $(k = \infty)$ form for the filter?

11.4-3 Suppose that we sequentially obtain observations of a parameter $\boldsymbol{\theta}$ of the form

$$\mathbf{z}_i = \mathbf{H}\boldsymbol{\theta} + \mathbf{n}_i \qquad i = 1, 2, \dots$$

where $\mathbf{n}_i$ is a white zero-mean noise process. We desire a linear sequential estimator of the form

$$\hat{\boldsymbol{\theta}}_{i+1} = \mathbf{F}\hat{\boldsymbol{\theta}}_i + \mathbf{K}\mathbf{z}_{i+1}$$

Determine the relationship of $\mathbf{F}$ and $\mathbf{K}$ such that the estimator will remain unbiased if it is initially unbiased. Note that $E\{\boldsymbol{\theta}\}$ is not necessarily zero.

11.4-4 Define the estimation error as

$$\tilde{\mathbf{x}}(k) = \mathbf{x}(k) - \hat{\mathbf{x}}(k)$$

Now show that the estimate $\hat{\mathbf{x}}(k)$ and $\tilde{\mathbf{x}}(k)$ are uncorrelated so that

$$\text{cov}\ \{\tilde{\mathbf{x}}(k), \hat{\mathbf{x}}(k)\} = \mathbf{0}$$

11.4-5 One can use the Kalman filter to estimate parameters by defining a state $\mathbf{x}(k) = \boldsymbol{\theta}$ and letting the state model for $\mathbf{x}(k + 1)$ be

$$\mathbf{x}(k + 1) = \mathbf{I}\mathbf{x}(k)$$

This implies that $\mathbf{x}(k)$ is constant. Use the Kalman filter on this model to derive the following sequential form for parameter estimation:

$$\hat{\boldsymbol{\theta}}(k) = \hat{\boldsymbol{\theta}}(k - 1) + \mathbf{K}(k)[\mathbf{z}(k) - \mathbf{H}(k)\hat{\boldsymbol{\theta}}(k - 1)]$$

$$\mathbf{K}(k) = \mathbf{V}(k - 1)\mathbf{H}^T(k)[\mathbf{H}(k)\mathbf{V}(k - 1)\mathbf{H}(k) + \mathbf{V}_v(k)]^{-1}$$

$$\mathbf{V}(k) = [\mathbf{I} - \mathbf{K}(k)\mathbf{H}(k)]\mathbf{V}(k - 1)$$

[Note that here $\hat{\boldsymbol{\theta}}(k)$ means the estimate of $\boldsymbol{\theta}$ based on the observation set $\mathbf{Z}(k)$.]

11.4-6 Use the matrix inversion lemma to derive directly the algorithm given in Prob. 11.4-5 from Eqs. (9.2-7) and (9.2-8). *Hint:* Let

$$\mathbf{V}_{m+1} = \mathbf{V}_m\mathbf{H}^T[\mathbf{H}\mathbf{V}_m\mathbf{H}^T + \mathbf{V_n}]^{-1}\mathbf{H}\mathbf{V}_m$$

11.4-7 There are some problems for which there is a known input $\mathbf{u}(k)$ to the plant so that Eq. (11.1-1) becomes

$$\mathbf{x}(k + 1) = \boldsymbol{\Phi}(k + 1)\mathbf{x}(k) + \boldsymbol{\Gamma}(k)\mathbf{w}(k) + \mathbf{u}(k)$$

Derive the Kalman filter for this case. Note that this algorithm can be used to handle the case where $\mathbf{w}(k)$ is not zero-mean.

11.4-8 In some problems, the observation model contains a known function $\mathbf{y}(k)$, so that Eq. (11.1-3) becomes

$$\mathbf{z}(k) = \mathbf{H}(k)\mathbf{x}(k) + \mathbf{v}(k) + \mathbf{y}(k)$$

Rederive the Kalman filter for this case.

A

TABLE OF DENSITIES

This appendix describes some of the most common probability density functions. A brief discussion of the significance of each density is given, and its properties are tabulated. The tables include the density function, mean, and variance. For completeness, the characteristic function is also included:

$$\Phi_x(\omega) = E\{\exp(j\omega x)\}$$

A.1 UNIFORM

A *uniform* variable is one whose value is known to be in a fixed range but where the probability that it is in a segment of that range depends only on the width of the segment. One example of such a variable is the phase of the ac voltage in an electrical outlet at the instant you turn on a light. These variables are frequently used because they require only limited structural assumptions and they are usually easy to work with. The properties of this variable are given in Table A.1.

Table A.1 Uniform density

$$p(x) = \begin{cases} \dfrac{1}{b-a} & a \le x \le b \\ 0 & \text{elsewhere} \end{cases}$$

$$E\{x\} = \frac{b+a}{2}$$

$$\text{var}\,\{x\} = \frac{(b-a)^2}{12}$$

$$\Phi_x(\omega) = \frac{2}{\omega(b-a)}\, e^{j\omega(b+a)/2} \sin\frac{\omega(b-a)}{2}$$

A.2 GAUSSIAN

This density is frequently called *normal*, particularly by probability theorists and statisticians. It is also called *laplacian* by the French,† but we shall use this name to describe the density discussed in Sec. A.4. The central limit theorem states roughly that the normalized sum of a large number of independent identically distributed random variables, almost regardless of their density function, will be a *gaussian* variable. Thus, it is not surprising that noise is frequently modeled as gaussian. Also, although it may look messy, the gaussian density is actually very easy to use.

The scalar gaussian density is tabulated in Table A.2. It is interesting to note that for a zero-mean gaussian random variable, $p(x)$ and $\Phi_x(\omega)$ have the same shape. This property is unique to the gaussian density. Another useful property is that the scalar form can be easily generalized to the vector form. Table A.3 contains a summary of an *l*-dimensional gaussian variable.

Table A.2 Scalar gaussian density

$$p(x) = \frac{1}{\sqrt{2\pi}\,\sigma} \exp\left[\frac{-(x-m)^2}{2\sigma^2}\right]$$

$$E\{x\} = m$$

$$\text{var}\{x\} = \sigma^2$$

$$\Phi_x(\omega) = \exp\frac{j\omega m - \omega^2\sigma^2}{2}$$

Table A.3 Vector gaussian density

$$p(\mathbf{x}) = [(2\pi)^l \det \mathbf{V}]^{-1/2} \exp\{-\tfrac{1}{2}[(\mathbf{x}-\boldsymbol{\mu})^T\mathbf{V}^{-1}(\mathbf{x}-\boldsymbol{\mu})]\}$$

$$E\{\mathbf{x}\} = \boldsymbol{\mu}$$

$$\text{var}\{\mathbf{x}\} = \mathbf{V}$$

$$\Phi_x(\boldsymbol{\omega}) = E[e^{j\boldsymbol{\omega}^T\mathbf{x}}] = \exp(j\boldsymbol{\omega}^T\boldsymbol{\mu} - \tfrac{1}{2}\boldsymbol{\omega}^T\mathbf{V}\boldsymbol{\omega})$$

A.3 EXPONENTIAL

An exponential random variable is often used to model the length of time a system will run before it fails. If one assumes that the probability that the system will fail in the next T seconds depends only on T and not on how long the system has been running, then the actual failure time is an exponential random variable. It is clear that an exponential variable, also called a *single-sided ex-*

†Laplace was a French mathematician.

ponential variable, should be easy to use. Its properties are presented in Table A.4.

Table A.4 Exponential density

$$p(x) = \begin{cases} \lambda e^{-\lambda} & x \geq 0 \\ 0 & x < 0 \end{cases}$$

$$E\{x\} = \frac{1}{\lambda}$$

$$\text{var } \{x\} = \frac{1}{\lambda^2}$$

$$\Phi_x(\omega) = \frac{\lambda}{\lambda - j\omega}$$

A.4 LAPLACIAN

The double-sided exponential, or *laplacian*, density is frequently used in examples. Its convenient form, zero mean, and symmetry make it a nice alternative to the gaussian density. Also, it is a good approximation to the density of amplitudes in human speech. It is tabulated in Table A.5.

Table A.5 Laplacian density

$$p(x) = \frac{\lambda}{2} e^{-\lambda |x|}$$

$$E\{x\} = 0$$

$$\text{var } \{x\} = \frac{2}{\lambda^2}$$

$$\Phi_x(\omega) = \frac{\lambda^2}{\lambda^2 + \omega^2}$$

A.5 RAYLEIGH

If **s** is a two-dimensional signal vector that is corrupted by zero-mean, additive, white gaussian noise **n**, then the distance between the received signal **r** and **s** is

$$x = |\mathbf{r} - \mathbf{s}|$$
$$= \sqrt{n_1^2 + n_2^2}$$

and x is a *Rayleigh* random variable. Such variables recur with some regularity, and their density is presented in Table A.6.

Table A.6 Rayleigh density

$$p(x) = \begin{cases} \dfrac{x}{\sigma^2}e^{-x^2/2\sigma^2} & x \geq 0 \\[2ex] 0 & x < 0 \end{cases}$$

$$E\{x\} = \sigma\sqrt{\frac{\pi}{2}}$$

$$\text{var}\{x\} = (s - \frac{\pi}{2})\,\sigma^2$$

A.6 BINOMIAL

A binary random variable whose value is 1 with probability p and 0 with probability $1 - p$ is called a *Bernoulli* random variable. It is the simplest of the discrete variables and is tabulated in Table A.7. Since it is a discrete variable, its density function contains impulses. If we have a set of I independent Bernoulli variables, then the number of such variables that are 1 is a *binomial* random variable. Its properties are listed in Table A.8. Note that the mean and the variance of the binomial variable are just I times the mean and the variance of the corresponding Bernoulli variable, and that the characteristic function is the Bernoulli characteristic function raised to the I power.

Table A.7 Bernoulli density

$$p(x) = (1 - p)\delta(x) + p\delta(x - 1)$$
$$E\{x\} = p$$
$$\text{var}\{x\} = p(1 - p)$$
$$\Phi_x(\omega) = 1 - p + pe^{j\omega}$$

Table A.8 Binomial density

$$p(x) = \sum_{i=0}^{I} (\tbinom{I}{i})p^i(1 - p)^{I-i}\delta(x - i)$$
$$E\{x\} = pI$$
$$\text{var}\{x\} = p(1 - p)I$$
$$\Phi_x(\omega) = [1 - p + pe^{j\omega}]^I$$

A.7 POISSON

If one has a large number of independent events that can occur uniformly over a long interval, then the number of such events that occur in a fixed interval is a

Poisson variable, as given in Table A.9. The time between pairs of occurrences is an exponential variable. If the parameter of the exponential variable is λ and the interval is T, then the Poisson parameter α satisfies $\alpha = \lambda T$.

Table A.9 Poisson density

$$p(x) = \sum_{i=0}^{\infty} \frac{\alpha^i e^{\alpha}}{i!} \delta(x - i)$$

$E\{x\} = \alpha$

$\text{var}\{x\} = \alpha$

$\Phi_x(\omega) = e^{\alpha}(e^{j\omega} - 1)$

PROBABILITY TABLES

This appendix contains a set of three probability tables which are useful in decision-theory problems.

Table B.1 Q Function

$$Q(x) = \int_x^\infty \frac{1}{\sqrt{2\pi}} e^{-\xi^2/2} d\xi = 1 - Q(-x)$$

x	$Q(x)$	x	$Q(x)$	x	$Q(x)$
0.00	0.5000	1.10	0.1357		
0.05	0.4801	1.15	0.1251	2.10	0.0179
0.10	0.4602	1.20	0.1151	2.15	0.0158
0.15	0.4404	1.25	0.1056	2.20	0.0139
0.20	0.4207	1.282	0.1000	2.25	0.0122
0.25	0.4013	1.30	0.0968	2.30	0.0107
0.30	0.3821	1.35	0.0885	2.326	0.0100
0.35	0.3632	1.40	0.0808	2.35	0.0094
0.40	0.3446	1.45	0.0735	2.40	0.0082
0.45	0.3264	1.50	0.0668	2.45	0.0071
0.50	0.3085	1.55	0.0606	2.50	0.0062
0.55	0.2912	1.60	0.0548	2.55	0.0054
0.60	0.2743	1.645	0.0500	2.576	0.0050
0.65	0.2578	1.65	0.0495	2.60	0.0047
0.675	0.2500	1.70	0.0446	2.65	0.0040
0.70	0.2420	1.75	0.0401	2.70	0.0035
				2.75	0.0030
0.75	0.2266	1.80	0.0359	2.80	0.0026
0.80	0.2119	1.85	0.0322	2.85	0.0022
0.842	0.2000				
0.85	0.1977	1.90	0.0287	2.90	0.0019
0.90	0.1841	1.95	0.0256	2.95	0.0016
0.95	0.1711	1.960	0.0250	3.00	0.0013
1.00	0.1587	2.00	0.0228	3.090	0.0010
1.05	0.1469	2.05	0.0202	3.291	0.0005

Source: Adapted from A. M. Mood, "Introduction to the Theory of Statistics," Copyright, 1950, McGraw-Hill Book Company, New York.

Occasionally it is desirable to approximate $Q(x)$ with an analytic expression. There are several such approximations; a set of particularly good approximations are

$$\frac{1}{\sqrt{2\pi}} \frac{2}{x + \sqrt{x^2 + 4}} e^{-x^2/2} \leq Q(x) \leq \frac{1}{\sqrt{2\pi}} \frac{2}{x + \sqrt{x^2 + 8/\pi}} e^{-x^2/2} \quad \text{(B.1-1)}$$

Somewhat looser but simpler bounds are given by

$$Q(x) \leq \frac{1}{x\sqrt{2\pi}} e^{-x^2/2} \quad \text{(B.1-2)}$$

and

$$Q(x) \leq \tfrac{1}{2} e^{-x^2/2} \quad \text{(B.1-3)}$$

The bound given by Eq. (B.1-2) is quite accurate for large $(x > 2)$ values of x, while the bound of Eq. (B.1-3) is accurate only for very small values of x.

Table B.2 Cumulative binomial distribution†

$$P\{x \geq x' \,|\, n, p\} = \sum_{i=x'}^{n} \binom{n}{i} p^i (1-p)^{n-i}$$

Entries in the table are values of $\sum_{i=x'}^{i=n} \binom{n}{i} p^i(1-p)^{n-i}$ for the indicated value of n, p, and

x'. When $p > 0.5$, the value of $\sum_{i=x'}^{i=n} \binom{n}{i} p^i(1-p)^{n-i}$ for a given n, x', and p is equal to 1 minus

the tabular entry for the given n with $n - x' + 1$ in place of the given value of x' and $1 - p$ in place of the given value of p.

						p					
n	x'	.05	.10	.15	.20	.25	.30	.35	.40	.45	.50
2	1	.0975	.1900	.2775	.3600	.4375	.5100	.5775	.6400	.6975	.7500
	2	.0025	.0100	.0225	.0400	.0625	.0900	.1225	.1600	.2025	.2500
3	1	.1426	.2710	.3859	.4880	.5781	.6570	.7254	.7840	.8336	.8750
	2	.0072	.0280	.0608	.1040	.1562	.2160	.2818	.3520	.4252	.5000
	3	.0001	.0010	.0034	.0080	.0156	.0270	.0429	.0640	.0911	.1250
4	1	.1855	.3439	.4780	.5904	.6836	.7599	.8215	.8704	.9085	.9375
	2	.0140	.0523	.1095	.1808	.2617	.3483	.4370	.5248	.6090	.6875
	3	.0005	.0037	.0120	.0272	.0508	.0837	.1265	.1792	.2415	.3125
	4	.0000	.0001	.0005	.0016	.0039	.0081	.0150	.0256	.0410	.0625
5	1	.2262	.4095	.5563	.6723	.7627	.8319	.8840	.9222	.9497	.9688
	2	.0226	.0815	.1648	.2627	.3672	.4718	.5716	.6630	.7438	.8125
	3	.0012	.0086	.0266	.0579	.1035	.1631	.2352	.3174	.4069	.5000
	4	.0000	.0005	.0022	.0067	.0156	.0308	.0540	.0870	.1312	.1875
	5	.0000	.0000	.0001	.0003	.0010	.0024	.0053	.0102	.0185	.0312
6	1	.2649	.4686	.6229	.7379	.8220	.8824	.9246	.9533	.9723	.9844
	2	.0328	.1143	.2235	.3446	.4661	.5798	.6809	.7667	.8364	.8906
	3	.0022	.0158	.0473	.0989	.1694	.2557	.3529	.4557	.5585	.6562
	4	.0001	.0013	.0059	.0170	.0376	.0705	.1174	.1792	.2553	.3438
	5	.0000	.0001	.0004	.0016	.0046	.0109	.0223	.0410	.0692	.1094
	6	.0000	.0000	.0000	.0001	.0002	.0007	.0018	.0041	.0083	.0156
7	1	.3017	.5217	.6794	.7903	.8665	.9176	.9510	.9720	.9848	.9922
	2	.0444	.1497	.2834	.4233	.5551	.6706	.7662	.8414	.8976	.9375
	3	.0038	.0257	.0738	.1480	.2436	.3529	.4677	.5801	.6836	.7734
	4	.0002	.0027	.0121	.0333	.0706	.1260	.1998	.2898	.3917	.5000
	5	.0000	.0002	.0012	.0047	.0129	.0288	.0556	.0963	.1529	.2266
	6	.0000	.0000	.0001	.0004	.0013	.0038	.0090	.0188	.0357	.0625
	7	.0000	.0000	.0000	.0000	.0001	.0002	.0006	.0016	.0037	.0078

†Linear interpolation with respect to p generally will not be accurate to more than two decimal places and sometimes less.

For extensive tables of $\sum_{i=x'}^{i=n} \binom{n}{i} p^i(1-p)^{n-i}$ see Tables of the Binomial Probability Distribution, Applied Math. ser. 6, National Bureau of Standards, Washington, D.C., 1950.

Source: Table B.2 is used by permission from R. S. Burington and D. C. May, Jr., "Handbook of Probability and Statistics with Tables," Copyright 1953, McGraw-Hill Book Co.

Table B.2 Cumulative binomial distribution (continued)

n	x'	.05	.10	.15	.20	.25	.30	.35	.40	.45	.50
8	1	.3366	.5695	.7275	.8322	.8999	.9424	.9681	.9832	.9916	.9961
	2	.0572	.1869	.3428	.4967	.6329	.7447	.8309	.8936	.9368	.9648
	3	.0058	.0381	.1052	.2031	.3215	.4482	.5722	.6846	.7799	.8555
	4	.0004	.0050	.0214	.0563	.1138	.1941	.2936	.4059	.5230	.6367
9	1	.3698	.6126	.7684	.8658	.9249	.9596	.9793	.9899	.9954	.9980
	2	.0712	.2252	.4005	.5638	.6997	.8040	.8789	.9295	.9615	.9805
	3	.0084	.0530	.1409	.2618	.3993	.5372	.6627	.7682	.8505	.9102
	4	.0006	.0083	.0339	.0856	.1657	.2703	.3911	.5174	.6386	.7461
	5	.0000	.0009	.0056	.0196	.0489	.0988	.1717	.2666	.3786	.5000
	6	.0000	.0001	.0006	.0031	.0100	.0253	.0536	.0994	.1658	.2539
	7	.0000	.0000	.0000	.0003	.0013	.0043	.0112	.0250	.0498	.0898
	8	.0000	.0000	.0000	.0000	.0001	.0004	.0014	.0038	.0091	.0195
	9	.0000	.0000	.0000	.0000	.0000	.0000	.0001	.0003	.0008	.0020
10	1	.4013	.6513	.8031	.8926	.9437	.9718	.9865	.9940	.9975	.9990
	2	.0861	.2639	.4557	.6242	.7560	.8507	.9140	.9536	.9767	.9893
	3	.0115	.0702	.1798	.3222	.4744	.6172	.7384	.8327	.9004	.9453
	4	.0010	.0128	.0500	.1209	.2241	.3504	.4862	.6177	.7340	.8281
	5	.0001	.0016	.0099	.0328	.0781	.1503	.2485	.3669	.4956	.6230
	6	.0000	.0001	.0014	.0064	.0197	.0473	.0949	.1662	.2616	.3770
	7	.0000	.0000	.0001	.0009	.0035	.0106	.0260	.0548	.1020	.1719
	8	.0000	.0000	.0000	.0001	.0004	.0016	.0048	.0123	.0274	.0547
	9	.0000	.0000	.0000	.0000	.0000	.0001	.0005	.0017	.0045	.0107
	10	.0000	.0000	.0000	.0000	.0000	.0000	.0000	.0001	.0003	.0010
11	1	.4312	.6862	.8327	.9141	.9578	.9802	.9912	.9964	.9986	.9995
	2	.1019	.3026	.5078	.6779	.8029	.8870	.9394	.9698	.9861	.9941
	3	.0152	.0896	.2212	.3826	.5448	.6873	.7999	.8811	.9348	.9673
	4	.0016	.0185	.0694	.1611	.2867	.4304	.5744	.7037	.8089	.8867
	5	.0001	.0028	.0159	.0504	.1146	.2103	.3317	.4672	.6029	.7256
	6	.0000	.0003	.0027	.0117	.0343	.0782	.1487	.2465	.3669	.5000
	7	.0000	.0000	.0003	.0020	.0076	.0216	.0501	.0994	.1738	.2744
	8	.0000	.0000	.0000	.0002	.0012	.0043	.0122	.0293	.0610	.1133
	9	.0000	.0000	.0000	.0000	.0001	.0006	.0020	.0059	.0148	.0327
	10	.0000	.0000	.0000	.0000	.0000	.0000	.0002	.0007	.0022	.0059
	11	.0000	.0000	.0000	.0000	.0000	.0000	.0000	.0000	.0002	.0005
12	1	.4596	.7176	.8578	.9313	.9683	.9862	.9943	.9978	.9992	.9998
	2	.1184	.3410	.5565	.7251	.8416	.9150	.9576	.9804	.9917	.9968
	3	.0196	.1109	.2642	.4417	.6093	.7472	.8487	.9166	.9579	.9807
	4	.0022	.0256	.0922	.2054	.3512	.5075	.6533	.7747	.8655	.9270
	5	.0002	.0043	.0239	.0726	.1576	.2763	.4167	.5618	.6956	.8062
	6	.0000	.0005	.0046	.0194	.0544	.1178	.2127	.3348	.4731	.6128
	7	.0000	.0001	.0007	.0039	.0143	.0368	.0846	.1582	.2607	.3872
	8	.0000	.0000	.0001	.0006	.0028	.0095	.0255	.0573	.1117	.1938
	9	.0000	.0000	.0000	.0001	.0004	.0017	.0056	.0153	.0356	.0730
	10	.0000	.0000	.0000	.0000	.0000	.0002	.0008	.0028	.0079	.0193
	11	.0000	.0000	.0000	.0000	.0000	.0000	.0001	.0003	.0011	.0032
	12	.0000	.0000	.0000	.0000	.0000	.0000	.0000	.0000	.0001	.0002

n	x'	.05	.10	.15	.20	.25	.30	.35	.40	.45	.50
								p			
	5	.0000	.0004	.0029	.0104	.0273	.0580	.1061	.1737	.2604	.3633
	6	.0000	.0000	.0002	.0012	.0042	.0113	.0253	.0498	.0885	.1445
	7	.0000	.0000	.0000	.0001	.0004	.0013	.0036	.0085	.0181	.0352
	8	.0000	.0000	.0000	.0000	.0000	.0001	.0002	.0007	.0017	.0039
13	1	.4867	.7458	.8791	.9450	.9762	.9903	.9963	.9987	.9996	.9999
	2	.1354	.3787	.6017	.7664	.8733	.9363	.9704	.9874	.9951	.9983
	3	.0245	.1339	.2704	.4983	.6674	.7975	.8868	.9421	.9731	.9888
	4	.0031	.0342	.0967	.2527	.4157	.5794	.7217	.8314	.9071	.9539
	5	.0003	.0065	.0260	.0991	.2060	.3457	.4995	.6470	.7721	.8666
	6	.0000	.0009	.0053	.0300	.0802	.1654	.2841	.4256	.5732	.7095
	7	.0000	.0001	.0013	.0070	.0243	.0624	.1295	.2288	.3563	.5000
	8	.0000	.0000	.0002	.0012	.0056	.0182	.0462	.0977	.1788	.2905
	9	.0000	.0000	.0000	.0002	.0010	.0040	.0126	.0321	.0698	.1334
	10	.0000	.0000	.0000	.0000	.0001	.0007	.0025	.0078	.0203	.0461
	11	.0000	.0000	.0000	.0000	.0000	.0001	.0003	.0013	.0041	.0112
	12	.0000	.0000	.0000	.0000	.0000	.0000	.0000	.0001	.0005	.0017
	13	.0000	.0000	.0000	.0000	.0000	.0000	.0000	.0000	.0000	.0001
14	1	.5123	.7712	.8972	.9560	.9822	.9932	.9976	.9992	.9998	.9999
	2	.1530	.4154	.6433	.8021	.8990	.9525	.9795	.9919	.9971	.9991
	3	.0301	.1584	.3521	.5519	.7189	.8392	.9161	.9602	.9830	.9935
	4	.0042	.0441	.1465	.3018	.4787	.6448	.7795	.8757	.9368	.9713
	5	.0004	.0092	.0467	.1298	.2585	.4158	.5773	.7207	.8328	.9102
	6	.0000	.0015	.0115	.0439	.1117	.2195	.3595	.5141	.6627	.7880
	7	.0000	.0002	.0022	.0116	.0383	.0933	.1836	.3075	.4539	.6047
	8	.0000	.0000	.0003	.0024	.0103	.0315	.0753	.1501	.2586	.3953
	9	.0000	.0000	.0000	.0004	.0022	.0083	.0243	.0583	.1189	.2120
	10	.0000	.0000	.0000	.0000	.0003	.0017	.0060	.0175	.0426	.0898
	11	.0000	.0000	.0000	.0000	.0000	.0002	.0011	.0039	.0114	.0287
	12	.0000	.0000	.0000	.0000	.0000	.0000	.0001	.0006	.0022	.0065
	13	.0000	.0000	.0000	.0000	.0000	.0000	.0000	.0001	.0003	.0009
	14	.0000	.0000	.0000	.0000	.0000	.0000	.0000	.0000	.0000	.0001
15	1	.5367	.7941	.9126	.9648	.9866	.9953	.9984	.9995	.9999	
	2	.1710	.4510	.6814	.8329	.9198	.9647	.9858	.9948	.9983	.9995
	3	.0362	.1841	.3958	.6020	.7639	.8732	.9383	.9729	.9893	.9963
	4	.0055	.0556	.1773	.3518	.5387	.7031	.8273	.9095	.9576	.9824
	5	.0006	.0127	.0617	.1642	.3135	.4845	.6481	.7827	.8796	.9408
	6	.0001	.0022	.0168	.0611	.1484	.2784	.4357	.5968	.7392	.8491
	7	.0000	.0003	.0036	.0181	.0566	.1311	.2452	.3902	.5478	.6964
	8	.0000	.0000	.0006	.0042	.0173	.0500	.1132	.2131	.3465	.5000
	9	.0000	.0000	.0001	.0008	.0042	.0152	.0422	.0950	.1818	.3036
	10	.0000	.0000	.0000	.0001	.0008	.0037	.0124	.0338	.0769	.1509
	11	.0000	.0000	.0000	.0000	.0001	.0007	.0028	.0093	.0255	.0592
	12	.0000	.0000	.0000	.0000	.0000	.0001	.0005	.0019	.0063	.0176
	13	.0000	.0000	.0000	.0000	.0000	.0000	.0001	.0003	.0011	.0037
	14	.0000	.0000	.0000	.0000	.0000	.0000	.0000	.0000	.0001	.0005
	15	.0000	.0000	.0000	.0000	.0000	.0000	.0000	.0000	.0000	.0000

Table B.2 Cumulative binomial distribution (continued)

n	x'	.05	.10	.15	.20	.25	.30	.35	.40	.45	.50
16	1	.5599	.8147	.9257	.9719	.9900	.9967	.9990	.9997	.9999	1.0000
	2	.1892	.4853	.7161	.8593	.9365	.9739	.9902	.9967	.9990	.999
	3	.0429	.2108	.4386	.6482	.8029	.9006	.9549	.9817	.9934	.9979
	4	.0070	.0684	.2101	.4019	.5950	.7541	.8661	.9349	.9719	.9894
	5	.0009	.0170	.0791	.2018	.3698	.5501	.7103	.8334	.9147	.9616
	6	.0001	.0033	.0235	.0817	.1897	.3402	.5100	.6712	.8024	.8949
	7	.0000	.0005	.0056	.0267	.0796	.1753	.3119	.4728	.6340	.7228
	8	.0000	.0001	.0011	.0070	.0271	.0744	.1594	.2839	.4371	.5982
	9	.0000	.0000	.0002	.0015	.0075	.0257	.0671	.1423	.2559	.4018
	10	.0000	.0000	.0000	.0002	.0016	.0071	.0229	.0583	.1241	.2272
	11	.0000	.0000	.0000	.0000	.0003	.0016	.0062	.0191	.0486	.1051
	12	.0000	.0000	.0000	.0000	.0000	.0003	.0013	.0049	.0149	.0384
	13	.0000	.0000	.0000	.0000	.0000	.0000	.0002	.0009	.0035	.0106
	14	.0000	.0000	.0000	.0000	.0000	.0000	.0000	.0001	.0006	.0021
	15	.0000	.0000	.0000	.0000	.0000	.0000	.0000	.0000	.0001	.0003
	16	.0000	.0000	.0000	.0000	.0000	.0000	.0000	.0000	.0000	.0000
17	1	.5819	.8332	.9369	.9775	.9925	.9977	.9993	.9998	1.0000	1.0000
	2	.2078	.5182	.7475	.8818	.9499	.9807	.9933	.9979	.9994	.9999
	3	.0503	.2382	.4802	.6904	.8363	.9226	.9673	.9877	.9959	.9988
	4	.0088	.0826	.2444	.4511	.6470	.7981	.8972	.9536	.9816	.9936
	5	.0012	.0221	.0987	.2418	.4261	.6113	.7652	.8740	.9404	.9755
	6	.0001	.0047	.0319	.1057	.2347	.4032	.5803	.7361	.8529	.9283
	7	.0000	.0008	.0083	.0377	.1071	.2248	.3812	.5522	.7098	.8338
	8	.0000	.0001	.0017	.0109	.0402	.1046	.2128	.3595	.5257	.6855
	9	.0000	.0000	.0003	.0026	.0124	.0403	.0994	.1989	.3374	.5000
	10	.0000	.0000	.0000	.0005	.0031	.0127	.0383	.0919	.1834	.3145
	11	.0000	.0000	.0000	.0001	.0006	.0032	.0120	.0348	.0826	.1662
	12	.0000	.0000	.0000	.0000	.0001	.0007	.0030	.0106	.0301	.0717
	13	.0000	.0000	.0000	.0000	.0000	.0001	.0006	.0025	.0086	.0245
	14	.0000	.0000	.0000	.0000	.0000	.0000	.0001	.0005	.0019	.0064
	15	.0000	.0000	.0000	.0000	.0000	.0000	.0000	.0001	.0003	.0012
	16	.0000	.0000	.0000	.0000	.0000	.0000	.0000	.0000	.0000	.0001
	17	.0000	.0000	.0000	.0000	.0000	.0000	.0000	.0000	.0000	.0000
18	1	.6028	.8499	.7464	.9820	.9944	.9984	.9996	.9999	1.0000	1.0000
	2	.2265	.5497	.7759	.9009	.9605	.9858	.9954	.9987	.9997	.9999
	3	.0581	.2662	.5203	.7287	.8647	.9400	.9764	.9918	.9975	.9993
	4	.0109	.0982	.2798	.4990	.6943	.8354	.9217	.9672	.9880	.9962
	5	.0015	.0282	.1206	.2836	.4813	.6673	.8114	.9058	.9589	.9846
	6	.0002	.0064	.0419	.1329	.2825	.4656	.6450	.7912	.8923	.9519
	7	.0000	.0012	.0118	.0513	.1390	.2783	.4509	.6257	.7742	.8811
	8	.0000	.0002	.0027	.0163	.0569	.1407	.2717	.4366	.6085	.7597
	9	.0000	.0000	.0005	.0043	.0193	.0596	.1391	.2632	.4222	.5927
	10	.0000	.0000	.0001	.0009	.0054	.0210	.0597	.1347	.2527	.4073
	11	.0000	.0000	.0000	.0002	.0012	.0061	.0212	.0576	.1280	.2403
	12	.0000	.0000	.0000	.0000	.0002	.0014	.0062	.0203	.0537	.1189

n	x'	.05	.10	.15	.20	.25	.30	.35	.40	.45	.50
	13	.0000	.0000	.0000	.0000	.0000	.0003	.0014	.0058	.0183	.0481
	14	.0000	.0000	.0000	.0000	.0000	.0000	.0003	.0013	.0049	.0154
	15	.0000	.0000	.0000	.0000	.0000	.0000	.0000	.0002	.0010	.0038
	16	.0000	.0000	.0000	.0000	.0000	.0000	.0000	.0000	.0001	.0007
	17	.0000	.0000	.0000	.0000	.0000	.0000	.0000	.0000	.0000	.0001
	18	.0000	.0000	.0000	.0000	.0000	.0000	.0000	.0000	.0000	.0000
19	1	.6226	.8649	.9544	.9856	.9958	.9989	.9997	.9999	1.0000	1.0000
	2	.2453	.5797	.8015	.9171	.9690	.9896	.9969	.9992	.9998	1.0000
	3	.0665	.2946	.5587	.7631	.8887	.9538	.9830	.9945	.9985	.9996
	4	.0132	.1150	.3159	.5449	.7369	.8668	.9409	.9770	.9923	.9978
	5	.0020	.0352	.1444	.3267	.5346	.7178	.8500	.9304	.9720	.9904
	6	.0002	.0086	.0537	.1631	.3322	.5261	.7032	.8371	.9223	.9682
	7	.0000	.0017	.0163	.0676	.1749	.3345	.5188	.6919	.8273	.9165
	8	.0000	.0003	.0041	.0233	.0775	.1820	.3344	.5122	.6831	.8204
	9	.0000	.0000	.0008	.0067	.0287	.0839	.1855	.3325	.5060	.6762
	10	.0000	.0000	.0001	.0016	.0089	.0326	.0875	.1861	.3290	.5000
	11	.0000	.0000	.0000	.0003	.0023	.0105	.0347	.0885	.1841	.3238
	12	.0000	.0000	.0000	.0000	.0005	.0028	.0114	.0352	.0871	.1796
	13	.0000	.0000	.0000	.0000	.0001	.0006	.0031	.0116	.0342	.0835
	14	.0000	.0000	.0000	.0000	.0000	.0001	.0007	.0031	.0109	.0318
	15	.0000	.0000	.0000	.0000	.0000	.0000	.0001	.0006	.0028	.0096
	16	.0000	.0000	.0000	.0000	.0000	.0000	.0000	.0001	.0005	.0022
	17	.0000	.0000	.0000	.0000	.0000	.0000	.0000	.0000	.0001	.0004
	18	.0000	.0000	.0000	.0000	.0000	.0000	.0000	.0000	.0000	.0000
	19	.0000	.0000	.0000	.0000	.0000	.0000	.0000	.0000	.0000	.0000
20	1	.6415	.8784	.9612	.9885	.9968	.9992	.9998	1.0000	1.0000	1.0000
	2	.2642	.6083	.8244	.9308	.9757	.9924	.9979	.9995	.9999	1.0000
	3	.0755	.3231	.5951	.7939	.9087	.9645	.9879	.9964	.9991	.9998
	4	.0159	.1330	.3523	.5886	.7748	.8929	.9556	.9840	.9951	.9987
	5	.0026	.0432	.1702	.3704	.5852	.7625	.8818	.9490	.9811	.9941
	6	.0003	.0113	.0673	.1958	.3828	.5836	.7546	.8744	.9447	.9793
	7	.0000	.0024	.0219	.0867	.2142	.3920	.5834	.7500	.8701	.9423
	8	.0000	.0004	.0059	.0321	.1018	.2277	.3990	.5841	.7480	.8684
	9	.0000	.0001	.0013	.0100	.0409	.1133	.2376	.4044	.5857	.7483
	10	.0000	.0000	.0002	.0026	.0139	.0430	.1218	.2447	.4086	.5881
	11	.0000	.0000	.0000	.0006	.0039	.0171	.0532	.1275	.2493	.4119
	12	.0000	.0000	.0000	.0001	.0009	.0051	.0196	.0565	.1308	.2517
	13	.0000	.0000	.0000	.0000	.0002	.0013	.0060	.0210	.0580	.1316
	14	.0000	.0000	.0000	.0000	.0000	.0003	.0015	.0065	.0214	.0577
	15	.0000	.0000	.0000	.0000	.0000	.0000	.0003	.0016	.0064	.0207
	16	.0000	.0000	.0000	.0000	.0000	.0000	.0000	.0003	.0015	.0059
	17	.0000	.0000	.0000	.0000	.0000	.0000	.0000	.0000	.0003	.0013
	18	.0000	.0000	.0000	.0000	.0000	.0000	.0000	.0000	.0000	.0002
	19	.0000	.0000	.0000	.0000	.0000	.0000	.0000	.0000	.0000	.0000
	20	.0000	.0000	.0000	.0000	.0000	.0000	.0000	.0000	.0000	.0000

Table B.3 Wilcoxon-test false-alarm probability

The entries in this table are the false-alarm probability $P\{d_2|m_1\}$ associated with a Wilcoxon test with I samples and a threshold T.

T	3	4	5	6	7	8	9
2	.625						
3	.375						
4	.250	.562					
5	.125	.438					
6		.312					
7		.188	.500				
8		.125	.406				
9		.062	.312				
10			.219	.500			
11			.156	.422			
12			.094	.344			
13			.062	.281	.531		
14			.031	.219	.469		
15				.156	.406		
16				.109	.344		
17				.078	.289	.527	
18				.047	.234	.473	
19				.031	.188	.422	
20				.016	.148	.371	
21					.109	.320	
22					.078	.273	.500
23					.055	.230	.455
24					.039	.191	.410
25					.023	.156	.367
26					.016	.125	.326
27					.008	.098	.285
28						.074	.248
29						.055	.213
30						.039	.180
31						.027	.150
32						.020	.125
33						.012	.102
34						.008	.082
35						.004	.064
36							.049
37							.037
38							.027
39							.020
40							.014
41							.010
42							.006
43							.004
44							.002

Table B.3 Wilcoxon-test false-alarm probability (*continued*)

T	10	11	12	13	14	15
27	.500					
28	.461					
29	.423					
30	.385					
31	.348					
32	.312	.517				
33	.278	.483				
34	.246	.449				
35	.216	.416				
36	.188	.382				
37	.161	.350				
38	.138	.319	.515			
39	.116	.289	.485			
40	.097	.260	.455			
41	.080	.232	.425			
42	.065	.207	.396			
43	.053	.183	.367			
44	.042	.160	.339			
45	.032	.139	.311	.500		
46	.024	.120	.285	.473		
47	.019	.103	.259	.446		
48	.014	.087	.235	.420		
49	.010	.074	.212	.393		
50	.007	.062	.190	.368		
51	.005	.051	.170	.342		
52	.003	.042	.151	.318	.500	
53	.002	.034	.133	.294	.476	
54	.001	.027	.117	.271	.452	
55		.021	.102	.249	.428	
56		.016	.088	.227	.404	
57		.012	.076	.207	.380	
58		.009	.065	.188	.357	
59		.007	.055	.170	.335	.511
60		.005	.046	.153	.313	.489
61		.003	.039	.137	.292	.467
62		.002	.032	.122	.271	.445
63		.001	.026	.108	.251	.423
64		.001	.021	.095	.232	.402
65		.000	.017	.084	.213	.381
66			.013	.073	.196	.360
67			.010	.064	.179	.339
68			.008	.055	.163	.319
69			.006	.047	.148	.300
70			.005	.040	.134	.281
71			.003	.034	.121	.262

Table B.3 Wilcoxon-test false-alarm probability (*continued*)

T	10	11	12	13	14	15
72			.002	.029	.108	.244
73			.002	.024	.097	.227
74			.001	.020	.086	.211
75			.001	.016	.077	.195
76			.000	.013	.068	.180
77			.000	.011	.059	.165
78				.009	.052	.151
79				.007	.045	.138
80				.005	.039	.126
81				.004	.034	.115
82				.003	.029	.104
83				.002	.025	.094
84				.002	.021	.084
85				.001	.018	.076
86				.001	.015	.068
87				.001	.012	.060
88				.000	.010	.053
89				.000	.008	.047
90				.000	.007	.042
91					.005	.036
92					.004	.032
93					.003	.028
94					.003	.024
95					.002	.021
96					.002	.018
97					.001	.015
98					.001	.013
99					.001	.011
100					.000	.009
101					.000	.008
102					.000	.006
103					.000	.005
104					.000	.004
105						.003
106						.003
107						.002
108						.002
109						.001
110						.001
111						.001
112						.001
113						.000
114						.000
115						.000
116						.000
117						.000
118						.000
119						.000

REFERENCES

Cramér, H.: "Mathematical Methods of Statistics," Princeton University Press, Princeton, N.J., 1946.

Deutsch, R.: "Estimation Theory," Prentice-Hall, Inc., Englewood Cliffs, N.J., 1965.

Feller, W.: "An Introduction to Probability Theory and Its Applications," vol. 1, John Wiley & Sons, Inc., New York, 1957.

Gibbons, J. D.: "Nonparametric Statistical Inference," McGraw-Hill Book Company, New York, 1971.

Gibson, J. D., and J. L. Melsa: "Introduction to Nonparametric Detection with Applications," Academic Press, Inc., New York, 1975.

Hancock, J., and P. Wintz: "Signal Detection Theory," McGraw-Hill Book Company, New York, 1966.

Helstrom, C. W.: "Sequential Detection," chap. 7 of "Communication Theory," A. V. Balakrishnan (ed.), McGraw-Hill Book Company, New York, 1968.

Jazwinski, A. H.: "Stochastic Processes and Filtering Theory," Academic Press, Inc., New York, 1970.

Melsa, J. L., and A. P. Sage: "An Introduction to Probability and Stochastic Processes," Prentice-Hall, Inc., Englewood Cliffs, N.J., 1973.

Mendel, J. M.: "Discrete Techniques of Parameter Estimation," Marcel Dekker, New York, 1973.

Middleton, D.: "Topics in Communication Theory," McGraw-Hill Book Company, New York, 1965.

Papoulis, A.: "The Fourier Integral and Its Applications," McGraw-Hill Book Company, New York, 1962.

Papoulis, A.: "Probability, Random Variables and Stochastic Processes," McGraw-Hill Book Company, New York, 1965.

Parzen, E.: "Modern Probability Theory and Its Applications," John Wiley & Sons, Inc., New York, 1960.

Parzen, E.: "Stochastic Processes," Holden-Day, Inc., San Francisco, 1962.

Raemer, H. R.: "Statistical Communication Theory and Applications," Prentice-Hall, Englewood Cliffs, N.J., 1969.

Rao, C. R.: "Information and Accuracy Attainable in the Estimation of Statistical Parameters," *Bull. Calcutta Math. Soc.*, vol. 37, pp. 81–91, 1945.

Sage, A. P., and J. L. Melsa: "Estimation Theory with Applications to Communications and Control," McGraw-Hill Book Company, New York, 1971.

Sakrison, D.: "Communication Theory: Transmission of Waveforms and Digital Information," John Wiley & Sons, Inc., New York, 1968.

Turin, G. L.: "Notes on Digital Communication," Van Norstrand Reinhold Company, New York, 1969.

Van Trees, H. L.: "Detection, Estimation and Modulation Theory, Part I," John Wiley & Sons, Inc., New York, 1968.

Wald, A.: "Sequential Analysis," John Wiley & Sons, Inc., New York, 1947.

Weber, C. L.: "Elements of Detection and Signal Design," McGraw-Hill Book Company, New York, 1968.

Wozencraft, J. M., and I. M. Jacobs: "Principles of Communication Engineering," John Wiley & Sons, Inc., New York, 1965.